Membranes and their Cellular Functions

Membranes and their Cellular Functions

J.B. Finean, R. Coleman and R.H. Michell
Department of Biochemistry, University of Birmingham

Illustrations by T.A. Bramley

THIRD EDITION

BLACKWELL SCIENTIFIC PUBLICATIONS

OXFORD LONDON EDINBURGH BOSTON PALO ALTO MELBOURNE

© 1974, 1978, 1984 Blackwell Scientific Publications
Editorial Offices:
Osney Mead, Oxford OX2 0EL
8 John Street, London WC1N 2ES
9 Forrest Road, Edinburgh EH1 2QH
52 Beacon Street, Boston, Massachusetts 02108, USA
706 Cowper Street, Palo Alto,
   California 94301, USA
99 Barry Street, Carlton, Victoria 3053, Australia

First published 1974
Second edition 1978
Reprinted 1979, 1981
Third edition 1984

Set by Fourjay Typesetters, Oxford
Printed and bound in Great Britain
at the Alden Press, Oxford

DISTRIBUTORS

USA and Canada
   Blackwell Scientific Publications Inc
   PO Box 50009, Palo Alto
   California 94303

Australia
   Blackwell Scientific Book Distributors
   31 Advantage Road, Highett
   Victoria 3190

British Library
Cataloguing in Publication Data

Finean, J.B.
   Membranes and their cellular functions. — 3rd ed.
   1. Cell membranes   2. Cell physiology
   I. Title   II. Coleman, R.   Michell, R.H.
   574.87′5   QH601

   ISBN 0-632-01204-8

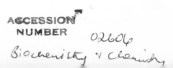

Contents

Preface to the third edition

The first edition of this book was published ten years ago to meet the growing need for a brief introductory text that would present a broad view of the significance of membranes in the activities of cells. It consisted mainly of a general description of membrane structure and of the functions of membranes.

In the second edition we were able to identify many of the specific molecular components of membranes responsible for particular functions. The third edition reflects the continuation of this trend, with details of molecular mechanisms of some membrane processes beginning to emerge from our rapidly increasing knowledge of the molecular structures of membrane components.

Through intensive discussion we have continued to maintain a concise text, supplemented by numerous original diagrams and by cartoons executed by a former colleague. We gratefully acknowledge the advantages bestowed by our department with its excellent library, secretarial and visual aids facilities. In particular, we acknowledge the skill of Mrs Pauline Hill who has both modified many of the original illustrations and translated our new ideas into appropriate drawings.

Many colleagues, both past and present, have helped us to develop a broad interest in membrane structure and function. We are grateful to them all, and particularly to the late Alastair Frazer and Georg Hübscher to whom we dedicated the first edition.

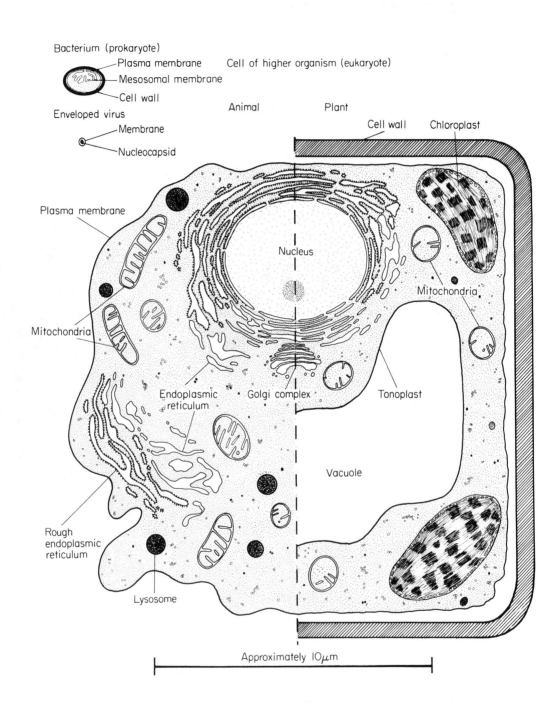

Bacterium (prokaryote)
— Plasma membrane
— Mesosomal membrane
— Cell wall

Cell of higher organism (eukaryote)

Enveloped virus
— Membrane
— Nucleocapsid

Animal

Plant

Cell wall

Chloroplast

Plasma membrane

Mitochondria

Nucleus

Mitochondria

Endoplasmic
reticulum

Golgi complex

Tonoplast

Rough
endoplasmic
reticulum

Vacuole

Lysosome

Approximately 10μm

1 Distribution, isolation and general functions

Free-living cells and some living cells in multicellular organisms can be observed under the light microscope with little or no preparative manipulations, particularly if phase contrast or interference contrast optics are employed. It is immediately apparent that such cells are bounded by some form of resilient barrier which always includes a supple membrane (the plasma membrane, also known as the cell surface membrane or cytoplasmic membrane). In some organisms (e.g., bacteria, fungi, higher plants) this is supplemented by a substantially rigid external wall. Combination of light microscopy with lapsed-time cinematography (e.g., for speeding up images of slow cellular migration) and with stroboscopic slow-motion cinematography (e.g., for analysing rapid flagellar motions) demonstrates very vividly that cells are not static structures. They may flow 'purposefully' across solid substrates (e.g., slime moulds or phagocytic blood leucocytes) or swim with the aid of cilia, flagellae or other motile elaborations of the cell surface (e.g., sperm, or ciliates such as *Paramecium*). Even in static cells the cell surface may be mobile and the intracellular components often, though not always, exhibit ordered patterns of movement. The streaming of cytoplasm that carries chloroplasts around the periphery of plant cell and the radial movement of pigment granules in chromatophores (that gives rise to colour changes in many animals) provide examples of such movement.

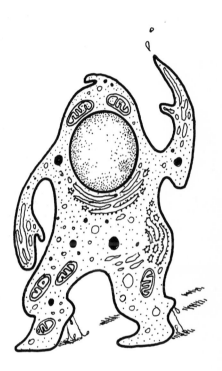

Although nuclei can be clearly distinguished in such living cells, other intracellular components can be detected but not clearly identified. Mitochondria can be distinguished by the use of stains applied to the living cell (vital stains). Some further detail can be seen in the light microscope, but only if more drastic fixation, staining, embedding and sectioning procedures are introduced: great caution must therefore be exercised in relating such stained images to the living cell.

Although the existence of plasma membranes can be inferred from light microscopy, direct images of such membranes can be resolved only by using shorter wavelength

1

radiation in the electron microscope. To use this improved resolution effectively it is necessary to examine extremely thin samples, in which image overlap is minimized, and to enhance the contrast in the image by staining, so that fine structural details can be distinguished. Our current picture of the elaboration of membrane structures, both at cell surfaces and in intracellular organelles, has therefore been derived mainly from electron microscopy of thin, stained sections of fixed tissues; its relevance to living cells, however, has been re-affirmed by electron microscopy of replicas of fracture faces in tissue that has been rapidly deep-frozen (i.e., freeze–fracture electron microscopy, see p. 4). Thus the line-drawing of cell structure given in the frontispiece can be regarded as a realistic, if simplified, representation of the contribution of membranes to the architecture of the cell.

see p. 4

Cellular membranes, both at the cell surface and as the barriers which delineate intracellular compartments, are essentially hydrated lipoprotein structures. The physical and chemical nature of these membranes and the ways in which they function, especially in animal cells, are the topics covered in this book.

A typical procedure for the preparation of cellular material for electron microscopy involves fixation in buffered osmium tetroxide, dehydration, cutting of ultrathin sections and staining of these with a salt of a heavy metal, for example uranyl acetate. When such prepared sections are examined with an electron microscope, sections through the lipoprotein membranes are readily identifiable with characteristic trilamellar features present in the resulting micrographs. These images appear as pairs of closely spaced, and generally continuous, parallel dense lines separated by a less dense region. What is seen is not a direct image of the physiologically active membrane, but largely a pattern of deposition of electron–opaque metal which has been determined by the membranes of the original specimen and perhaps modified by the subsequent preparative procedures. Thus, the image does not exactly represent either all or part of the native membrane. It is, however, a reliable and characteristic feature derived from membranes and its details probably provide some indication of the variations and elaborations which existed in the parent membranes.

The dimension most frequently quoted for one of these trilamellar images is its overall width. This varies in different membranes and variation is also apparent between values reported by different workers for the same membrane. The

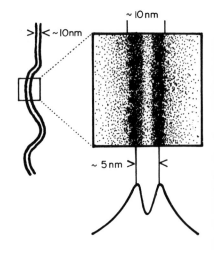

electron
microscopy

trilamellar
images

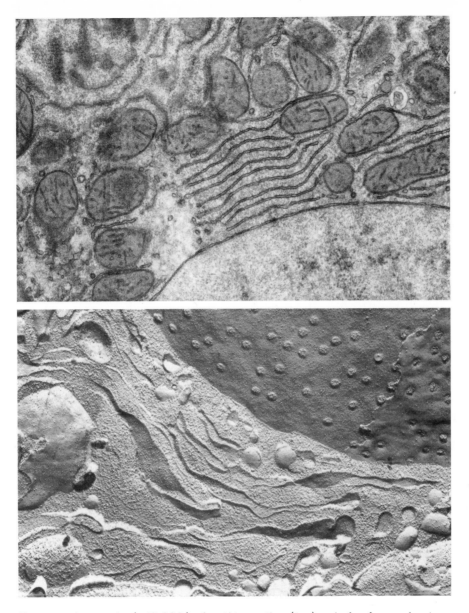

Electron micrographs (x10 000) of a thin section (top) and of a freeze-fracture replica (bottom) of the nucleus and adjacent cytoplasm in a liver cell (hepatocyte). Micrographs by J. Berriman and D. Mills

latter variation is probably due to subtly different preparative procedures or variability in the quality of microscope images. A more consistent dimension is obtained by measurement of the distance between peaks on a densitometer trace across the image. The trilamellar feature corresponding to the plasma membrane may be 7–15 nm in overall width in different cells. Often, the image is asymmetric, with the two dense lines unequal in width or electron opacity. In membranes of intracellular organelles the trilamellar image is usually more uniformly symmetrical and the overall thickness (5–8 nm) is somewhat less.

freeze–fracture

Freeze–fracture electron micrographs are obtained from platinum–carbon replicas of fracture faces in rapidly frozen samples (see diagram). Fractures through such cellular samples follow to an appreciable extent the contours of cellular and intracellular structure, so that the replica will show some cell interiors as relief views in which the organelles are seen as protrusions or depressions with respect to the ice plane. Such fractures frequently reveal structural detail within the plane of the membrane (see p. 40).

1.1 Cell surfaces

In free-living cells, electron micrographs frequently show a relatively homogeneous trilamellar image over the entire surface, but the existence of local membrane specializations is often revealed by freeze–fracture studies, for example at the boundary between cell body and cilium.

However, in differentiated cells which are organized into tissues and sustain long-term interactions with their neighbours there are variations in the detailed structure of the surface membrane at these points of interaction that can be seen even in transmission micrographs. Desmosomes form foci upon which cytoplasmic filaments converge and at which the external surfaces of the plasma membranes of adjacent cells adhere tightly. Tight junctions are cell–cell contacts where the trilamellar images of the plasma membranes of adjacent cells come into intimate contact. When such junctions are viewed by freeze–fracture microscopy (p. 6) it is seen that they consist of multiple linear arrays of particles: these junctions restrict diffusion between the apposed surfaces of adjacent cells. Gap junctions are areas of cell–cell contact in which the trilamellar images in tissue section display a small, but constant, separation (~2 nm). Infiltration of the 'gap' with an electron-dense material such as lanthanum hydroxide

junctions between cells

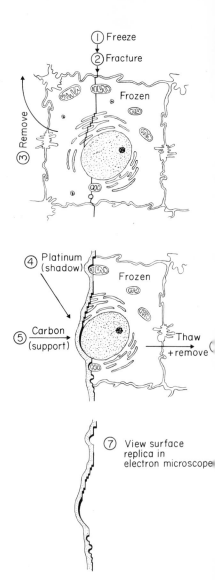

(1) Freeze
(2) Fracture
Frozen
(3) Remove
(4) Platinum (shadow)
Frozen
(5) Carbon (support)
Thaw + remove
(7) View surface replica in electron microscope

reveals, however, that the two membranes are linked by structures 7–8 nm in diameter with a centre-to-centre spacing of 9–10 nm. More detailed structural and functional studies reveal that these are actually areas at which the closely apposed membranes of adjacent cells are specialized so as to allow ions and metabolic intermediates to diffuse directly between the cytoplasmic compartments of adjacent cells, but without destroying the normal barrier to the entry of extracellular materials (see p. 130).

Particular cells often show special modifications, usually confined to discrete areas of the cell surface, that facilitate the performance of some characteristic function. Motile cilia and flagellae of eukaryote cells are used both for locomotion in free-living cells and for sustaining a flow of the overlying fluid in fixed cells (e.g., the gills of invertebrates or tracheal epithelium in vertebrates). These organelles are cylindrical projections of the membrane that are supported by and interact with a ring of nine pairs of microtubules which surrounds a central pair of tubules: the tubules are anchored to a centriole in the cytoplasm at the base of each cilium.

The plasma membrane is also thrown into an orderly array of cylindrical outward projections in the 'brush border' structures that are characteristic of absorptive cell layers, for example in the intestinal mucosa, renal tubules and placenta. The microvilli which make up brush borders again have ordered filamentous cores, but in this case the major component is actin: the filaments interact laterally with the membrane, with a protein plaque at the tip of each microvillus and with a myosin-like protein in the terminal web below the brush border (see diagrams on p. 6).

In some cells, for example kidney tubule cells and the salt glands through which seabirds excrete excess salt, proliferations of the plasma membrane may also be directed inwards into the basal regions of the cells, to increase the efficiency of the link between intracellular energy metabolism and the energy-requiring solute pumping activities of the plasma membrane.

Many of the nerve fibres of vertebrates are given improved current-carrying properties by being invested with an insulating myelin sheath over most of their length. This is a multi-layered spiral extension of plasma membrane laid down around the axon by specialized satellite (Schwann or oligodendroglial) cells. Substantial membrane specialization is often seen at the synapses at which nerves communicate with their target cells. This includes both densely staining

cilia and flagella

microvilli

myelin

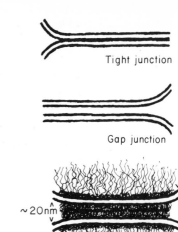

Tight junction

Gap junction

~10 nm
~20 nm

Desmosome

Epithelial cell (kidney tubule)

Brush border

Nucleus

Mitochondrion
Plasma membrane
Basement membrane

5

Scanning electron micrograph of isolated
intestinal epithelial cell (x 8000). Courtesy of Dr S. Knutton.

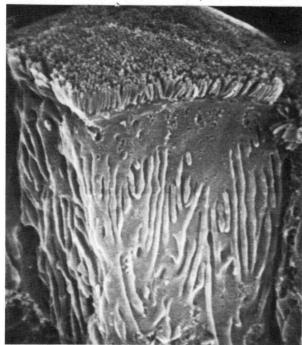

Microvilli on
luminal surface
(Brush border)

Irregular folding
on lateral surface

Brush border region of intestinal epithelial cell

Freeze-fracture
EM x ~ 45 000

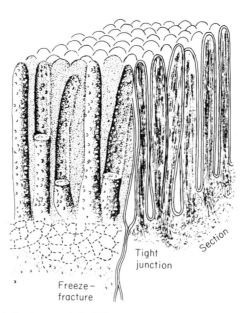

Tight
junction

Section

Freeze-
fracture

Thin section
EM x ~ 45 000

Micrographs courtesy of J. Berriman and D. Mills

elaborations on the cytoplasmic surfaces of the apposed membranes and also some form of stainable material in the space between them.

At the cytoplasmic surface of the trilamellar image of plasma membrane, there is frequently a filamentous layer. This may be thin (e.g., in the erythrocyte) or of substantial thickness (e.g., below the mobile leading edge of a cell moving across a surface), and sometimes it may be obviously ordered (e.g., in brush borders). Such structures seem universally to include actin, together with other proteins, and to be implicated in the determination of cell shape and movement.

cytoskeletal
layer

In a large number of animal cells there is a substantial layer of carbohydrate-containing material (glycocalyx) external to the trilamellar unit. When stained with thorium dioxide or other metallic stains, this appears in electron micrographs as a coarse, fibrillar structure extending outwards a considerable distance (up to 10 nm) from the trilamellar image of the plasma membrane. It is particularly marked in, for example, the brush border region of intestinal epithelial cells (the 'fuzzy coat') and in *Amoebae* where it appears sufficiently dense to appreciably restrict the access of particulate material to the immediate environment of the plasma membrane. Egg cells are also enclosed in a substantial 'gelatinous' coat, but this appears to be a fairly discrete layer, whereas those of the *Amoebae* and intestinal mucosa appear likely to be more fully integrated into the plasma membrane structure (Chapter 2.3).

glycocalyx

The cells of many organisms, particularly green plants, algae, fungi and most bacteria, possess a well-defined cell wall outside the plasma membrane. This is frequently a relatively massive structure consisting of several distinct layers, and its principal functions undoubtedly include protection of the fragile interior of the cell from physical stresses, including the tendency to osmotic swelling of cells living in hypotonic environments. For example, the majority of bacteria live in osmotically hostile environments and thus have cell walls, but these are absent from organisms (extreme halophiles) which live in hypertonic salt solutions and from *Mycoplasma* and *Acholeplasma* which are usually parasitic in animal cells.

cell wall

The walls vary greatly in morphology and in chemical composition, but in most cases they consist largely of either polysaccharide (cellulose, glucan, mannan, etc. in plants and fungi) or of extensively cross-linked polymers whose constituents include amino acids and sugars (the peptidoglycans present in all eubacteria). In gram-positive bacteria the only structure outside the plasma membrane is a relatively massive

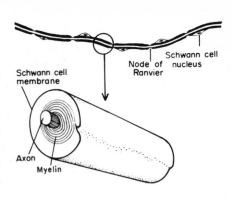

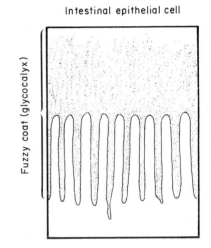

Intestinal epithelial cell

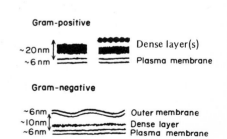

and extensively cross-linked peptidoglycan cell wall, but in gram-negative organisms this structure is thinner and is itself surrounded by an 'outer membrane' which is rich in lipid and lipopolysaccharide and appears trilamellar in electron micrographs.

1.2   Intracellular membranes

prokaryotes

Prokaryotic organisms (eubacteria and archaebacteria) do not have a defined nucleus. They have a plasma membrane, but further differentiation of membrane systems within the cells is limited. Most cyanobacteria (blue–green algae) have flattened sacs of phytosynthetic membranes (thylakoids) close to their plasma membrane, and purple photosynthetic bacteria (e.g., *Rhodospirillum* sp.) feature inward elaborations of their photosynthetic plasma membrane. Bacteria also exhibit variable quantities of intracytoplasmic 'mesosomal' membranes that are involved in DNA replication and cell division. All internal membrane elaborations in prokaryotes appear to show continuity with the plasma membrane.

eukaryotes

In eukaryotic cells (cells of animals, plants, fungi and protista) there is usually a variety of cytoplasmic organelles with structures which involve membranes, although in exceptional circumstances (the mammalian erythrocyte) a cell may differentiate to the stage of retaining only the plasma membrane.

nucleus

nuclear pores

The genetic material in eukaryotic cells is confined to one nucleus (or occasionally more) which has a well-defined membrane boundary. This consists of a pair of concentrically arranged membrane elements which are in continuity around the edges of pores about 75 nm in diameter. The pores pierce the double structure at a density of approximately $50/\mu m^2$. Within them, there is a characteristic structure which includes eight elements arranged around the edge of the pore and some central components. These pores form a controlled route for movement of materials between nucleus and cytoplasm. The nuclear envelope disappears during cell division, possibly becoming merged with the endoplasmic reticulum (with which it often shows continuity in electron micrographs), and reappears in the daughter cells.

The abundance and extent of development of each of the other membrane-defined organelles varies considerably in relation to the nature and intensity of the activities of the cell being studied. The most extensive membrane system is usually the endoplasmic reticulum, which consists mainly of a

endoplasmic reticulum

Endoplasmic reticulum

Nucleus

Ribosomes   Nuclear pores   Nuclear envelope

system of flattened tubes or sacs referred to as cisternae. These form a network of channels, sometimes narrow and sometimes opening out into larger chambers, which occupy a substantial proportion of the cytoplasm. In most cells the cytoplasmic faces of a majority of the cisternae carry attached granules (ribosomes). Further ribosomes exist free in the cytoplasm, the distribution between free and membrane-bound being a reflexion of cellular function. Some endoplasmic reticulum membranes are free of ribosomes. The rough- and the smooth-surfaced endoplasmic reticulum membranes form different parts of a continuous membrane system.

Many of the smooth-surfaced membrane cisternae of the cell are often distinguished from the endoplasmic reticulum by being organized into discrete structures or areas known as Golgi complex(es) or, in some plant and invertebrate cells, dictyosomes. These typically consist of a series of parallel stacked smooth membrane cisternae. There may be one large Golgi complex, usually close to the nucleus, or several scattered throughout the cytoplasm. Although usually distinctive, the Golgi complex often appears morphologically related to adjacent endoplasmic reticulum, lysosomes and secretory granules: when these relationships are clear-cut, then the face of the Golgi complex that is adjacent to the endoplasmic reticulum is referred to as the *cis* face, and secretory vesicles are elaborated from the *trans* face.

There are also a variety of approximately spherical organelles of various sizes and electron opacities, each of which consists of a single membrane envelope enclosing some form of material. These contents consist of hydrolytic enzymes (lysosomes), certain oxidative enzymes (peroxisomes), material destined for secretion (secretory granules or synaptic vesicles), or ingested material (phagocytic vacuoles or pinocytic vesicles). Some Golgi and secretory granule membranes involved in secretion show a greater thickness than other intracellular membranes, suggesting a similarity to the plasma membrane.

Often the most striking and the most numerous of the cytoplasmic organelles in aerobic cells are mitochondria. These organelles feature two membrane elements, an outer smooth membrane envelope and a more complex inner membrane system. The latter appears to be in the form of a bag which separates the space enclosed within the outer membrane into two distinct compartments, one being enclosed within the other. The inner membrane shows tubular or plate-like infoldings, known as cristae, their number and arrange-

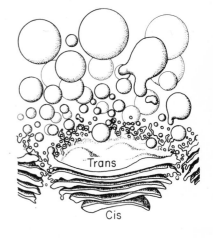

Trans

Cis

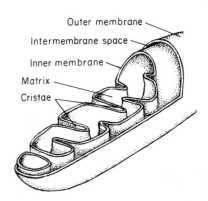

Outer membrane
Intermembrane space
Inner membrane
Matrix
Cristae

Golgi complex
dictyosomes

lysosomes
peroxisomes

secretory
granules

mitochondria

9

ment showing great variation from tissue to tissue and even in different mitochondria in a single cell. In most cells, a high proportion of the mitochondria appear sausage-shaped and relatively short but there is microscopic evidence of a proportion of much larger and more irregularly shaped mitochondria in many tissues and even of a single complex mitochondrion with many tubular projections in yeast cells. The fundamental division of the space within the mitochondrion into two compartments (intermembrane space and matrix) is, however, always apparent.

chloroplasts

Plant tissues contain another family of organelles, the plastids, of which the chloroplasts found in photosynthetic tissues are the most familiar. As in mitochondria, an outer membrane forms a simple envelope which encloses a more complex arrangement of internal membranes. In the chloroplast this includes loose arrays of approximately parallel extended membranes arranged in pairs (lamellae) and regions (grana) in which parallel membrane pairs (thylakoids) are densely packed.

tonoplast

Plant cells also contain one or more vacuoles. These are bounded by a single membrane (the tonoplast); they store organic substances and take up water by osmosis, thus helping to maintain the turgor of the plant.

Although the various membrane systems and discrete organelles in the eukaryote cell often appear independent when seen in electron microscopic images, it is now clear that, with the possible exception of mitochondria and plastids, there is a considerable degree of functional continuity between different intracellular membranes and between these and the plasma membrane. In addition, a variety of ordered filamentous and tubular elements extend throughout the 'cytosol' which bathes these organelles: these appear to play major roles in dictating cytoplasmic organization and cell shape.

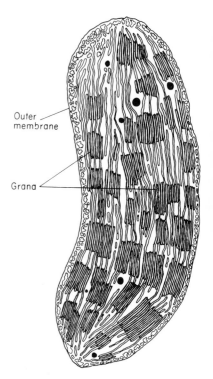

Outer membrane

Grana

1.3 General approaches to the study of membranes

Studies of intact tissues and cells, and of these after mild fixation, have yielded appreciable information on the chemical nature and physical properties of membrane barriers, and on the chemical constituents and enzyme activities associated with the various cellular compartments delineated by membranes. Information derived from studies of the osmotic properties of cells (Chapter 3) and of their electrical properties (Chapter 4) are described elsewhere.

histochemistry

Histochemical techniques, in which the location of a particular constituent or enzyme activity is made visible by a specific staining reaction, have been particularly important. For example, acid phosphatase can be shown to be present in small cytoplasmic organelles by histochemical techniques using chromogenic substrates to colour these organelles prior to light microscopy. Further studies, in which the electron microscope is used and the enzyme activity is detected by precipitating liberated inorganic phosphate with lead (an electron-dense metal), can give detailed information on the nature of the organelles involved. Molecules against which antibodies are either naturally available or can be raised may be visualized by light or electron microscopy through the use of fluorescent antibodies or antibodies linked to readily visualized enzymes (e.g., peroxidase) or to large (e.g., haemocyanin) or electron-dense (e.g., ferritin) molecules. Methods in which microscopy is combined with autoradiography can give detailed information on the localization within cells of molecules that have been radioactively labelled.

The participation of individual membranes or organelles in the functioning of an organism is most easily studied if the process(es) of interest can be isolated from the complexity of the whole organism. The extent of such isolation varies from the study of intact organs through to experiments with purified molecular constituents such as enzymes. Such simplification, though valuable, is fraught with dangers. Among the possible dangers are the loss of external control over cells, for example by hormones, the breakdown of the inter-relationships that exist between reactions located in different parts of the cell, and the removal of spatial and functional constraints imposed by membranes.

Between the two extremes mentioned above lie other experimental approaches which include studies of particular types of cells in isolation from their parent organs and the investigation of isolated organelles or membrane fragments which retain many of their original metabolic activities and much of their structural organization. Isolation of such subcellular fractions from many sources is now routine. It consists of the selection of a relatively homogeneous population of the cells to be studied, breakage of these gently in a protective medium and separation of the various particles in the homogenate by centrifugation.

The starting material for subcellular fractionation is either a

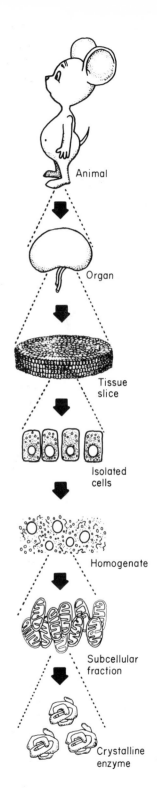

Animal

Organ

Tissue slice

Isolated cells

Homogenate

Subcellular fraction

Crystalline enzyme

solid tissue or a population of free-living cells taken from the body or grown in cell culture. Tissues are often heterogeneous, due both to the presence of blood (which can be removed by perfusion) and to the existence of more than one intrinsic cell population. Frequently, this heterogeneity is ignored or does not seriously hamper the isolation of a particular material in reasonable purity, but sometimes it is necessary first to isolate a homogeneous cell population. Some procedures for isolation of dispersed cells from solid tissues are purely mechanical, but these often give rather low yields of damaged cells, especially from highly differentiated tissues. Usually, therefore, the tissue is first treated with enzymes (most often collagenase and/or hyaluronidase) or chelators, for example EDTA, to weaken intercellular associations and then subjected to gentle mechanical treatment to disaggregate the cells. Under favourable conditions, cells dissociated in this way can be very healthy; they exclude membrane-impermeable dyes, display complex cell functions—for example, integrated biochemical pathways and responses such as secretion—and may even survive and grow in tissue culture. Sometimes the cell suspensions obtained from body fluids (e.g., plasma) or by tissue dissociation are heterogeneous, in which case different cell-types must be separated, usually by low speed differential rate or density-gradient centrifugation, or by free-flow electrophoresis. Plants, bacteria and fungi present a further problem, in that methods of homogenization which are capable of rupturing their tough cell walls are unlikely to leave delicate intracellular organelles undamaged. A frequent way of circumventing this problem is to remove or weaken the wall before homogenizing the cells. This is done by prior incubation with enzymes, usually glycosidases, which specifically degrade the structural polymers of which the walls are constructed: lysozyme and enzymes isolated from snail gut are frequently used. The modified cells produced by these treatments are referred to as spheroplasts or, if the wall is completely removed, protoplasts.

isolation of cells

homogenization

The cells in the selected population are homogenized by the gentlest method compatible with efficient rupture of their plasma membranes and, if possible, the preservation of intact intracellular organelles. This often involves a liquid shearing force imparted by expressing the cell suspension through a narrow orifice or by rotating a cylindrical pestle in a concentric tube containing the cell suspension. Alternatively, cavitation may be induced in cells either by equilibrating them with high-pressure nitrogen and then releasing the pressure abruptly or by the rotating metal blades of a blender. Very resistant cells may be ground up with minute glass beads, or a frozen cell mass may be extruded through a narrow orifice.

suspending
medium

The suspending medium used for homogenization and subsequent procedures is usually a buffered aqueous solution of a non-electrolyte which is not extensively metabolized and which does not rapidly permeate through membranes. Often this solute is sucrose. The concentration is usually chosen to be approximately iso-osmotic with the intracellular environment (about 250–350 mosmol/1). The ionic environment which surrounds organelles within the cell is not maintained in these non-ionic media, and it therefore seems likely that some properties of isolated organelles may be substantially affected by prolonged exposure to these non-physiological media. Sometimes a hypotonic solution may be used so as to impose an extra stress (osmotic) on the cells and facilitate their rupture.

Centrifugation techniques which exploit differences in size and density between different particles are used to separate the organelles and membrane fragments present in the homogenates.

differential
centrifugation

'microsomes'

Differential centrifugation sediments particles at different rates which depend largely on the sizes of the particles. Hence, in the usual procedures, the largest particles (nuclei) are sedimented first and the smallest ('microsomes' and ribosomes) last. 'Microsomes' are a mixture of small membrane vesicles and fragments of somewhat variable composition. Some of these will have existed in the cells before homogenization, but the majority arise from more extended membrane systems (including endoplasmic reticulum, plasma membrane and Golgi complex) during homogenization.

Centrifugation techniques
(key to particle types)

	Small	Large
Low density	○	O
High density	●	●

Differential rate
sedimentation in an
angle rotor

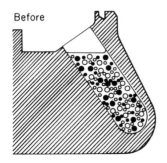

Before

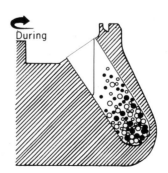

During

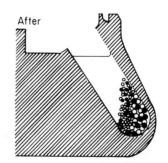

After

In isopycnic density-gradient centrifugation, particles are centrifuged through media of graded densities until they float in the media of their own densities; low particle densities often indicate a high lipid content and high densities a high content of protein and/or nucleic acids. The gradients used may show either a continuous decrease in density from bottom to top or may be formed by laying layers of different densities one above the other. The solute whose concentration is varied is often of low molecular weight, in which case the gradient is also a gradient of osmotic pressure. In such gradients, organelles impermeable to the solute (e.g., lysosomes) will shrink and thus increase in density as they sediment, whereas permeable organelles (e.g., peroxisomes) will retain their original dimensions and density. Alternatively, the osmotic pressure may be held relatively constant with a solute of low molecular weight, and the density variations imparted by varying the concentration of a dense high molecular weight solute; such solutes include Ficoll (polysucrose), Metrizamide (an iodinated benzamido-derivative of glucose) and Percoll (colloidal silica coated with polyvinylpyrrolidone).

Differential centrifugation in angle rotors can be a relatively large-scale procedure, but does not usually give complete resolution of mixtures of organelles, whereas isopycnic centrifugation in swinging bucket rotors gives good resolution of mixtures, but on a relatively small scale. Subcellular fractionation procedures, therefore, often consist of a sequence of separations based initially on size and then on density, finally yielding moderate amounts of isolated subcellular fractions purer than could be obtained by either technique alone.

Zonal rotors, in which separations based on either sedimentation rate or density can be carried out on a moderate scale and with high resolution, largely overcome these limitations but are expensive and more complex to operate.

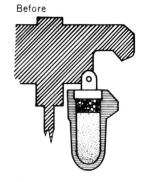

Before

During

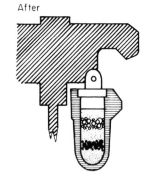

After

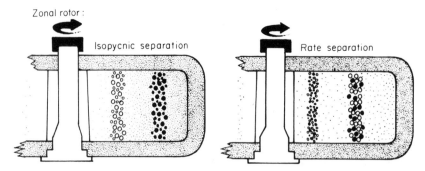

Zonal rotor:

Isopycnic separation

Rate separation

Centrifugation techniques
(key to particle types)

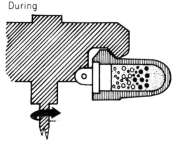

	Small	Large
Low density	○	⭕
High density	•	⬤

In some situations, a component isolated from a cell still consists of a complex structure which includes more than one

14

type of membrane and compartment, for example mitochondria, chloroplasts or pinched-off nerve endings. In such cases, it is often profitable to apply further disruption and fractionation techniques to try to isolate and localize particular constituents within the complex organelles.

density
perturbation

In situations where the native densities of functionally distinct cell components are sufficiently close to hinder or preclude their separation by centrifugation techniques, it may be possible to change the density of one of them preferentially without seriously affecting the molecular structure or functional characteristics. Lysosomes become readily separable (as secondary lysosomes) from other subcellular components following the ingestion by the cells of non-metabolizable material of high or low density, for example dextran or Triton WR 1339 respectively. Similarly, phagocytic vacuoles can be readily isolated from homogenates of phagocytes which have ingested latex particles. The membrane itself may be made more dense by specific attachment of a heavy label. For example, lymphocyte plasma membrane can be labelled by attachment of phage particles by concanavalin A and glutaraldehyde, and several types of plasma membrane are made more dense by incorporation of digitonin.

Other physical and chemical characteristics of membranes have also been exploited in alternative isolation procedures. Differences in electrical charges on membranes have been exploited in the large-scale separation of specialized regions of plasma membrane from homogenized kidney tubule cells by free-flow electrophoresis. Membrane fragments carrying specific oligosaccharides or antigens have been separated by binding to appropriate affinity adsorbents (glass or sepharose beads coated with lectins or antibodies).

free-flow
electrophoresis

Subcellular fractionation can be used in two quite different ways: as an analytical technique for defining the intracellular location of a particular component or process, or as a preparative method for isolating a chosen entity in quantity and in a pure enough state for some particular study. In the former case, the emhasis is upon defining the relative distributions of different components amongst the subcellular fractions isolated from an homogenate and, as a result, identifying the intracellular locations of particular components or processes. This can be particularly important in the identification of the enzymic constituents of organelles, such as the plasma membrane and lysosomes, which only constitute a small proportion of the cell mass and are consequently difficult to isolate in a pure form.

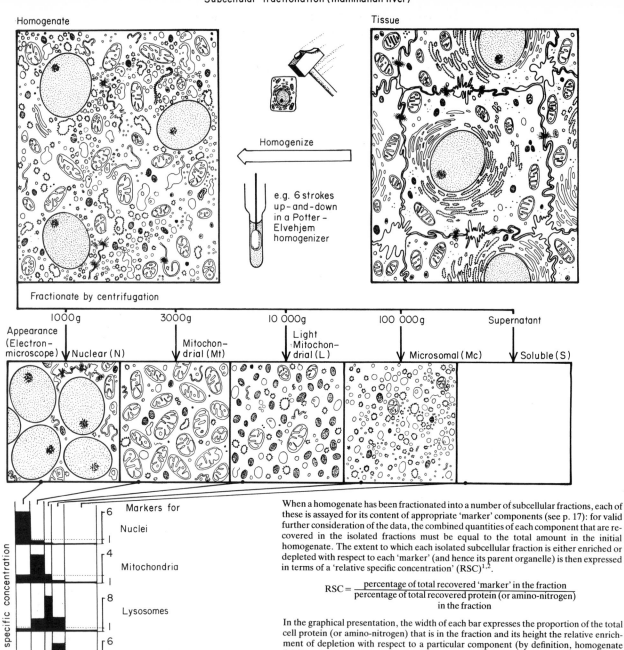

Homogenate

Tissue

Homogenize

e.g. 6 strokes up–and–down in a Potter–Elvehjem homogenizer

Fractionate by centrifugation

| 1000g | 3000g | 10 000g | 100 000g | Supernatant |

Appearance (Electron-microscope) ↓ Nuclear (N) ↓ Mitochondrial (Mt) ↓ Light Mitochondrial (L) ↓ Microsomal (Mc) ↓ Soluble (S)

Relative specific concentration

Markers for

Nuclei — 6, 1

Mitochondria — 4, 1

Lysosomes — 8, 1

Endoplasmic reticulum — 6, 1

Cytosol — 3, 1

N Mt L Mc S

% recovered protein

When a homogenate has been fractionated into a number of subcellular fractions, each of these is assayed for its content of appropriate 'marker' components (see p. 17): for valid further consideration of the data, the combined quantities of each component that are recovered in the isolated fractions must be equal to the total amount in the initial homogenate. The extent to which each isolated subcellular fraction is either enriched or depleted with respect to each 'marker' (and hence its parent organelle) is then expressed in terms of a 'relative specific concentration' (RSC)[1,2].

$$RSC = \frac{\text{percentage of total recovered 'marker' in the fraction}}{\text{percentage of total recovered protein (or amino-nitrogen) in the fraction}}$$

In the graphical presentation, the width of each bar expresses the proportion of the total cell protein (or amino-nitrogen) that is in the fraction and its height the relative enrichment of depletion with respect to a particular component (by definition, homogenate RSC for every component is 1.0). The area of each bar thus represents the proportion of that component which was found in the specified fraction.

1. Note that the 'theoretical' maximum RSC for any cellular component is inversely proportional to the total contribution to the cell mass made by the organelle in which it resides (e.g., if one-tenth of cell mass, then maximum RSC = 10).

2. RSC is a general term applicable to any cell component. When enzyme activities are considered, then the alternative term RSA (relative specific activity) is often employed. However, RSA is also frequently used to refer to the ratio:

$$\frac{\text{specific activity of fraction}}{\text{specific activity of homogenate}}$$

This is a less rigorous, but widely used, measure of the enzyme enrichment achieved during subcellular fractionation.

Further studies may then be conducted in which subcellular fractionation is used to prepare material for detailed studies. When some highly characteristic process is to be studied then this may be undertaken using appropriately enriched subcellular preparations that are only of limited purity: for example, selected lysosomal and plasma membrane enzyme activities are often investigated using subcellular fractions in which the relevant organelle forms only a small proportion of the total material. By contrast, reliable chemical or physical analyses of such organelles can only be undertaken using essentially pure material.

Isolated subcellular fractions are never entirely homogeneous, so it is essential that all isolated fractions are thoroughly characterized. This assessment may include optical and electron microscopy and the measurement, relative to the homogenate, of the concentrations of a variety of 'markers'. The markers are chemical, enzymic or antigenic constituents which have previously been shown to be localized or concentrated at known cellular sites and which can therefore be used to define the distribution in the isolated fractions of material from these sites. When distributions of markers are measured it is essential to ensure that all the material present in the original homogenate is accounted for.

'markers'

The choice of markers is normally simplified by the fact that particular constituents tend to occur at the same sites in different types of cell. However, enzymes that are appropriate markers for one tissue may sometimes not occur in others; for example, glucose-6-phosphatase is only a useful endoplasmic reticulum marker in those gluconeogenic tissues which possess the enzyme.

Some membrane systems in the cell display both biochemical heterogeneity and close functional inter-relationships with other cell components, for example endoplasmic reticulum, Golgi complex and plasma membrane (see Chapters 6 and 7). As a result, the distributions of some 'marker' enzymes cannot be regarded as absolute mirrors of the distributions of a particular organelle: peripheral regions of Golgi cisternae sometimes exhibit some 5′-nucleotidase activity and small amounts of acid phosphatase can occur in the endoplasmic reticulum. Examples of heterogeneity within a single membrane system would include graded functional variations from the *cis* to the *trans* face (see p. 9) of stacks of Golgi cisternae and lateral segregation of functions over different areas of the plasma membrane—for example, disaccharidase on the brush border and hormone-stimulated adenylate cyclase on the basolateral

Commonly used 'markers'

Nuclei
DNA
Histones

Endoplasmic reticulum
Glucose-6-phosphatase
Cytochrome P_{450}
Esterase (vs. naphthylacetate)
NADH-cytochrome *c* reductase

Plasma membranes
5′-nucleotidase
Na^+/K^+-ATPase
Hormone-stimulated adenylate cyclase

Golgi complex
UDP-galactose: *N*-acetylglucosamine
    galactosyltransferase
Thiamine pyrophosphatase

Peroxisomes
Catalase
D-amino acid oxidase

Mitochondria
Glutamate dehydrogenase (matrix)
Succinate dehydrogenase
Cytochrome oxidase (inner membrane)
DCCD-sensitive ATPase
Adenylate kinase (intermembrane space)
Monoamine oxidase (outer membrane)

Chloroplasts
Chlorophyll (thylakoids)
Ribulose bisphosphate carboxylase
    (soluble)

Cytosol
Lactate dehydrogenase
6-phosphogluconate dehydrogenase

aspect in intestinal epithelial cells. Enzymes which are on the inner face of isolated membrane vesicles or are in solution within the vesicles are often not freely accessible to substrates present in the incubation medium bathing the sealed vesicles. When the membranes are disrupted, for example by hypotonicity, detergents or ultrasonic treatment, this 'latency' disappears and the enzymes can be quantitatively assayed. Such latency, which may be a valuable pointer to intracellular compartmentation and was crucial in the discovery of lysosomes, must always be eliminated during the design of quantitative assays for intracellular enzymes.

1.4 The functional significance of cellular organization

As we have seen, the activities of cells are contained within a boundary, the plasma membrane. In prokaryotic cells there is relatively little intracellular differentiation and what there is is mainly determined by factors other than membrane boundaries. Mechanisms for the complete internalization of extracellular macromolecular material by endocytosis (invagination of plasma membrane and formation of pinched-off vesicles) are not present. Smaller molecules, do, however, enter and leave, and specific proteins and other macromolecules are somehow passed into the extracellular medium.

compartmentation

The interior of eukaryotic cells, on the other hand, is partitioned into a number of intracellular compartments whose physical boundaries are lipoprotein membranes. The variety of processes which together constitute the functioning of the cell occur within these compartments and both on and in the membranes. The compartmentation is of considerable benefit to the cell. For example, metabolites and enzymes of particular pathways can interact very efficiently with each other if they are concentrated in a small fraction of the total space within the cell (either in an aqueous compartment or in a membrane). These pathways can also be to a large degree isolated from opposing or competing reactions; one simple example of this is that the biosynthesis of many cellular constituents and their degradation usually occurs in different intracellular compartments. Furthermore, integration of the processes occurring in different compartments into a coherent whole is facilitated by the presence, in the barriers delineating the compartments, of special mechanisms for facilitating and controlling the movements of materials between them.

18

The processes most central to the survival and reproduction of a eukaryote cell occur in a space comprising the interior of the nucleus and the cytosol, in communication through the pores in the nuclear envelope. In the nucleus, deoxyribonucleic acid (DNA) is organized, with other molecules, into chromosomes and is, at the appropriate time, replicated: during this process it is connected to the nuclear membrane. In addition, the various types of ribonucleic acid necessary for synthesis of proteins (transfer RNAs, ribosomal RNAs and messenger RNAs) are transcribed from the DNA and processed into their functional forms within the nucleus. The RNAs are passed out through the nuclear pores into the cytosol, the ribosomal RNAs and possibly the messenger RNAs being in the form of specific complexes with protein. The method of this transfer is not clear but seems not to allow free movement of other molecules through the pores at the same time.

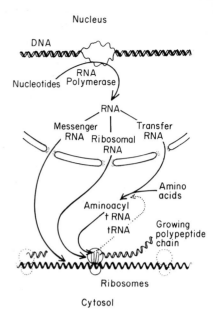

The cytosol compartment into which the RNAs are transferred and in which they fulfil their functions is the key area in which most of the biosynthetic processes of the cell occur. Here 'soluble' enzymes catalyse glycolysis, a fundamental ATP-yielding process. Glycolysis and an ancillary sequence of reactions, the pentose phosphate pathway, generate essential biosynthetic intermediates and the latter produces NADPH (a reducing agent involved in many biosynthetic processes, including those for fatty acids and cholesterol). Fatty acids are synthesized by a multienzyme complex in the cytosol. They are incorporated into phospholipids essential for membrane structure and into triacylglycerol by enzymes located in the endoplasmic reticulum membranes. These membranes are also the site of the final stages in the synthesis of cholesterol, another important membrane lipid. Intracellular soluble proteins and some membrane proteins are synthesized on ribosomes free in the cytosol, whilst secretory proteins and other membrane proteins are synthesized on ribosomes bound to endoplasmic reticulum membranes (see Chapters 6 and 7).

The cytosol is also in contact with the plasma membrane whose key role is the control of the movements of ions, nutrients and metabolites into and out of the cell. For most substances, the plasma membrane simply acts as a barrier which limits their movement, but for some, particularly those of special metabolic significance, such as sugars, amino acids and certain ions, its role is more specific (Chapter 3). In such cases, the membrane possesses mechanisms which facilitate their movements across the cell's perimeter down concentration gradients. Sometimes more sophisticated mechanisms

glycolysis

pentose phosphate pathway

biosynthetic processes

transport across plasma membrane

are present which require the expenditure of metabolic energy and thus allow the cells to actively accumulate substances they need or to expel those whose intracellular concentrations must be kept low. The plasma membrane also mediates the triggering of cellular responses to external influences such as neurotransmitters, antigens and many hormones.

The glycolytic pathway, although central to the metabolism of all organisms, only makes available in a metabolically useful form a small fraction of the energy locked up in carbohydrate molecules. The yields of ATP via the tricarboxylic acid cycle and oxidative phosphorylation, metabolic sequences which occur in mitochondria of all aerobic (O_2-using) cells, are much greater. Pyruvate, a 3-carbon metabolite of glucose produced by the glycolytic pathway, enters mitochondria and is oxidized, being converted to CO_2 and acetyl-CoA. The latter is then oxidized to produce two further CO_2 molecules: this occurs in a series of controlled steps which constitute the tricarboxylic acid cycle. In mitochondria, appropriate reactions also exist to convert other molecules (e.g., amino acids, fatty acids) either to acetyl-CoA or to intermediates of the tricarboxylic acid cycle, thus allowing their oxidation. NADH and $FADH_2$, the reduced forms of two redox coenzymes, are generated during these processes. These are then oxidized, thus initiating the sequential reduction of the various components of the respiratory chain (a sequence of enzymes and coenzymes which undergo cyclic reduction and oxidation), the final component of which reduces molecular oxygen (see Chapter 4). The free energy liberated during the passage of reducing equivalents along the respiratory chain is used to generate an electrochemical gradient of protons ($\Delta\bar{\mu}_{H^+}$) across the inner mitochondrial membrane. Dissipation of this $\Delta\bar{\mu}_{H^+}$ provides energy to drive the synthesis of ATP and for other purposes such as active transport of solutes across the inner mitochondrial membrane. The yield of ATP from one molecule of glucose is thus increased from the two molecules yielded by anaerobic glycolysis to more than 30 molecules. The enzymes of the tricarboxylic acid cycle are localized in the mitochondrial matrix and inner membrane and those of the respiratory chain and ATP synthesis form separate multienzyme complexes in the inner mitochondrial membrane: in prokaryotes these processes occur at the plasma membrane.

In green plants and cyanobacteria the thylakoids contain an energy-trapping system whose components include chlorophylls. As a result of the action of this system, the

tricarboxylic
acid cycle

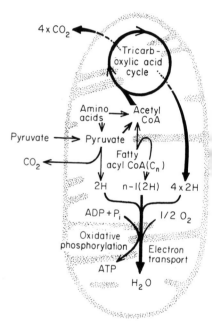

20

energy of sunlight is transduced into a $\Delta\bar{\mu}_{H^+}$. Dissipation of this provides ATP and reduced coenzymes, some of which are consumed in the reduction of atmospheric CO_2 to carbon compounds such as carbohydrates.

Cells synthesize a variety of materials, not only for their growth and multiplication and for export, but also for their own maintenance. In the latter process, which occurs continually even in non-growing, non-exporting cells, the concentrations in the cell of the synthesized constituents may show no change: synthesis must therefore be balanced by an equivalent rate of degradation. This dynamic balance, in which the chemical composition of a system can remain unchanged but its constituents are continually renewed, is normal metabolic turnover. Furthermore, there is sometimes a need for the removal of damaged or obsolete components and, occasionally, for the complete destruction of cells, for example during the disappearance of a tadpole's tail or during the metamorphosis occurring in a pupating insect. These reactions are mainly catalysed by the hydrolytic enzymes present in lysosomes. These enzymes, which are capable of degrading most, if not all, cellular constituents, are enclosed by an impermeable membrane which restricts their action. When macromolecular materials are taken into cells, the plasma membrane is involved in the initial events and lysosomes later play a role in dismantling the ingested material.

The picture of cell function presented so far is an extremely simplified one which describes only some of the key processes involved in the domestic economy of cells. Most cells show this pattern of processes but, particularly in complex organisms, the relative emphasis of different processes varies greatly and a variety of other reactions are linked into this pattern. In this way, cells become differentiated in order to perform specialist roles in the economy of the entire organisms.

Such specialization is often apparent in the degree of proliferation and in the inter-relationships between different membrane systems within a cell. Respiratory electron transport and oxidative phosphorylation are intimately associated with mitochondrial cristae. Thus, cells with a large and continuous (aerobic) energy requirement, for example insect flight muscle, mammalian cardiac muscle and kidney, contain large or numerous mitochondria with extensive cristae. Such mitochondria have a much higher content of respiratory enzymes and a higher respiration rate than mitochondria such as those of liver which perform more varied functions and have fewer and smaller cristae.

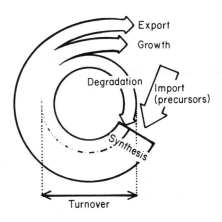

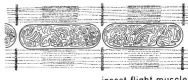

Mitochondria in:

insect flight muscle

liver cell

photosynthesis

turnover

hydrolytic enzymes

specialization

Many cells include in their special activities the synthesis and secretion of macromolecules for extracellular use, for example in communication (hormones), the assembly of extracellular structures (precursors of cell walls and collagen), lubrication (mucins), transport of essential constituents (transferrin), recognition and neutralization of foreign material (immunoglobulins), and digestion (enzymes and zymogens). Such processes involve integration of the activities of several organelles, with the Golgi complex playing a pivotal role; sometimes, its importance is apparent from its morphological emphasis.

Many free-living cells show a cellular organization in which different regions of the cell are clearly differentiated for different functions (e.g., the morphologically and functionally distinct front and back ends of a swimming *Paramecium*), and even motile cells that show no morphologically obvious polarity may develop functional polarity in response to an environmental stimulus (e.g., chemotactic migration of leucocytes towards sites of infection). In complex multicellular organisms, this type of polarization of cellular function reaches a particularly high degree of development in epithelial cell layers that separate two or more physiologically distinct environments—for example, the intestinal epithelium that separates intestinal lumen from bloodstream. In such cases, there are often substantial unidirectional flows of particular solutes through the cells. Many of the mechanisms responsible for achieving these polarized cell activities are in membranes, so it is essential that cells can biosynthesize and maintain their membrane complement in such a way as to sustain such essential functional polarity.

Further Reading

Fawcett D.W. (1980) *The Cell: its Organelles and Inclusions.* 2nd edn. W.B. Saunders Co., Philadelphia and London.

Hopkins C.D. (1978) *Structure and Function of Cells.* W.B. Saunders Co., Philadelphia and London.

Rogers H.J., Perkins H.R. & Ward J.N. (1980) *Microbial Cell Walls and Membranes.* Chapman & Hall, London.

Reid R.H. & Leech R.M. (1980) *Biochemistry and Structure of Cell Organelles.* Blackie, Glasgow and London.

Alberts B., Bray D., Lewis J., Raff M., Roberts K. & Watson J.D. (1983) *Molecular Biology of the Cell.* Garland, New York.

Lehninger A.L. (1982) *Principles of Biochemistry.* Worth, New York.

De Duve C. (1971) Tissue fractionation, past and present. *J Cell Biol* **50**, 20D–55D.

Fleischer S. & Packer L. (1974) *Methods in Enzymology.* Volume 31, Biomembranes, Part A. Academic Press, London and New York.

Maddy A.H. (ed.) (1976) *Biochemical Analysis of Membranes.* Chapman & Hall, London.

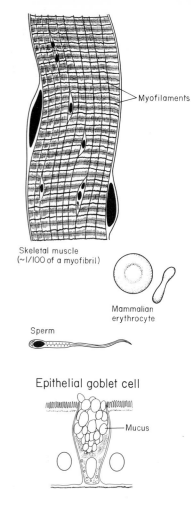

Myofilaments

Skeletal muscle
(~1/100 of a myofibril)

Mammalian erythrocyte

Sperm

Epithelial goblet cell

Mucus

Adipocyte (fat cell)

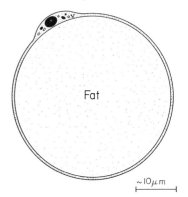

Fat

~10 μm

Lazarides E. & Revel J.P. (1979) The molecular basis of cell movement. *Scientific American* May, 88–100.

Dustin P. (1980) Microtubules. *Scientific American* August, 58–68.

Doolittle W.K. (1980) Revolutionary concepts in evolutionary cell biology. *Trends Biochem Sci* **5,** 146–148.

Woese C.R. (1981) Archaebacteria. *Scientific American* June, 94–106.

De Duve C. (1983) Microbodies in the living cell. *Scientific American* May, 52–62.

See also pp. 212, 213.

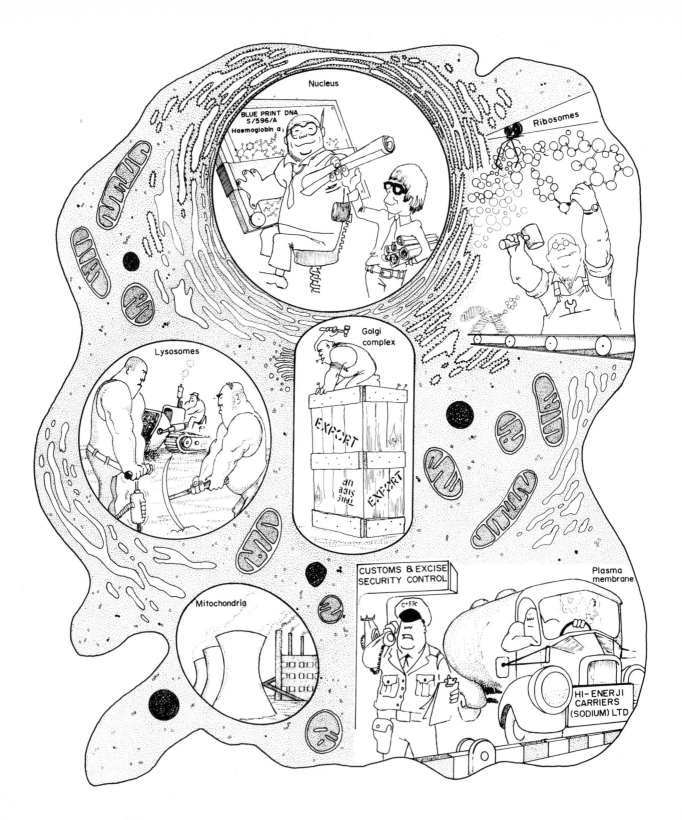

2 Composition and structure

Studies of the turnover of molecular components of membranes using radioactively labelled precursors have demonstrated that membranes are not static structures but are in a dynamic state. Membrane constituents are rapidly and continuously replaced at various rates (Chapter 7) and specific new molecular components can be added to pre-existing structures. Nevertheless, the spatial patterns which such molecular components form in membranes are probably essentially constant. Structural studies can provide no more than an average picture of the dynamic structure, but this picture may still express fundamental relationships which are essential for membrane functions.

Structural information has accumulated from a wide range of experimental techniques and varies considerably with respect to the averaging of data both in space and time. For example, a chemical analysis which requires the isolation of a large quantity of membrane will provide a broadly space-averaged picture of membrane composition, whereas some spectroscopic techniques can provide information on the physical state of a single molecular component in a matter of nano-seconds. In the integration of information from diverse approaches due consideration must be given to such factors.

hydrated lipoprotein structures

All cellular membranes appear to involve hydrated lipoprotein structures which give rise to trilamellar images in electron micrographs of tissue sections. Membranes may differ in the detail of their trilamellar images and of their chemical compositions but the general similarities are such as to suggest that there are fundamental similarities in their molecular organizations.

membrane water

Two significant assessments of the water component of membranes have been made. Calorimetric and nuclear magnetic resonance studies have detected a 'bound' water component and x-ray diffraction methods have identified a water content essential for the integrity of membrane lipoprotein structure. In both cases, the amount of water involved has been estimated to be of the order of 30 per cent as related to the dried weight of the membrane.

It is very probable that the effects of membrane surface structure extend well out into the aqueous environment. Water molecules in the immediate vicinity of cell membranes will be at least partially immobilized and the presence of charged groups at the membrane surface (see p. 37) will influence the distribution of mobile counter-ions. Surfaces of isolated cells normally carry net negative charges which can be detected and compared by microelectrophoresis techniques. These surface fixed charges lead to the formation of a diffuse

electrical double layer electrical double layer in which the charge at the surface is balanced by charges of opposite sign in the medium immediately adjacent to the surface. The potential arising from the electrostatic field created by the surface charges therefore decreases exponentially with distance from the surface. As the surface moves through the bulk medium it carries with it a thin layer of the medium including some of the counter-ions. Con-

zeta potential sequently, the potential at the surface of shear (zeta potential) which is measured by kinetic techniques such as microelectrophoresis is a few millivolts lower than the true surface potential. Zeta potentials of -10 to -39 mV have been measured for a variety of cells.

The potential due to surface fixed charges may be derived from the zeta potential by application of the Gouy–Chapman theory (assumes a uniform surface charge balanced by point charge counter-ions in the medium) or of the Stern theory (takes into consideration the finite sizes of the counter-ions and introduces an ion-free layer immediately adjacent to the surface). Estimates of surface charge densities derived from such calculations have been mainly in the range 1–5×10^{-10} C/ μm^2.

This special aqueous layer immediately adjacent to membrane surfaces may exert a considerable effect on membrane activities. Thus, the ion concentrations close to the active centres of membrane proteins may differ substantially from those in the bulk phase; the cell surface pH is probably about 0.3–0.4 units lower than the pH in the bulk medium.

2.1 Protein components

Most membrane preparations contain rather more protein than lipid but in the nerve myelin sheath protein may be as little as 20 per cent of the total dry mass; this probably reflects its exceptionally low metabolic activity. The exact proportion of protein in a membrane preparation is, to some extent, dependent on the procedure chosen for its isolation. This is be-

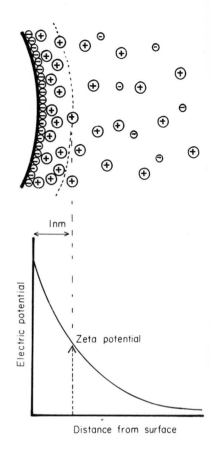

cause most isolation procedures do not preserve the conditions experienced by the membrane within cells and therefore membranes may either lose some of their more loosely bound proteins during isolation or bind components with which they do not normally associate.

The components which take part in physiologically meaningful associations with membranes but which are incorporated into the membrane so loosely that they can be displaced by mild treatments such as manipulation of pH or ionic strength are termed extrinsic proteins, for example the spectrin and actin which form the filamentous layer at the inner surface of the erythrocyte membrane. It seems probable that the main forces binding these proteins to the membranes are polar interactions with tightly bound membrane proteins and with lipids. It is possible that some proteins normally thought to belong in the soluble phase may also fall within this category.

There are also proteins which can be displaced only by disrupting membrane structure with organic solvents, detergents or degradative enzymes. Such proteins appear to be firmly incorporated into membrane structure and have been identified as intrinsic components. Optical studies (circular dichroism and optical rotatory dispersion) of intact membranes indicate that membrane proteins generally possess a high proportion of α-helical and random coil configurations, with rather little β-structure, suggesting that they are usually compact rather than extended structures.

A first indication of the protein composition of a membrane preparation may be obtained from an analysis in which the membranes are first dissociated in a reducing medium (e.g., urea and mercaptoethanol) containing sodium dodecyl sulphate (SDS), so as to unfold the constituent polypeptide chains and coat them with negatively charged dodecyl sulphate. Electrophoresis in polyacrylamide gels will then separate the polypeptide chains according to size. This provides a profile of polypeptide chain composition which is characteristic of the membrane and gives an indication of the complexity of its protein composition. In such a profile, polypeptides that are of similar molecular weights but which are derived from different proteins will not be distinguished; nor will any relationship be apparent between polypeptides that are of different sizes but which were derived from a single functional protein in the membrane. Thus, a polypeptide band on such a gel does not necessarily represent an individual protein, but it may serve as a reference for a subsequent, more

extrinsic
(peripheral) proteins

intrinsic
(integral) proteins

polypeptide chain
configurations

SDS gel
electrophoresis

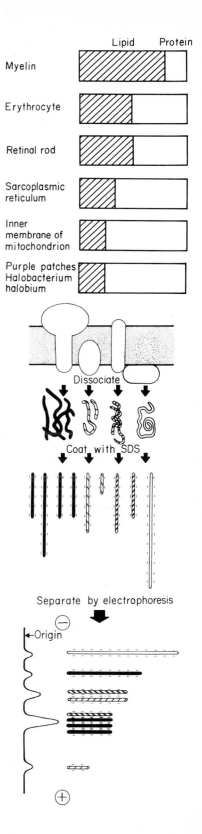

27

direct identification of a protein in terms of distinctive structural and functional properties. Changes in this characteristic polypeptide chain profile, following either chemical labelling or superficial proteolytic degradation of membranes, can also contribute information on the spatial localization of proteins in intact membranes.

isolation

The most successful procedures for the transfer of intrinsic proteins into aqueous systems appropriate for fractionation and characterization studies involve the use of detergents under non-denaturing conditions. The most effective detergents for this purpose have been the non-ionic detergents, such as Triton X-100 and octylglucoside, and moderately ionic detergents, such as deoxycholate. These detergents have lipid-like qualities which allow them to substitute, to some extent, for lipid in association with proteins, but they are also more hydrophilic than lipids. Consequently, they can both mobilize intrinsic protein molecules into detergent or detergent–lipid micelles in an aqueous environment and, once there, help to maintain the configuration of the proteins during many standard procedures for protein fractionation and purification. Removal of the detergent from the aqueous medium surrounding intrinsic proteins leads to aggregation and often to precipitation.

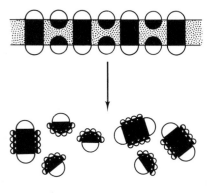

The application of these techniques has allowed the isolation of many intrinsic membrane proteins in pure form and with retention of their typical biological (e.g., enzymic or antigenic) activities.

This behaviour of intrinsic proteins implies that they possess surface regions consisting predominantly of amino acid residues with non-polar side-chains and that, in membranes, these are normally accommodated in the non-polar environment provided by the hydrophobic portions of lipids.

non-polar segments

The presence of these predominantly non-polar surface regions on the proteins is confirmed by the observation that intrinsic membrane proteins, unlike soluble proteins, bind substantial quantities of detergent and that their electrophoretic mobilities can be modified by association with charged detergents. In some intrinsic proteins, these predominantly non-polar surface domains are sufficiently extensive to endow the molecule with a significantly greater proportion of non-polar residues than extrinsic membrane proteins or soluble proteins. This is not, however, a characteristic of all intrinsic proteins, since these molecules range from those which are predominantly polar on their surfaces, with only a small non-polar segment interacting with the hydrophobic phase of the mem-

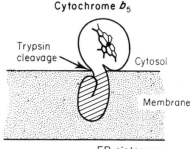

Cytochrome b_5

Trypsin cleavage

Cytosol

Membrane

ER cisternum

brane, to those which may be almost entirely immersed in the membrane interior. Probable examples of the latter include an enzyme from *Staphylococcus aureus,* soluble in organic solvents but not in water, which phosphorylates a very hydrophobic C_{55}-polyisoprenoid alcohol, and some of the very lipophilic polypeptides involved in electron transport and ATP synthesis in mitochondria and chloroplasts (Chapter 4).

amino acid
analyses

Amino acid sequence data are now available for many intrinsic proteins. Many such sequences have been established by traditional methods of proteolytic and chemical fragmentation combined with amino acid sequencing. However, information of this type can now be obtained more readily by determination of the nucleotide sequences of DNA molecules complementary in sequence either to mRNA or to the structural genes that encode the amino acid sequences of membrane proteins. This approach yields the amino acid sequences of the initial polypeptide transcripts, including segments that are removed or modified before or during the incorporation of polypeptides into membranes (Chapter 7). Predominantly non-polar segments can be readily identified in such sequences and their potential for insertion into or through the interior of the membrane inferred.

In cytochrome b_5 and many other membrane proteins it is clear that a non-polar sequence is concerned in the binding of the protein to the membrane, since the lipophilic segment remains embedded in the membrane even when the larger catalytic portion of the molecule is cleaved off and released into solution by limited proteolysis with trypsin. In some cases (e.g., in intestinal aminopeptidase and in glycophorin, the major erythrocyte sialoglycoprotein), such enzymic degradation, combined with chemical or antibody labelling of parts of intrinsic proteins exposed at the surfaces of a membrane, has established that the non-polar amino acid sequences span the membrane.

It would seem that to span the non-polar core of the mammalian plasma membrane requires at least 20 non-polar amino acid residues. If this sequence of residues is to form a continuous helical configuration that would direct all the non-polar residues outwards to interact with the surrounding lipid, then it must exclude histidine and proline. The polypeptides which are thought to span the membrane once fulfil this condition, and most of them also feature charged residues to either end of the non-polar sequence (Chapter 7).

In the case of bacteriorhodopsin, the protein component of the two-dimensional crystalline regions (purple patches) of

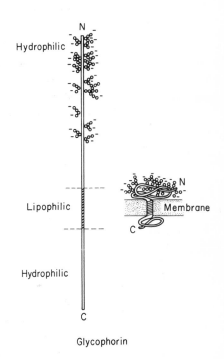

Glycophorin

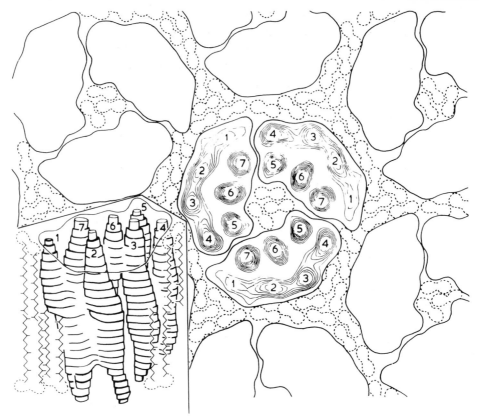

Bacteriorhodopsin

the membrane of *Halobacterium halobium*, a detailed structural analysis by x-ray and electron-optical techniques has shown that the polypeptide chain has seven membrane-spanning segments, all of which are of rod-like appearance and could be α-helices. The amino acid sequence has now been determined and the probable membrane-spanning segments identified. These include a few charged residues but it seems likely that these will be accommodated within the cluster of spanning segments, an arrangement that might be of significance in relation to the provision of a somewhat polar pore through which protons might travel.

Lipophilic amino acid sequences which have the potential to form membrane-spanning α-helices have also been identified in polypeptides involved in several other selective transport systems (Chapters 3 and 7), but details of the transport pathways are yet to be established. Membrane-spanning polypeptides are also involved in the formation of multi-subunit (water-filled) channels through membranes (Chapters 5

multiple-spanning
polypeptides

30

and 8), and in receptor proteins that transmit information between the two surfaces of membranes (Chapter 5).

multi-subunit
spanning
complexes

Aggregates of several types of polypeptides or subunits (sometimes referred to as heterogeneous oligomers or heteroligomers) have also been identified with specific activities in mitochondrial membranes and some have been crystallized in a form suitable for direct structural analysis by diffraction and electron microscopy. Cytochrome oxidase, for example, which includes six different types of polypeptide, has been crystallized from detergent solution and analysed to a resolution of 2.5 nm. The six-subunit monomer has a distorted Y-shape and it is suggested that the 'arms' of the monomer project from the matrix side of the inner mitochondrial membrane whilst the 'stem' is embedded in the lipid layer, so that more than 50 per cent of the molecule projects into the aqueous phase. Ubiquinone:cytochrome c reductase is a still more complex mitochondrial membrane component which includes at least eight subunits (identified in diagram, see also Chapter 4) in the monomer. This complex has been crystallized in a lipid bilayer, and a 2.5 nm resolution analysis identifies the structural unit as a dimer of parallel units which span the membrane in such a way that the c cytochromes project into the intermembrane space.

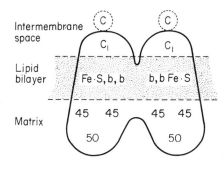

Ubiquinone–cytochrome C reductase

Numerous other functionally significant associations of polypeptides or subunits have been identified, mainly through isolation procedures which reveal the minimum functional unit and by chemical cross-linking prior to isolation from the membrane. Present indications are that such multi-subunit (or oligomeric) protein complexes may be a dominant theme in many membrane activities (Chapters 4 and 5).

2.2 Lipid components

lipid
characteristics

The lipids of membranes are amphiphilic molecules. They feature both a hydrocarbon region which is lipophilic and has very low affinity for water (i.e., much lower than water–water attraction, so that it is, in effect, squeezed out of any water phase) and a hydrophilic grouping which is usually smaller and is commonly referred to as the polar headgroup. Such molecules tend to aggregate with their lipophilic regions located in, or forming, a continuous non-polar environment; the polar groups form interfaces with each other, with other polar entities or with an aqueous phase.

In simple dispersions of membrane lipid in excess water the lipid molecules form extended (continuous) bilayer structures

31

in which both hydrophilic and lipophilic affinities are well accommodated. Such bilayer systems, either in the form of 'bimolecular lipid membranes' or of 'liposomes' (multi-lamellar or single bilayer vesicles) have been used extensively as model membranes in which characteristics of a variety of membrane components and membrane activities have been studied.

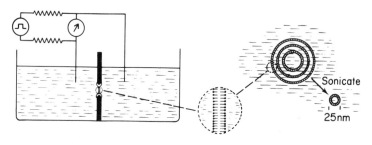

Bimolecular Lipid Membrane (BLM)   Liposomes

Sonicate

25nm

Some lipid molecules can be exchanged or even extracted from membranes by exposure to aqueous dispersions of other lipid-containing aggregates (liposomes or lipoproteins). Some of the cholesterol and some of the less polar of the phospholipids can be extracted into solvents such as ether and acetone under conditions (for example at reduced temperatures) which appear not to grossly disrupt the general membrane structure. Most phospholipids, however, can be efficiently extracted only with organic solvents such as mixtures of chloroform and methanol which destroy the molecular organization of the membrane. Extraction of extremely anionic lipids such as phosphatidylinositol 4-phosphate and 4,5-bisphosphate requires acidic conditions. Factors controlling lipid extraction may include not only the location of lipid molecules in the membrane and the forces holding them there, but also the composition of the lipid phase and the facility with which the various lipids can be accommodated in the solvent. Subsequent subfractionation of the lipids reveals a variety of solubility characteristics ranging from the nonpolar solvent requirements of the uncharged neutral lipids to the ready solubility in water of some of the glycosphingolipids with extensive hydrophilic oligosaccharide headgroups. The latter are not extractable from the membrane with water but prove to be water-soluble when isolated.

In most animal cell membranes the dominant lipids are glycerophospholipids but some membranes, particularly cell surface membranes, also contain substantial proportions of sphingolipids and neutral (less polar) lipids, mainly choles-terol. Glycerophospholipids are derivatives of glycerol which have a phosphate-containing substituent as well as two (occa-sionally one) fatty acid or ether substituents. In the case of both the headgroup and the hydrocarbon moiety there are several alternative substituents, but phospholipid classes with particular headgroups tend to have preferred hydrocarbon chain complements. A single membrane therefore contains a large number of chemically distinguishable species of glycero-phospholipid which are collected into relatively few classes in most analyses. In sphingolipids, the hydrophobic portion of the molecule is ceramide (an *N*-acyl derivative of sphingosine, a long chain amino alcohol) and the headgroup may be either a phosphate-containing substituent (usually phosphoryl-choline) or, in the glycosphingolipids, a sugar grouping which may include from one to more than 20 saccharide residues. The variety and complexity of membrane carbohydrate, both on lipids and proteins, are discussed in Section 2.3.

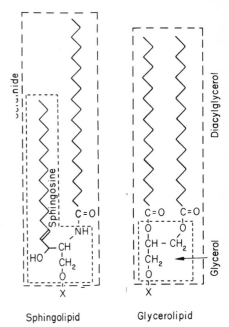

Sphingolipid   Glycerolipid

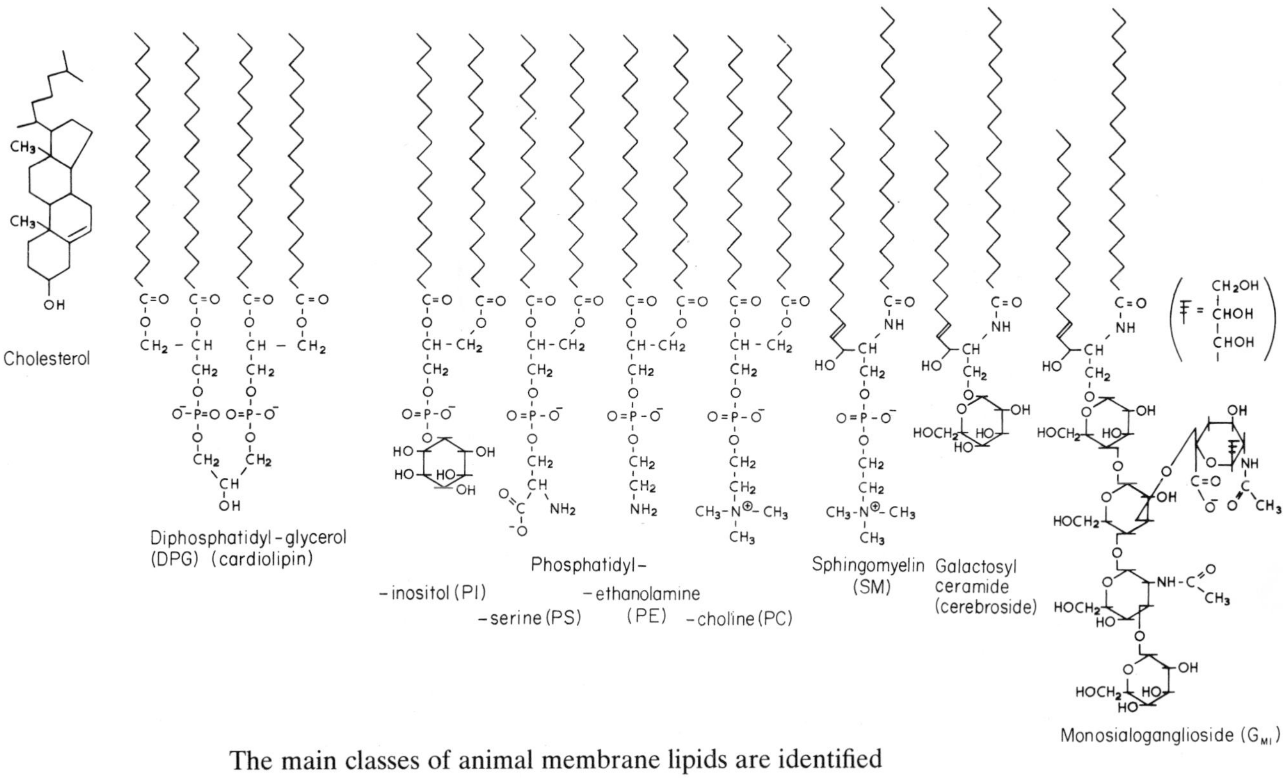

Cholesterol

Diphosphatidyl-glycerol (DPG) (cardiolipin)

Phosphatidyl-

– inositol (PI)
– serine (PS)   – ethanolamine (PE)   – choline (PC)

Sphingomyelin (SM)

Galactosyl ceramide (cerebroside)

Monosialoganglioside (G$_{MI}$)

The main classes of animal membrane lipids are identified in the accompanying diagram. Detailed studies of molecular conformation have been limited to a few synthetic phos-pholipids with fully saturated fatty acyl chains. One of the

33

most striking features is the orientation of the three glycerol carbons approximately in line with the 3-fatty acyl chain direction, so the 2-chain has to make an approximately 90° bend to enable it to align with the 3-chain. The two chains thus become displaced axially by 0.37 nm (about three methylene residues). The orientation of the P–N dipole in the phospholipid headgroup shows some variation, dependent on the size of the headgroup, but, in general, it lies close to the plane of the lipid layer. There is evidence that this conformation is maintained in aqueous dispersions of phospholipids.

Lipid analyses of membranes have revealed some striking general similarities, especially between equivalent membranes in different cells. In all animal cell membranes a substantial proportion (35–75 per cent) of the phospholipid molecules (PC, SM and LPC) have the zwitterionic phosphorylcholine headgroup. Moreover, in erythrocyte membranes from different animals, the joint contributions of PC and SM are maintained relatively constant whilst their individual proportions vary over a wide range. In animal membranes, the strongly negatively charged glycerophospholipids (PS, PI, DPG) together constitute a relatively constant proportion (15–25 per cent) and PE also contributes an appreciable net negative charge at physiological pH.

Analyses of surface membrane preparations from a wide range of animal cells have demonstrated a characteristically high cholesterol content, often about equimolar with the phospholipids. These membranes are also relatively rich in

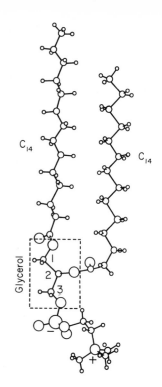

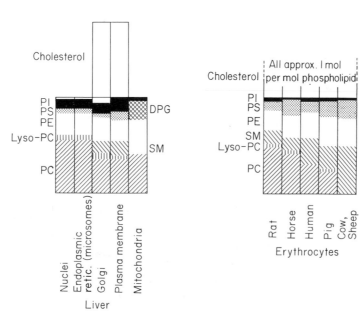

sphingolipids: a few possess as much sphingolipid as glycerophospholipid. In contrast, mitochondria, nuclear membranes and endoplasmic reticulum contain little sphingolipid or cholesterol. Golgi membranes and the membranes of secretory vesicles and secondary lysosomes have lipid compositions intermediate between those of the plasma membrane and the major intracellular organelles: this may reflect their relationship with the plasma membrane in endo- and exocytosis (Chapter 6). DPG is a strongly negatively charged lipid that is found in substantial amounts in mitochondria but not in other animal cell membranes. It is, however, a major lipid of many eubacteria and this has been cited as evidence in support of the view that mitochondria evolved from symbiotic eubacteria.

The fatty acyl and ether chains of lipids in animal cell membranes are unbranched and contain even numbers of carbon atoms, mainly 14–24, and the double bonds (0–6) are of *cis* configuration. Glycerophospholipid acyl chains tend to range from the shorter saturated types (C_{16} and C_{18}) to longer-chain polyunsaturated fatty acids (C_{20}–C_{24} with 4–6 double bonds), whereas the major acyl residues of sphingolipids are often of the longer chain saturated types (C_{20}–C_{24}). Sphingolipids often, in addition, contain substantial proportions of very long-chain saturated fatty acyl residues with a hydroxyl group adjacent to the carbonyl group. Perhaps, as a result of these differences, average levels of unsaturation tend to be significantly higher in the lipids of some cytoplasmic organelles than in the plasma membrane lipids of the same cell. One general effect of the higher cholesterol content and lower levels of unsaturation may be to make the lipid phase of plasma membranes less disordered (less fluid) than the lipid of cytoplasmic organelles. There is some evidence that diet may influence the fatty acid compositions of membrane lipids, but even when this happens, there is a strong tendency to retain in the lipids a relatively unchanged complement of certain 'essential' polyunsaturated acids.

In plant cells, the membranes of the organelles which they have in common with animal cells appear to have very similar lipid compositions, except that the major sterol is usually stigmasterol or cytosterol. Chloroplasts, however, show significant similarities to cyanobacteria in that they both contain mono- and digalactosyldiacylglycerol, sulphated glycosyldiacylglycerol and phosphatidylglycerol. Such similarities support the idea that chloroplasts and blue–green algae share a common ancestry. Chloroplasts also contain other lipids

Saturated   Polyunsaturated

Photosynthetic
pigments

Galactolipids

Sulpholipids

Phospholipids

(PC, PE and PI) which are characteristic of eukaryotes and might be expected to have been acquired from the general lipid metabolism of the host cell.

The yeast protoplast membrane contains about 40 per cent lipid, the bulk of which appears to be neutral lipid, ergosterol, and only 15–25 per cent is phospholipid. PE (33 per cent) and PC (23 per cent) are major components but the more highly charged phospholipids (PS, PI and PA) together account for almost 40 per cent.

The lipid composition of bacterial membranes presents great variety which depends not only on the strain of bacteria but also on the culture conditions and the stage of growth. Membrane fractions from bacteria, which may include plasma membrane, mesosomal membrane and sometimes the outer membrane, contain from 10 to 30 per cent lipid. The lipid content of membrane from wall-less bacteria (L-forms) and from *Mycoplasma* and *Acholeplasma* is somewhat higher.

The dominant phospholipids in membranes of gram-positive bacteria are phosphatidylglycerol (PG), amino-acyl derivatives of PG, and DPG, but PE is the most abundant phospholipid in gram-negative organisms. The lipid compositions of the L-forms differ substantially from those of the parent bacteria and are much more readily modified by manipulation of the culture medium. For example, cholesterol from the medium may be incorporated into the membranes of the L-form whereas it is completely absent from the parent organism. *Mycoplasma* are normally sterol-dependent whereas the closely related *Acholeplasma* species will incorporate sterol if available in the medium but are not dependent on it for growth. However, without cholesterol the membranes are more fragile.

In some strains of *Mycoplasma* and *Acholeplasma* and of bacteria, fatty acids from the culture medium are incorporated unchanged into the membrane lipids so that the fatty acid patterns of lipids in the membranes can be manipulated for experimental purposes. Branched chains and chains containing ring structures produce disorder in bacterial lipids in the same way as double bonds in eukaryote lipids.

The lipids of the *Archaebacteria* are very different: this group of bacteria comprises methanogens, extreme thermoacidophiles and extreme halophiles (including *Halobacterium* sp.). The major lipids are glycerolipids analogous to, amongst others, phosphatidylglycerol, but in these organisms the hydrocarbon substituents are branched phytol chains (as in chlorophyll, see Chapter 4) which are ether-linked to the 2-

and 3- positions of the glycerol (rather than the usual 1- and 2- positions), and headgroups are attached to the 1-carbon of the glycerol.

2.3 Carbohydrate components

Chemical analyses of plasma membrane and intracellular membrane systems have established that although the former carries the bulk of the cellular carbohydrate (including the glycocalyx), there are significant amounts also associated with membranes of subcellular organelles such as lysosomes, nuclei, Golgi complex and mitochondria. The carbohydrate content (in terms of total hexose) of plasma membrane preparations from mammalian cells ranges from 1 to 8 per cent of the total dried mass, but in an *Amoeba* a recent estimation has indicated as much as 25 per cent. The carbohydrate residues of the mammalian cell surface generally include sialic acid, L-fucose, galactose, mannose (and sometimes glucose), *N*-acetyl galactosamine and *N*-acetyl glucosamine. These sugars are assembled into a great variety of heterosaccharide chains which are not readily removed from the cell surface by washing, even in the presence of chelators. They are linked covalently to protein and lipid components of the membrane and are an integral part of the structure.

More detailed information on the structures of the heterosaccharides exposed at the cell surface has been obtained using specific binding agents such as lectins (proteins, often from plant seeds, with relatively specific binding affinities for certain carbohydrate groupings) and from material liberated by enzymes such as specific glycosidases which release particular sugars (for example sialic acid by neuraminidase) or by proteolytic enzymes which liberate the intact heterosaccharide attached to a peptide fragment. From such studies, sialic acid has been identified as a principal terminal sugar on heterosaccharide chains and as one of the principal contributors to the negative charge on cell surfaces (see p. 26). This charge can be reduced substantially by the action of neuraminidase, but there is a striking lack of proportionality between the amount of sialic acid liberated and the observed decrease in negative charge.

Many heterosaccharides at cell surfaces act as binding sites for viruses, lectins, etc., or display antigenic characteristics that may be retained even when they are liberated from the membrane by proteases or endoglycosidases. Detailed characterization of the carbohydrate structures responsible

cell surface charge

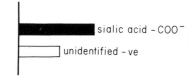

Contributions to surface charge in plasma membranes

Human erythrocyte

sialic acid – COO⁻

unidentified – ve

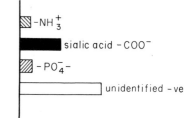

Human lymphocyte

– NH₃⁺

sialic acid – COO⁻

– PO₄⁻ –

unidentified – ve

for human blood group antigenicity, which is also expressed on numerous cell surfaces other than that of the erythrocyte, was facilitated by the occurrence of similar, if not identical, antigenic determinants on glycoproteins that are produced in large quantities by secretory glands. The ABO antigenic system is based on three determinants (A, B and H) which are characteristic both of membrane glycosphingolipids and of large heterosaccharides attached to band 3 polypeptides: the structures of A_2, B_2 and H_2-specific neutral glycolipids are shown in the margin. Individuals of the O blood group carry both anti-A and anti-B antibodies in their plasma but their cells carry neither A nor B antigens. They do, however, carry an H antigen which is, in effect, the precursor of both A and B. Group A individuals carry the A determinant on their cells and anti-B antibodies in their plasma and group B individuals have the reverse arrangement, whilst AB individuals carry both A and B antigens and neither antibody. Antigens of the Lewis group (Le_a and Le_b) and of the I group (I and i) are also expressed on, respectively, small and large glycosphingolipids.

blood group antigens

Membrane glycoproteins, like soluble glycoproteins, have each heterosaccharide side-chain attached either through an alkali-stable *N*-glycosidic linkage between an *N*-acetylglucosamine residue and an asparagine residue of the peptide backbone, or through an alkali-labile *O*-glycosidic bond between an *N*-acetylgalactosamine residue and either a serine or a threonine residue of the peptide. The heterosaccharides attached to serine or threonine are trisaccharides or tetrasaccharides, and there may be many such groupings close together along a single polypeptide chain, for example the 15 *O*-linked heterosaccharides (see diagram) that are all within 50 amino acid residues of the *N*-terminus of erythrocyte glycophorin A (see p. 29). In addition, within this span is a larger, asparagine-linked heterosaccharide. One of the surface glycoproteins of thymocytes is large (mol. wt 95 000, 60 per cent carbohydrate, with approximately 1 heterosaccharide grouping per 5 amino acids) and bears *O*-glycosidically-linked heterosaccharide groupings.

linkage to polypeptides

The majority of membrane glycoproteins—probably representing the majority of proteins exposed at cell surfaces—bear only asparagine-linked heterosaccharide chains. The core sugar sequence of these heterosaccharides usually consists of two *N*-acetylglucosamines followed by a branched structure of three or more mannoses, with the individual character of each heterosaccharide conferred by a variety of sugars attached as

$$\prime = \underset{(N\,Ac)}{\overset{\prime}{NHCOCH_3}} \qquad \ddagger = \begin{array}{c} CH_2OH \\ | \\ CHOH \\ | \\ CHOH \\ \llcorner \end{array}$$

O - linked heterosaccharides
of glycophorin A

38

branches or extensions to this core structure: typical examples include the mannose-rich heterosaccharides of rhodopsin (see diagram) and the acidic sialylated heterosaccharides of the G-protein of the envelope of vesicular stomatitis virus (see diagram). Different proteins bear few or many such heterosaccharide chains, with each contributing a mass equivalent to about 15–25 amino acid residues to the total glycopeptide. Recent studies have also identified much larger heterosaccharide structures (mol. wt 7000–11 000) on band 3 and band 4.5 polypeptides of the erythrocyte membrane. These are probably linked to the polypeptide through a typical *N*-acetylglucosamine/mannose core structure, but the majority of their mass consists either of a linear oligomer of alternating galactose and *N*-acetylglucosamine (fetal form), or of a similar structure with frequent 6-linked side-chains on galactose residues. These 'erythroglycan' heterosaccharides bear both ABO and I antigenic determinants (I on the adult form, i on the fetal).

2.4 Spatial relationships

The most direct information on the general spatial distributions of protein and lipid components in membranes has come from x-ray diffraction studies of a few favourable membrane systems and from electron microscope studies. The myelin sheaths of nerve fibres and the photoreceptor cells (rods and cones) of the retina feature regular and extensive stacking of membranes from which x-ray diffraction patterns can be recorded with the minimum of sample manipulation. Direct interpretations of the diffraction intensities, in terms of variations of electron density through the membranes, have provided profiles which show relatively low electron densities at the centres of the membranes and peaks of electron density towards the surfaces. In the case of myelin membranes, the minimum electron density approximates to that of liquid hydrocarbon, and the electron density profile as a whole is readily accounted for in terms of a structure in which the lipid component is in the form of a bilayer with the central hydrocarbon region in a disordered (fluid) state. The phosphate groups of the phospholipid molecules will be near the surfaces of the bilayer and are probably major contributors to the peaks of electron density.

X-ray data from other membranes which require isolation and concentration to produce a diffracting system are generally less detailed. They are, however, sufficient to provide a

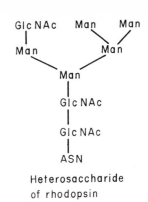

Heterosaccharide
of rhodopsin

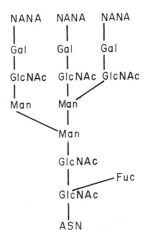

Heterosaccharide
of G−protein of
vesicular stomatitis
virus

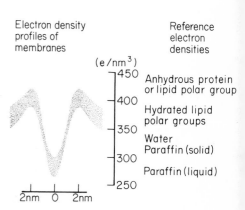

Electron density
profiles of
membranes

Reference
electron
densities

clear indication that the central regions of membranes are generally of relatively low electron densities. This would be consistent with an arrangement of the lipid components predominantly in bilayer form. Comparisons of natural membranes with their lipid extracts by a variety of techniques (differential thermal calorimetry, nuclear magnetic resonance, freeze-fracturing and measurements of electrical parameters and of permeability to non-electrolytes) have provided very similar indications. In fact, wherever there is a positive indication concerning the arrangement of lipid in membranes, it is for the lipid to be in bilayer form and located centrally.

Within the bilayer, there is evidence of some heterogeneity of distribution of individual lipid types or classes and of variations in the physical state of lipids in specific regions. An asymmetry of distribution of phospholipids between the cytoplasmic and the external leaflets of the bilayer in the erythrocyte membrane has been demonstrated both by chemical labelling and by hydrolysis of exposed molecules by specific phospholipases. Preliminary data from several other membranes have indicated that orientation of the more highly charged phospholipids towards the cytosol and of choline phospholipids towards the cell exterior and into the interiors of the organelles might be a general feature of mammalian membrane structure. Glycosphingolipids, as might be expected from their functions, are directed predominantly towards the cell exterior. There is, as yet, no clear indication as to whether or not cholesterol is also asymmetrically distributed.

The amphiphilic character of some intrinsic proteins (Section 2.1) clearly requires that parts of these molecules be inserted into the non-polar centre of the lipid layer and that some even span the whole of the non-polar region. Such penetration of the interior of the membrane by protein can be visualized in electron micrographs of replicas of freeze-fractured membrane preparations (see Chapter 1). This preparative procedure exposes the non-polar interior of the membrane and it is widely accepted that the projections ('particles') seen in the replicas of the exposed faces represent protein components which penetrate into the hydrocarbon region of the membrane. Most membrane replicas show a fairly high density of projections and pits and, in the case of the erythrocyte membrane, it has been estimated that they represent a total penetration of the membrane interior of about 30 per cent.

The extent to which individual proteins are exposed at either or both surfaces of membranes can be deduced from

lipid bilayer

lipid asymmetry

location of proteins

freeze-fracture

Erythrocyte membrane lipid

Outside

Inside

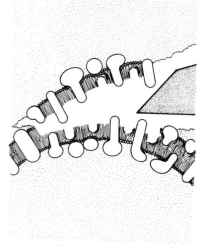

Freeze – fracture

characteristics such as accessibility of receptors, enzymes or transport systems to substrates or inhibitors, and from studies of labelling or chemical modification by specific chemical or enzyme reagents of known permeability characteristics. A number of chemical reagents which react with amino groups have been widely applied, but some difficulties of interpretation have arisen because of uncertainties concerning permeabilities and reaction conditions at the membrane surfaces. Perhaps the most conclusive information is obtained when the label is applied either as or by an impermeable macromolecule, for example ferritin-labelled antibodies, radioiodination of exposed tyrosyl groups by lactoperoxidase-catalysed iodination. Information obtained from limited proteolytic attack with enzymes such as trypsin and pronase is also free from uncertainties arising from the permeation of the modifying agent. With present techniques, identification of components that are exposed on the external surface of a cell or organelle is much more certain than for the internal surface. The general picture of protein distribution in membranes which has emerged from such studies emphasizes the asymmetric disposition of both extrinsic and intrinsic proteins. Individual proteins are confined to one or the other membrane surface or, if they span the membrane, are structurally asymmetric and always oriented in the same direction.

asymmetry of protein distribution

2.5 Molecular motions

A generally dynamic view of membrane structure, in which molecules are constantly in motion and in which interactions between molecules are constantly changing, has emerged from the application of a variety of spectroscopic techniques to the study of molecular motions in membranes. This has led to a popular description of membranes as 'fluid-mosaic' structures, but it is now necessary to add that within these generally fluid structures there is often considerable restriction and restraint. 'Fluidity' is a characteristic endowed particularly by lipid components, but the integration and control of membrane activities requires specific interactions between proteins, both intrinsic and extrinsic.

Lipid bilayer systems exhibit two major physical states: the gel phase (hydrocarbon chains relatively immobile and closely packed) and the liquid crystalline phase (hydrocarbon chains mobile and loosely packed), with a characteristic transition temperature or temperature range at which there is a change from one dominant state to the other. Major phase transitions

phase transition

41

can be seen: (1) as changes in molecular mobilities, particularly as described by spectroscopic techniques such as nuclear magnetic resonance (NMR); (2) as heat uptake during chain melting, by differentiation scanning calorimetry (DSC); and (3) as changes in structural characteristics, seen by x-ray diffraction and freeze-fracture electron microscopy. In addition to such major transitions, there may be more subtle changes in lipid mobilities that are detectable by spectroscopic methods and perhaps also by DSC. Lipid mixtures, such as those in membranes, tend to exhibit transitions that encompass a broad temperature range, and, under such circumstances, areas of both gel and liquid crystalline phases may exist simultaneously, thus giving a lateral phase separation within a lipid bilayer.

lipid
mobilities

At physiological temperatures most of the lipid hydrocarbon in membranes flexes and oscillates, much as in a hydrated lipid bilayer system above the gel–liquid crystalline phase transition, with mobilities highest in the regions of terminal methyl groups and progressively more restricted towards the polar surfaces. There is also evidence for rapid diffusion of lipid molecules within the plane of the membrane at rates similar to those in purely lipid systems, but this does not necessarily apply to all of the lipid molecules in all physiological situations. Indeed, one of the most persistent uncertainties in most spectroscopic studies of the mobilities of membrane components is the extent to which the dominant signals quantitatively report on the motions of membrane constituents.

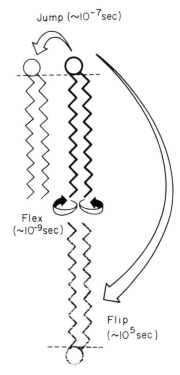

Jump (~10^{-7} sec)

Flex (~10^{-9} sec)

Flip (~10^{5} sec)

Inversions of lipid molecules (and of amphiphilic proteins) from one side of the membrane to the other (flip–flop) would be expected to be very infrequent because of the high energy expenditure that such movement would require. In lipid bilayer systems, this is indeed so and the flip rates are barely detectable, but there is evidence to suggest that some natural membranes (though probably not all) possess special mechanisms which, at times, operate to greatly accelerate flip–flop of lipids. The preservation of molecular asymmetry of membranes requires, however, that such inversion mechanisms must be limited and very selective.

Within the generally fluid lipid bilayer of membranes many protein molecules are free to rotate about an axis perpendicular to the plane of the bilayer and to diffuse laterally. Flash photolysis methods have been used to measure the decay of dichroism (e.g., of the retinal of rhodopsin) caused by molecular rotation. Saturation transfer electron paramagnetic resonance (EPR) has also provided data on the rotation of a

protein
rotation

number of important membrane proteins, both in the native membrane and incorporated into an artificial lipid bilayer following purification. Some intrinsic proteins, such as the rhodopsin of retinal rods and the Ca^{2+}-dependent ATPase of sarcoplasmic reticulum, show rotational rates commensurate with their existence in the membrane as independent molecules immersed in a medium of viscosity akin to olive oil but others, such as the cytochrome oxidase complex in the mitochondrial inner membrane, show no detectable rotation. Band 3 proteins in the erythrocyte membrane show two components with substantially different rates of rotation; the more rapid rotation and the slower, temperature-dependent rotation may represent, respectively, dimers and larger oligomers. Such mobilities also show some variability in relation to the state of the membrane, as affected, for instance, by conditions of isolation or by mild treatment of the membrane with agents such as proteolytic enzymes. Some proteins which appear to be relatively immobilized in a native membrane (e.g., bacteriorhodopsin in the purple membrane), show greater freedom to rotate or to diffuse when incorporated at higher dilution in artificial lipid bilayers.

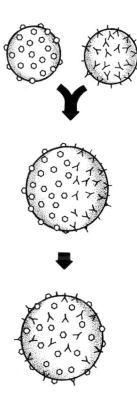

Lateral movement of proteins in membranes was first demonstrated in experiments in which plasma membrane glycoproteins were labelled with fluorescent or electron-dense markers. When two strains of cells in tissue culture were labelled with different-coloured fluorescent antibodies directed specifically against their surface antigens, they each took on a uniform labelling over their surface. When such cells were mixed and fused at 37° to form heterokaryons the two populations of antigen–antibody complexes rapidly intermixed to yield an even fluorescence of intermediate colour over the whole heterokaryon. In other studies, the distribution of fluorescent or of ferritin-labelled anti-immunoglobulin antibodies on B-lymphocytes was observed initially to be diffuse, but the binding of divalent antibody to the cell's surface led first to aggregation into discrete patches and then to rapid,

lateral movement of antigens

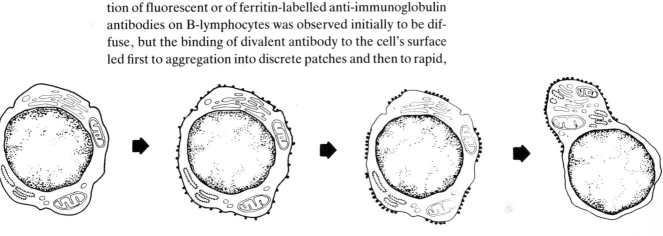

energy-dependent migration to one end of the cell (capping) and pinocytosis of the labelled complexes. There is further discussion of aggregation and endocytosis of surface-bound ligands in Chapter 6.

These early experiments provided a dramatic, qualitative demonstration of the free and directed mobilities of antibody–glycoprotein complexes at cell surfaces, but later, quantitative work, particularly using fluorescence photobleaching and recovery (FPR) methods has provided evidence of marked variations in the rates of such movements. Rhodopsin molecules, which both rotational and lateral diffusion measurements suggest to be constrained only by the viscosity of the surrounding lipid, have a lateral diffusion coefficient of $3\text{--}4 \times 10^{-9}\,\mathrm{cm^2/sec}$ in the disc membrane of retinal rod outer segments, but an extensive range of receptors and lectin-binding proteins at the surfaces of isolated or cultured cells has given values at least a factor of ten lower than this. Such differences cannot readily be explained either by variations in lipid viscosity or by formation of small aggregates of intrinsic proteins, but are suggestive of interactions with a controlling network of protein at the cytoplasmic side of the membrane. Perhaps the simplest and most readily studied example of such a network is the spectrin–actin complex which forms a filamentous layer at the cytoplasmic face of the erythrocyte membrane. It is now generally accepted that elongated spectrin molecules (mol.wts 220 000 and 240 000) form a two-dimensional meshwork through interaction with membrane actin (band 5, mol.wt 43 000), ankyrin (mol.wt 200 000) and other less well-identified polypeptides, and that this meshwork is anchored to membrane-spanning, band 3 polypeptides (mol.wt approx. 100 000). This could account for the restricted mobilities of at least some of the band 3 polypeptides in erythrocyte membranes and for the increased mobilities observed under conditions which disrupt the spectrin–actin meshwork. Actin-containing meshworks beneath many other plasma membranes are less well defined but in many cells there is also evidence for linkage between intrinsic proteins and the more gross filaments of the cytoskeleton. Evidence for the influence of such interactions on protein motion comes from modifications to such motions by pharmacological agents such as cytochalasins E or B which interfere with microfilament assembly. Capping phenomena, for example, are inhibited by cytochalasin B.

A still more positive indication of a physical link between an intrinsic membrane protein and the cytoskeleton has come from the demonstration (by a sophisticated FPR method) that

links to cytoskeleton

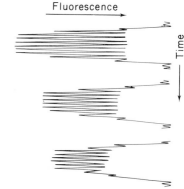

(1) Tag membrane with fluorescent ligand
(2) Bleach with stripes of laser light

(3) Lateral diffusion of both bleached and unbleached molecules is seen as exponential decrease of contrast between adjacent bleached and unbleached stripes

Fluorescence

Time

Fluorescence Photobleaching and Recovery Technique

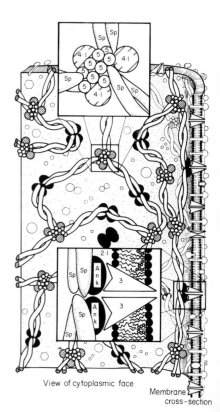

View of cytoplasmic face

Membrane cross-section

44

surface concanavalin A receptors of mouse embryo fibroblasts move faster in a direction aligned with underlying cytoplasmic filaments than in a direction perpendicular to the filaments.

lipid
heterogeneity

Lipids in membranes also show some restriction of their mobilities. Spectroscopic techniques, especially electron paramagnetic resonance, frequently distinguish between populations of lipid molecules that have different mobilities: these may represent the two halves of the membrane bilayer and/or non-uniform distribution of lipid within the plane of the membrane. There has been considerable speculation about the extent to which restriction of lipid mobilities might be caused by interactions with intrinsic proteins. Such proteins do perturb the lipid molecules within their immediate vicinity and they modify (usually elevate) the phase transition temperature of lipid when they are introduced into 'model membrane' systems. The activities of proteins, in turn, are often sensitive to the lipid environment: activities are modified by changes in the chemical nature of the lipid which surrounds them and by environmental changes (e.g., in temperature) which modify the physical state of the lipid. The lipid may be important for the maintenance of the protein molecules in an active configuration, for correct orientation with respect to the lipid–water interface and for provision of a non-polar environment suitable for interaction with particular substrates.

A lipid-dependence of many membrane activities has been inferred from the effects of experimental modification of the lipid environment and from the reactivation of purified membrane proteins by dispersion in 'model membrane' systems. Thus, in many cases in which the fatty acid composition of membrane lipids has been substantially modified by sustained changes in environmental temperature or in the pattern of

lipid-dependence

fatty acid intake during growth (e.g., in bacterial fatty acid auxotrophs grown in the presence of different fatty acids, see p. 46), corresponding changes in activation energies for enzyme activities have been detected. Treatment of membranes with lipid-perturbing agents such as organic solvents, detergents and phospholipases also tend to modify and even to abolish membrane activities, but the demonstration of genuine lipid-dependence requires a quantitative assessment of both inactivation and of reactivation of the functions of membrane proteins through the removal and restoration of lipid components.

Normal function can often be restored by lipids, or even by detergents which simply provide an appropriate non-polar environment, but studies of some purified membrane enzymes incorporated into model membrane systems have suggested more specific requirements for lipids with optimum chain lengths and degrees of unsaturation and even with specific headgroups for sustaining or restoring enzyme activity. Thus, studies of the reactivation of purified sarcoplasmic reticulum Ca^{2+}-ATPase have demonstrated that to sustain high ATPase activity the hydrocarbon chain length in the surrounding lipid must be greater than 14 carbons and unsaturated. Phosphatidylcholine is more effective than phosphatidylethanolamine, although the inclusion of both in membrane vesicles is necessary for the demonstration of Ca^{2+}-transport. Some enzymes show even more specific lipid requirements, for example mitochondrial β-hydroxybutyrate dehydrogenase is only active in the presence of phosphatidylcholine, and the sugar phosphotransferase of *E. coli* requires phosphatidylglycerol (see p. 33). The significance of such requirements for specific headgroups is not yet apparent.

Further information on the influence of the lipid environment on membrane proteins has come from attempts to correlate temperature-dependent changes in the activities of proteins and in the physical state of the membrane lipids. The temperature-dependence of activities can be conveniently expressed as Arrhenius plots (log activity vs. 1/T). For membrane activities such plots are frequently resolved into two or more intersecting straight lines with different gradients which relate to different activation energies. The temperatures at which discontinuities occur in Arrhenius plots of membrane activities sometimes correspond to temperatures at which changes in the physical state of the bulk of the membrane lipid can be detected. Such observations are taken to emphasize the influence of the general lipid environment on the activities of membrane proteins. However, shifts between two activation energies sometimes do not coincide with major lipid phase transitions but are still sensitive to changes in membrane lipid composition: it is then inferred that the membrane lipid is not in a uniform physical state and that the protein is influenced by membrane lipid that does not participate in the bulk lipid phase transition.

Such observations, taken together with the physical measurements of lipid mobility, gave rise to the idea that the lipids that surround intrinsic membrane proteins might constitute distinctive 'microdomains' or 'boundary layers' that are in a physical state different from the bulk of the membrane lipid and by which the proteins are particularly influenced. Experi-

enzyme
activity and
lipid-transitions

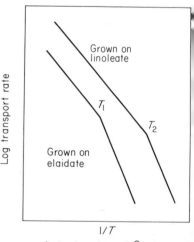

Arrhenius plots of β-glucoside transport in bacteria requiring unsaturated fatty acid.

46

ments to determine the minimum amounts of lipid needed for activity have suggested that some 'boundary layers' may be only one molecule thick. There is no doubt that introduction of protein into pure lipid systems causes some reduction of lipid mobility. ESR probes have demonstrated that lipid molecules which would normally exchange places in 10^{-9}s are immobilized for at least 10^{-8}s, but studies by NMR reveal that these molecules are still very mobile: no restriction of motion is detectable on a 10^{-5}s time-scale. Furthermore, it is not certain that all of these perturbations are attributable to boundary lipid of the type described above; much of the relevant experimental data might equally well be explained in terms of the creation of a 'trapped lipid' phase with distinctive physical characteristics by an aggregation of protein molecules, induced either by changes in protein concentration or by lipid phase transitions. Thus, the demonstration, even under relatively physiological conditions, that some lipid molecules in membranes are not freely mobile does not necessarily imply the existence of distinctive 'boundary layers' of restrained lipid molecules around individual intrinsic proteins. Neither is it clear whether such relatively modest restrictions upon lipid mobility around proteins would have any substantial effect on their functions.

'boundary layer'

Microdomain

Further Reading

Finean J.B. & Michell R.H. (eds.) (1981) Membrane Structure. *New Comprehensive Biochemistry,* Volume 1. Elsevier, Amsterdam.

Bretscher M.S. & Raff M.C. (1975) Mammalian plasma membranes. *Nature* **258,** 43–49.

Fleischer S. & Packer L. (1974) *Methods in Enzymology.* Volume 32, Biomembranes, Part B. Academic Press, London and New York.

Branton D., Cohen C.M. & Tyler J. (1981) Interaction of cytoskeletal proteins on the human erythrocyte membrane. *Cell* **24,** 24–32.

Korn E.D. (1982) Actin polymerization and its regulation by proteins from non-muscle cells. *Physiol. Rev.* **62,** 672–737.

Henderson R. (1977) The purple membrane from *Halobacterium halobium. Ann. Rev. Biophys. Bioeng.* **6,** 87–110.

Luytenberg B. (1981) Composition and function of the outer membrane of *Escherichia coli. Trends in Biochem. Sci.* **6,** 262–266.

Capaldi R.A. (1982) Structure of intrinsic membrane proteins. *Trends in Biochem. Sci.* **7,** 293–295.

Helenius A. & Simons K. (1975) Solubilization of membranes by detergents. *Biochim. Biophys. Acta* **415,** 57–108.

Hawthorne J.N. & Ansell G.B. (1983) Phospholipids. *New Comprehensive Biochemistry,* Volume 4. Elsevier, Amsterdam.

Gurr M.I. & James A.T. (1980) *Lipid Biochemistry.* 3rd edn. Chapman and Hall, London.

Buldt G. & Wohlgemuth R. (1981) The headgroup conformation of phospholipids in membranes. *J. Membrane Biol.* **58,** 81–100.

Houslay M.D. & Stanley K.K. (1982) *Dynamics of Biological Membranes.* John Wiley & Sons, Chichester.

Gennis R.B. & Jonas A. (1977) Protein–lipid interactions. *Ann. Rev. Biophys. Bioeng.* **6,** 195–238.

Chapman D., Gomez-Fernandez J.C. & Goni F.M. (1979) Intrinsic protein–lipid interactions. *FEBS Letters* **98,** 211–223.

Bennett J.P., McGill K.A. & Warren G.B. (1981) The role of lipids in the functioning of a membrane protein: the sarcoplasmic reticulum calcium pump. *Current Topics in Membranes and Transport* **14,** 127–164.

Karnovsky M.J., Kleinfeld A.L., Hoover R.L. & Klausner R.D. (1982) The concept of lipid domains in membranes, *J. Cell Biol.* **94,** 1–6.

See also pp. 212, 213.

3 Passage of small molecules

Membranes are permeability barriers that control the passage of molecules between the cell and its environment and between one cell compartment and another. While their permeabilities to most molecules are low, individual membranes show high permeabilities for particular molecules, suggesting the involvement of specific transport mechanisms. The presence of such mechanisms in membranes ensures that the functions of a cell can be carried on at an adequate rate; in some cases the transport system may even be involved in metabolic regulation.

When a transport system maintains or builds up a concentration gradient, energy is consumed. The general features of transport systems will be covered in this chapter but the link between transport and cellular energy will be considered both in this chapter and in Chapter 4.

3.1 Movement of water and dissolved gases

gases

Gases such as oxygen and carbon dioxide, which are important in cellular metabolism, pass in and out of the cell in a dissolved state and the limiting factor in the rate of transfer is the extent to which gases are soluble in the aqueous environment. Carbon dioxide is very soluble in water and passes freely through membranes but oxygen has a much more limited solubility and this becomes a limiting factor in cellular metabolism.

Water exchanges rapidly across cell membranes. This can be demonstrated by introducing tritiated water on one side and noting the rapid equilibration.

osmosis

When solutions separated by a membrane differ in concentration the diffusion of water in one direction exceeds that in the other and there is a net transfer of water across the membrane. This process is referred to as osmosis. The net movement of water continues until the concentrations of solute become the same on both sides of the membrane or until the

osmotic pressure

force generated by the osmosis (the osmotic pressure) is

49

balanced by some opposing pressure resulting from the tendency of one solution to increase in volume at the expense of the other.

Theoretically, the osmotic pressure across a perfect semipermeable membrane of 1 mol/kg solution of any non-electrolyte should be equivalent to 22.4 atmospheres at 0°C. In fact, it deviates somewhat from this value because of the finite volume of the solute molecules and their physical interactions.

Osmosis is involved in the regulation of water distribution in a variety of situations in plants and in animals. Thus, the intake of water through the root systems of plants builds up a considerable 'root pressure' which forces water into the plant stem. This root pressure is derived largely from osmosis but transfer of water through the stem to the leaves is sustained by the process of transpiration which effectively sucks up water through the stem to replace that evaporated from the leaves.

transpiration

In plants the hydrostatic pressure generated by osmotic flow (turgor pressure) is balanced by the cell walls which form a rigid structural framework. Any unicellular organism in a hypotonic environment either provides itself with a protective cell wall which limits any swelling due to osmotic inflow of water or it actively expels such water. In *Amoebae,* this excess water is accumulated in membrane-limited contractile vacuoles which are emptied through the plasma membrane. Multicellular organisms have a variety of regulatory mechanisms, the operation of which ensures that the osmotic pressure of the internal environment is maintained at a constant level. Consequently, their cells do not possess their own regulatory mechanisms and do not survive when exposed to extremes of hypotonicity. In these organisms osmosis is exploited in specialized processes which maintain homeostasis. For example, the kidney in birds and mammals can produce a highly concentrated urine (up to 5000 mosmol/l, 15–20 times the isotonic level, in the desert rat), and concentrated saline is secreted from the salt glands in marine animals (see p. 96). Osmotic phenomena are also exploited in adjusting buoyancy in some marine animals and in providing resistance to dehydration in arid environments.

turgor pressure

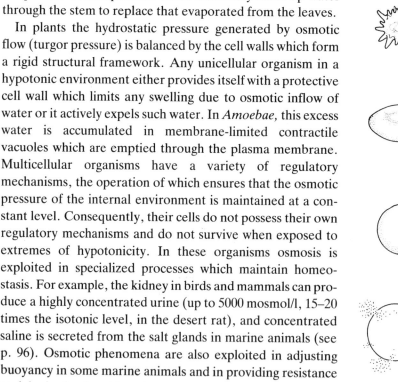

Mammalian
erythrocyte

Plant
cell

3.2 Passive movement of solutes

The existence of a concentration gradient of solute molecules across a membrane tends to cause a net movement of solute molecules down this concentration gradient. It should be noted that fluxes occur in both directions and that the net flux is the sum of these two movements.

In the simplest case, the rate of flow [the flux per unit area (J)] of uncharged molecules in the direction of a gradient can be described by the law of simple diffusion (Fick's law) which may be expressed as

simple diffusion

Fick's law

$$J = -D\frac{dC}{dx}$$

negative sign signifies that solute moves in direction of decreasing concentration

where D is a simple diffusion coefficient and dC/dx is the concentration gradient (chemical gradient). D can be expressed as ω C.RT/C where ω is a mobility, C is the concentration of solute at the plane of flux measurement and RT/C is the kinetic energy term.

Movements of ionized solutes are, in addition, influenced by electrical gradients but the rate of flow of the solute may still be described in simple terms by the Nernst–Planck equation:

Nernst–Planck equation

$$J = -\omega C \left(\frac{RT}{C}\frac{dC}{dx} + zF\frac{d\Psi}{dx} \right)$$

z = No. of electrical charges on permeating molecule
F = the Faraday (96 500 coulomb/mol)
$\frac{d\Psi}{dx}$ = charge gradient across membrane

where the expression in brackets is the combined force due to concentration and electrical gradients.

Solute movements through membranes that are described adequately by these equations may be regarded as simple diffusion or passive permeation.

Studies of the rates of passive movement of a variety of solutes across cell surface membranes have provided significant information on the chemical and physical nature of these barriers. Quantitative analysis of permeability phenomena is complicated by the simultaneous movement of solute and solvent molecule. However, methods have been devised which circumvent this and facilitate quantitative comparisons of permeability characteristics of various natural and artificial membranes. For example, methods have been developed for following volume changes in erythrocytes which result from the creation of a transmembrane concentration gradient with respect to a penetrating non-electrolyte solute. The graph of volume change against time can be extrapolated to zero time to obtain an initial rate of transfer. Further extrapolations from experiments with a variety of solutes (for example glycerol, sucrose, urea, formamide) and a variety of concentration gradients, provided parameters which have been expressed in terms of radii of hypothetical pores through which permeants might pass. The calculations involve a number of

hypothetical pores

Hypothetical pore radii

Human erythrocyte	0.42 nm
Frog muscle fibre	0.40 nm
Squid axon	0.42 nm
Necturus kidney	0.56 nm

51

assumptions concerning the applicability of particular physical laws to movements of solutes through membranes, but the values obtained for 'pore radii' have provided a useful basis for comparing the permeability characteristics of different cell membranes to water and other small uncharged molecules. The nature and location of such pores are not known. They must, therefore, be regarded as hypothetical and the calculated 'pore radii' used solely as a basis for comparisons.

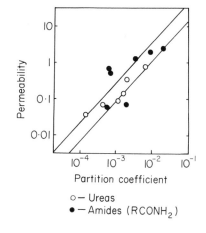

o — Ureas
● — Amides ($RCONH_2$)

lipid solubility

Studies of the rates of penetration of a wide variety of organic non-electrolytes into experimentally favourable plant and animal cells led to the suggestion by Overton in 1899 that solubility in oils or non-polar solvents was an important factor in determining rates of penetration. Observations made with the plant cell *Chara ceratophilla* gave an approximately linear relationship between permeability and oil–water partition coefficients of permeants. Size also has an effect which is only partially represented in the variation in oil–water partition coefficient. Thus, in the analysis of data on the penetration of small molecules into *Chara,* the approximation to linearity is considerably improved by introducing a molecular size factor into the relationship, that is, $P \times M^{1/2}$ against partition coefficient.

temperature dependence

The rates of penetration of several non-electrolytes across artificial lipid membranes (liposomes) and across membranes of isolated cells such as erythrocytes, tumour cells and bacteria show a marked temperature dependence. This has been taken as a strong indication that the solute molecules pass through the lipid hydrocarbon region of the membrane. This conclusion is supported by experiments in which the fluidity of the hydrocarbon region of the lipid layer has been varied by changing the proportions of unsaturated chains and of cholesterol in the lipid phase.

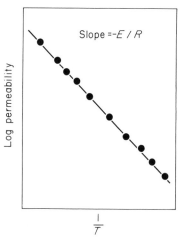

Determination of activation energy
(Arrhenius plot)

activation energies

The activation energy (E) required for penetration of molecules into membranes has been calculated from graphs of a function of permeation rate against reciprocal temperature. For example, values obtained for glycol, glycerol and erythritol correspond to the energies known to be required for the dehydration of these molecules (see margin). The removal of water of hydration from these solute molecules is therefore probably a prerequisite for entry into the lipid layer. For a non-electrolyte molecule moving passively in response to a chemical gradient, the major potential energy barrier probably reflects this necessity for the molecule to lose its water of hydration before it can pass beyond the polar barrier of the lipid headgroups.

Glycol	Glycerol	Erythritol
CH_2OH	CH_2OH	CH_2OH
$\mid$	$\mid$	$\mid$
CH_2OH	$CHOH$	$CHOH$
	$\mid$	$\mid$
	CH_2OH	$CHOH$
		$\mid$
		CH_2OH

$E = 60\,kJ/mol$ $77\,kJ/mol$ $87\,kJ/mol$

(4.2 kJ=1 kcal)

Most membranes show very low permeability to polar molecules, but there are a few apparently anomalous membranes, which show high and non-discriminating permeability to polar molecules (e.g., sugars, amino acids and nucleotides, but not their polymers) and with a linear relationship with concentration at all concentration levels. These membranes—the outer membranes of gram-negative bacteria, the outer membrane of mitochondria and the gap junction regions of the plasma membrane of apposed cells—possess pores formed by the aggregation of membrane-spanning protein molecules, for example 'porin' in bacteria and 'connexin' in gap junctions.

pores

3.3 Ion distribution

The movement and distribution of ions across cell membranes is greatly influenced by the presence in biological systems of charged macromolecules which cannot cross membrane barriers. On each side of the membrane the total number of positive charges must always equal the total number of negative charges. In the case of a simple situation, as for example one involving only solutions of sodium chloride, any movement of sodium or chloride ions across the dividing membrane must maintain the condition

$$[Na_i^+] \times [Cl_i^-] = [Na_e^+] \times [Cl_e^-]$$

so that

$$\frac{[Na_i^+]}{[Na_e^+]} = \frac{[Cl_e^-]}{[Cl_i^-]}$$

[] denotes concentration
i   denotes internal
e   denotes external

If charged macromolecules are present, then an equivalent number of oppositely charged diffusible ions must remain with them in the compartment in which they occur. This then leads at equilibrium to an unequal distribution of diffusible ions across the membrane. This is widely referred to as a Donnan equilibrium after F.G. Donnan who first investigated these phenomena.

Donnan equilibrium

Cells include protein and other macromolecules which at physiological pH have a net negative charge. If the concentration of these 'fixed' anions is X_i^- inside the compartment and the diffusible ions are entirely Na^+ and Cl^-, then at equilibrium

53

(1) $[Na_i^+] = [Cl_i^-] + [X_i^-]$

(2) $[Na_e^+] = [Cl_e^-]$

As $[Na_i^+] \times [Cl_i^-] = [Na_e^+] \times [Cl_e^-]$

then $\dfrac{[Na_i^+]}{[Na_e^+]} = \dfrac{[Cl_e^-]}{[Cl_i^-]} = \sqrt{\dfrac{[Cl_i^-] + [X_i^-]}{[Cl_i^-]}}$

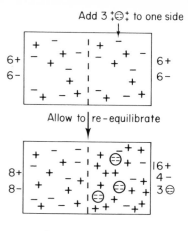

Add 3 $\cdot\ominus\cdot$ to one side

Allow to re-equilibrate

Donnan equilibrium

(obtained by substituting for $[Na_i^+]$ and $[Na_e^+]$ from (1) and (2)).

When, at equilibrium, the activities of the diffusible ions on either side of the membrane are unequal they set up an electrical transmembrane potential (Donnan potential).

For many of the cells of complex organisms there are substantial concentrations of charged macromolecules, mainly proteins, on both sides of the plasma membrane (and also of the intracellular membranes): in these situations Donnan effects may be relatively unimportant.

3.4 Mediated permeation

The penetration of glycerol into human or rat erythrocytes is much more rapid than into those of most other species, including pig, sheep and cow. There is evidence of an extra mechanism, the kinetics of which are readily distinguishable from passive permeation. This extra permeation shows a much lower activation energy and a somewhat less marked temperature dependence. It would therefore appear that, in this case, the glycerol molecules probably do not need to lose all of their water of hydration on entering the membrane and that their path is probably not directly through the hydrocarbon region of the membrane lipid. The mechanism is identified as a mediated permeation in which some specific constituents of the membrane, probably protein, play a role.

Similarly, entry of glucose, with five hydroxyls capable of forming hydrogen bonds, would be expected to require an activation energy above 80 kJ/mol but the measured activation energy for permeation of glucose into erythrocytes is approximately 16 kJ/mol. As a consequence, glucose crosses the erythrocyte membrane about five orders of magnitude faster than would be expected for passive permeation. Mediated permeation mechanisms may even operate for relatively hydrophobic molecules. For example, the entry of glucocorticoids into many cell types is far faster than would be predicted from their oil–water partition coefficients.

Passive permeation and mediated permeation are more generally distinguishable on the basis of differences in the kinetics and specificities of the two processes. A system which mediates solute movement is invariably of limited capacity and should eventually become saturated. As the chemical or electrochemical gradient is increased, the rate of permeation would be expected to approach and maintain a maximum provided that the solute concentration can be raised to an appropriate level. Note that there is always a component of the total flux which represents passive permeation by the solute: this may have to be allowed for before the saturation phenomenon can be precisely analysed.

The simple diffusion coefficient and the Nernst–Planck equations of passive permeation are not appropriate for describing the kinetics of mediated systems. The most useful attempts to analyse the kinetics of such systems have assumed that the most important factor is a specific interaction (defined by a characteristic affinity constant K_m) of the solute molecule with some component of the membrane. Unidirectional mediated flux of solute across the membrane is therefore described approximately by adopting a Michaelis–Menten type expression

$$J_{1 \to 2} = \frac{J_{max} C_1}{K_m + C_1}$$

where $J_{1 \to 2}$ is flux from compartment 1 to compartment 2, J_{max} is maximum rate of flux (i.e., the value at saturation of the mediated system) and C_1 is the concentration of solute in compartment 1. The next flux in these terms would be

$$J = J_{max} \left(\frac{C_1}{K_m + C_1} - \frac{C_2}{K_m + C_2} \right)$$

In many systems involving mediated permeation the electrochemical gradient is maintained by modifying the solute or removing it from the second compartment and the rate of mediated permeation is then closely approximated by $J = J_{1 \to 2}$. This formal similarity to enzyme kinetics means that certain types of mathematical treatments of data, developed for enzyme kinetics, can be used to determine J_{max} and K_m and, in addition, to characterize inhibitors of the mediated permeabilities.

Striking examples of saturation phenomena are to be found in the active transport systems which cause reabsorption of a variety of substances from the glomerular filtrate into the cells

saturation phenomena

Saturation kinetics
Specificity
Competitive inhibition
pH dependence
Specific inhibition

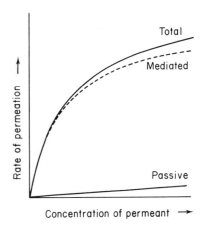

K_m, the affinity constant, is the permeant concentration at which $J = J_{max/2}$

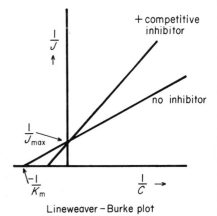

Lineweaver – Burke plot

55

lining the kidney tubules (Chapter 4). In some other systems, for example glucose transport into erythrocytes ($K_m = 25$ mM) and into hepatocytes ($K_m = 65$ mM), saturating concentrations for the transport systems are never approached under physiological conditions since blood glucose concentrations normally lie in the range of 5–10 mM.

specificity

Although mediation systems generally discriminate clearly between different types of solute molecules, for example between D- and L-stereoisomers of specific sugars and amino acids, they frequently transfer several closely related compounds. These solutes, therefore, compete with each other for a mediation mechanism. For example, the minimum structural requirements for a molecule to be recognized by the sugar transport system of mammalian intestine are met by 6-carbon pyranose sugars bearing a hydroxyl on carbon 2. D-glucose and D-galactose, which possess these features and which differ only in the orientation of one hydroxyl group, therefore compete with each other for penetration through certain membranes. However, many competitive inhibitors structurally related to permeant molecules simply associate with the mediation mechanisms and restrict access of permeant molecules: they do not themselves permeate through

competitive
inhibition

the membrane. Thus, 4,6-ethylideneglucose competitively inhibits the penetration of glucose into some cell types without itself being a permeant. Sometimes the characteristics of mediated permeation of a family of related compounds into different cells show different relative affinities for permeants or inhibitors, indicating that the molecular characteristics of the mediating mechanism, or mechanisms, vary somewhat from tissue to tissue. For example, phlorizin is a good inhibitor of glucose transport in intestine but in the erythrocyte a much better inhibitor is phloretin, which lacks the sugar residue of phlorizin.

In addition to those specific inhibitors which show a structural relationship to the permeant, many mediated permeation systems are specifically inhibited by molecules that have

specific
inhibition

no obvious structural relationship to the permeant. Phloretin inhibits sugar transport, ouabain (a steroid glucoside, Section 3.6) inhibits linked transport of Na^+ and K^+, and tetrodotoxin (a toxin from certain puffer fish, Chapter 5.5) prevents Na^+ movement through specific channels in excitable membranes.

Effects of pH, and non-competitive inhibition by heavy metal ions, thiol reagents, fluorodinitrobenzene and so on, which are known to modify the activities of protein molecules,

D-glucose   D-galactose

Phlorizin

56

also help to identify mediated permeation. For example, the mediated permeation of glycerol into human or rat erythrocytes, which occurs at pH 7, is blocked by reduction of the extracellular pH to less than pH 6 or by treatment of the cells with a low concentration (<0.1 mM) of Cu^{2+} ions. The low levels of inhibitory substances, particularly those of high specificity, that are needed to block mediated permeation indicate that each permeation system occupies only a small proportion of the total membrane area. Inhibitors have also been used extensively in the identification of mediated permeation systems of low affinity and high V_{max}.

exchange diffusion

Certain phenomena which can be expected as consequences of the action of mediated permeation systems have been widely used in their identification and characterization. However, the variety of experimental situations involved has led to some confusion in terminology. Exchange diffusion (compulsory exchange diffusion) describes the rapid exchange of permeant molecules across a membrane by a mediated permeation system. When the system is at equilibrium at high permeant concentration there is no net flux across the membrane, but if a small amount of radiolabelled permeant is then added to one side, a rapid unidirectional flux of labelled permeant is observed (in exchange for unlabelled permeant).

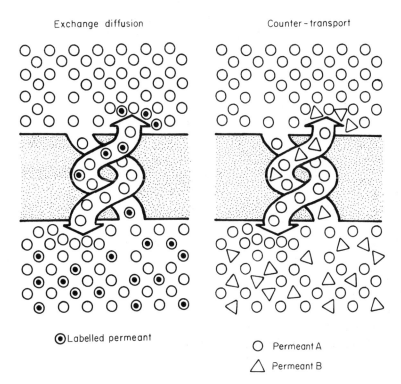

Exchange diffusion   Counter-transport

⊙ Labelled permeant

○ Permeant A

△ Permeant B

This demonstrates that even under conditions of negligible net flux (as measured chemically) and no net energy change, there is a rapid flow of molecules across the membrane in both directions. Exchange diffusion, as expected, obeys Michaelis–Menten kinetics and has a finite maximum rate.

counter-transport

Counter-transport (counter-flow or competitive exchange diffusion) occurs when a system with a single mediated permeation mechanism for substances A and B is at equilibrium with respect to A, i.e., $J^A_{1\to2} = J^A_{2\to1}$, and then permeant B is added to compartment 1. Competition by B reduces $J^A_{1\to2}$ without initially affecting $J^A_{2\to1}$ and the result is a transient net flux of A into compartment 1 even though no initial concentration gradient of A existed.

uniport

Many mediated permeation systems transport a single permeant: these are called uniports. In other systems, described collectively as cotransports, the movement of one permeant is dependent on the simultaneous movement of a different permeant either in the same direction (symport) or in the opposite direction (antiport). Symport systems include the cotransport of Na^+ and of certain sugars in intestinal epithelia or of H^+ and sugars in certain bacteria, and the best known antiport system is that which moves Na^+ and K^+ through the plasma membrane.

symport
antiport

Cotransport systems

Symport

Na^+

Glucose

K^+

Na^+

Antiport

3.5 Mediated permeation: down electrochemical gradient

The driving force for some mediated permeation systems is simply the chemical or electrochemical gradient, as with passive diffusion. In such cases, the movement of permeant is 'downhill' and these processes are termed 'facilitated diffusion'. The operation of a facilitated diffusion system should eventually lead to equilibration on either side of the membrane. However, many of the facilitated diffusion systems of mammalian tissues are for metabolites which are received from blood plasma, for example sugars, amino acids, purines and glycerol, and, in these cases, the continuous consumption by metabolism of the permeant molecule ensures that a concentration gradient is maintained. Mediated permeation systems are usually not present for compounds which are intermediates on metabolic pathways, and this often dictates that these intermediates are retained within the particular cellular compartment in which they are both synthesized and utilized. There sometimes exists, however, a facilitated diffusion system for the exit of the final metabolic product; for example,

facilitated
diffusion

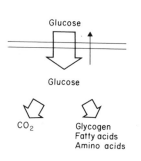

Glucose

Glucose

CO_2

Glycogen
Fatty acids
Amino acids

lactate, the end product of glycolysis, rapidly leaves red blood cells by a facilitated diffusion system.

Although many facilitated diffusion systems remain active all of the time and show constant kinetic characteristics, others vary in their activity as a consequence of changes in the environment. Some can be activated or inhibited by hormones. For example, glucose transport into skeletal muscle, cardiac muscle and adipose tissue is enhanced by insulin (see p. 125), while the equivalent systems in liver, erythrocytes, brain and several other tissues are unaffected. This allows selective control of the relative rates of glucose utilization by different tissues.

control of metabolism

A facilitated diffusion system for ions that is always active is the anion transport system of the erythrocyte, but many other mechanisms for selective ion permeation are interconvertible between active (open) and inactive (closed) states. Notable amongst these are: (i) the so-called Na^+ and K^+ 'gates' which respond to changes in membrane potential in excitable tissues such as nerve (pp. 96–101); (ii) ion channels coupled to neurotransmitter receptors (Chapter 5); and (iii) various plasma membrane ion permeation mechanisms which become active in response to a rise in cytoplasmic Ca^{2+} ion concentration. The latter, which in various cells include channels selective for K^+, for Na^+ or for Cl^-, often play a major part in the changes in membrane potential in cells that respond to hormones and neurotransmitters with a rise in cytosol $[Ca^{2+}]$ (Chapter 5.7).

ion 'gates'

3.6 Mediated permeation: against electrochemical gradient

Several of the transport processes which are of vital importance to living organisms involve mediated permeation mechanisms linked to a source of metabolic energy; this enables them to work against chemical or electrochemical gradients. Such processes are termed active transport. They fulfil the criteria already specified for mediated permeation systems, but are differentiated from other mediated systems by their ability to operate against electrochemical gradients and by their consumption of metabolic energy.

active transport

Because they can operate against concentration gradients, active transport processes are often used by cells to obtain compounds from environments where the concentrations are very low. In some cases, this causes almost complete removal of the permeants from the medium, for example absorption of nutrients from bacterial culture media and from intestinal

Glucose

Active transport –
some criteria for identification

Fulfils mediation criteria (see p. 55)
Operates against gradient
Depends upon energy metabolism

contents, or recovery of sugars and amino acids from the glomerular filtrate in kidney. Protoplasts prepared from *E. coli* (Chapter 1.3) can, if suspended in an osmotically protective medium, take up and metabolize lactose from a medium of very low lactose concentration. If the same experiment is then done either with a transportable, but non-metabolizable, analogue of lactose or with protoplasts from a mutant unable to metabolize lactose, then lactose can be accumulated in sufficient quantity to osmotically swell and lyse the protoplasts.

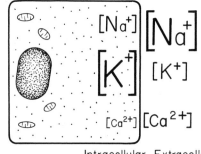

	Intracellular	Extracellul
$[Na^+]$	$\sim 10^{-2}M$	$\sim 10^{-1}M$
$[K^+]$	$\sim 10^{-1}M$	$\sim 10^{-2}M$
$[Ca^{2+}]$	$\sim 10^{-7}M$	$\sim 10^{-3}M$

Cellular ion gradients

ion gradients

Active transport systems (pumps) also create and maintain ionic gradients, allowing the cell precise control over its internal environment. One pump, often called the sodium pump, maintains a low Na^+/K^+ ratio inside cells in the face of a high Na^+/K^+ ratio in the intercellular fluid; the resulting gradients are essential for excitability, for the energization of other transport systems, and for the control of osmotic balance. Another pump maintains the intracellular Ca^{2+} concentration at a much lower level than that of the extracellular medium. The pumping of ions by cells which form an interface with the external environment (e.g., intestine, kidney) also allows complex organisms to control the ionic composition of the extracellular medium. Ion pumps are also used for the selective secretion of the ionic components of exocrine secretions. Most exocrine secretions are rich in Na^+ as compared with K^+ (e.g., sweat), gastric juice is rich in H^+, and pancreatic juice in HCO_3^-.

magnitude of gradients

The Na^+ and K^+ gradients at the surface of animal cells generally involve a difference in concentration at the two sides of about 10- to 15-fold, though in specialized tissues like avian salt gland, which secretes a 1 M NaCl solution, this difference can be much larger. Many of the other gradients generated by ion pumps are of much greater magnitude. For example, around mammalian cells the Ca^{2+} concentration (10^{-3} M) is about 10^3- to 10^5-fold higher than the intracellular activity of ionized calcium. In addition, a similar Ca^{2+} gradient exists in relaxed skeletal muscle between the cytosol containing the contractile elements and the interior of the sarcoplasmic reticulum, an intracellular membrane system capable of accumulating Ca^{2+} (for its function, see Chapter 4.6). An even more extreme gradient, this time of H^+ concentration, is from about 10^{-7} M intracellular to about 10^{-1} M extracellular across the plasma membrane of the acid-secreting parietal cells of the gastric mucosa.

energy requirement

In order to maintain such gradients, molecules or ions must be moved in a thermodynamically unfavourable direction ('uphill'). This process consumes energy, the amount being determined by the concentration gradient (non-ionized permeants) or electrochemical potential (ions). Energy is supplied by cellular energy metabolism. Interference with this supply inhibits active transport, and this serves as a diagnostic test for the presence of an active transport system for a particular material.

linkage to energy

The provision of the energy supply to active transport systems can take several forms (see also Chapter 4). Many systems use an electrochemical gradient of protons (proton-motive force) that is generated through redox, photochemical or ATP-hydrolysing reactions to drive proton (or hydroxyl)-linked symport or antiport systems; others derive the energy for the creation of ion gradients (e.g., of Na^+ or Ca^{2+}) directly from the hydrolysis of ATP. Ion gradients that are established in these ways then form a reservoir of energy that can be used by additional active transport systems which promote antiport or symport of permeants coupled to the ions of preformed gradients. In some systems, the membrane potential created by the ion asymmetries is used directly to drive (electrophorese) particular ions through specific transport systems against their own concentration gradients, thus tending to collapse the membrane potential.

demands on energy metabolism

The energy needed for active transport makes a high demand upon the metabolic capacity of many cells and may even dominate metabolism. In a resting man, active transport accounts for about 30–40 per cent of the total energy utilization. Oxygen uptake is probably the best general indicator of metabolism in the majority of tissues and it is significant that the oxygen uptake rates of many tissues which have prominent active transport activities are high.

Although all cells maintain ionic gradients, nervous tissue must continuously re-establish these gradients in the face of repeated depolarization and accompanying ion leakage (Chapter 4.8). In a resting man, the brain, although accounting for only about one-fiftieth of the body weight, consumes about one-fifth of the oxygen used by the whole body.

The human kidney produces 100–200 l of glomerular filtrate per day, but only 1–2 l of urine are excreted; most of the salts and essentially all of the amino acids and sugars which were present in the glomeruler filtrate are reabsorbed, mainly through Na^+-linked symports (Chapter 4.7). The drug, ouabain, which is primarily an inhibitor of the active co-transport of sodium and potassium, causes a depression of some 70–80 per cent in the oxygen uptake by the kidney tissue.

Energy requirements of transport

$$\Delta G = RT \ln \frac{C_1}{C_1}$$

ΔG is the free energy change (work) required to move 1 mol permeant from concentration C_2 (low) to C_1 (high). For an ionized permeant

$$\Delta G = RT \ln \frac{C_1}{C_2} + zF\Delta\psi$$

where z is the valence of the ion, F is the Faraday and $\Delta\psi$ is the potential difference across the membrane

Factors which reduce active transport

	Interferes with
F^-, iodoacetate	glycolysis
Malonate fluorocitrate	TCA cycle
CN^-, N_3^-	resp. chain
Oligomycin	ox. phosph.
2,4-dinitrophenol	ox. phosph.
Anoxia	resp. chain

Ouabain

61

This suggests that active transport is the main user of metabolic energy in the kidney.

group transport systems

The above comments apply to active transport systems in which the permeant crosses the membrane without being chemically modified. There is also a small number of transport systems, known collectively as group transport systems, in which there is covalent modification of the permeant during the translocation event. For example, entry of some sugars into certain bacteria through group transport systems involves phosphorylation of the sugars, with phosphoenolpyruvate as the ultimate phosphate donor; these systems catalyse group transport of the glycosyl group.

It has been observed that during sugar absorption in mammalian small intestine, there is sometimes a more rapid uptake of monosaccharides derived from disaccharides than of monosaccharides free in the gut lumen. It is assumed that this arises from some form of association in the brush-border membrane between the disaccharidase and a monosaccharide transport system. Similarly, there is a close association between transport and hydrolysis during the activity of the glucose-6-phosphatase of the mammalian hepatic endoplasmic reticulum. Here, however, the substrate is first transported from the cytosol to the endoplasmic reticulum lumen by a DIDS-sensitive transport process and is then hydrolysed by an active site at the lumenal surface of the membrane.

Associations between enzymes and transport systems

DIDS: 4,4'-Diisothiocyano-2,2'-stilbene disulphonate

3.7 Ionophores

Ion permeabilities of lipid bilayers and of natural membranes can be greatly increased by incorporation of a range of small molecules which includes both synthetic compounds and compounds synthesized by microorganisms, some of which have been used as antibiotics. These ionophores have been intensively studied as tools which enhance ion permeabilities and also because of the potential relevance of their mode of action to permeabilities of natural membranes.

Some ionophores, including nigericin and monensin, are negatively charged at neutral pH and form electrically neutral complexes with alkali cations and protons. Others possess no ionizable groups and form charged complexes with the appropriate ions: these include cyclic and linear polypeptides (the gramicidins and alamethicins), cyclic molecules consisting of alternating amino acids and α-hydroxy acids (valinomycin and the enniatins), cyclic molecules containing four lactone rings (the macrotetrolides, e.g., nonactin), and cyclic polyethers (the crown compounds). Compounds such as trialkyltins and triphenyltin are ionophores for anions.

cation–ionophore complexes

Many ionophores form stable complexes with cations and x-ray crystallographic analyses have demonstrated that each cation is stably coordinated with the ionophore. Non-polar groups of the ionophore are directed outwards so that the ion becomes enclosed in a purse-like structure with a polar lining and a non-polar exterior. Studies of the energetics of formation of these complexes have indicated that the compounds may gradually fold around the ions at the lipid–water interface. During this process, the water molecules associated with the ions are replaced one by one as the ions become coordinated with the ionophores: this stepwise displacement of water of hydration reduces the potential energy barrier to penetration into the membrane.

Valinomycin-K^+

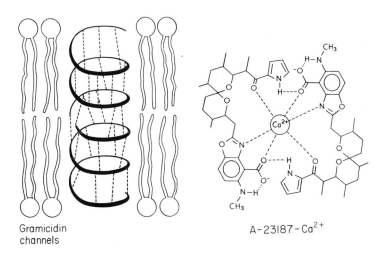

Gramicidin channels

A-23187-Ca^{2+}

carrier mechanism

Studies of valinomycin-mediated ion movement across lipid membranes under the influence of a range of electrochemical potentials have indicated that ion–valinomycin complexes diffuse as independent entities through the lipid barrier. Furthermore, movement through the hydrocarbon phase of the membrane is more rapid than through the water–lipid boundary. Studies of the kinetics of ion movement mediated by several ionophores also show that there is a strict stoichiometry between the ionophore and the ion carried, for example 1:1 for valinomycin:K^+ and 2:1 for A23187:Ca^{2+}.

In contrast, the characteristics of ion movement through lipid bilayers promoted by gramicidins A, B and C are more consistent with single file movement through channels. The

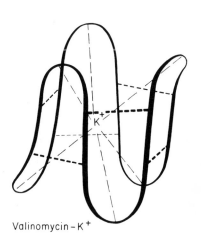

Valinomycin-K^+

pore mechanism

sizes of these molecules and the kinetics of the process suggest that two gramicidin molecules combine to form a water-filled channel through the lipid layer. Efficient channel formation by alamethicin (probably involving five molecules) requires an applied electrical potential and can be used to mimic in lipid bilayers many of the characteristics of action potentials in natural excitable membranes.

The pore-forming ionophores allow the passage of a range of monovalent cations and of protons; the channels, in addition, allow the passage of water. The ion carriers, in contrast, do not promote water flow and show somewhat greater ion specificities. These range from the relatively unspecific nigericin, which allows K^+, Na^+ and H^+ to cross and therefore effects an essentially electroneutral exchange of ions, to valinomycin which shows a preference of $10\,000:1$ for K^+ over Na^+ and does not transport protons. Thus, valinomycin will only mediate a net flux of K^+ if a permeant anion is also provided, the membrane is permeable to another cation, or a high membrane potential is maintained. A few ionophores, for example A23187 and ionomycin, show high affinities for divalent cations, particularly Mn^{2+}, Ca^{2+} and Mg^{2+}.

selectivity

temperature effect

Lowering the temperature to below the gel to liquid–crystalline phase transition temperature of the membrane lipid virtually abolishes ion movement promoted by the diffusing ionophores but has little effect on the channel-forming ones. This is probably due to restriction of diffusion in the immobilized lipid layer.

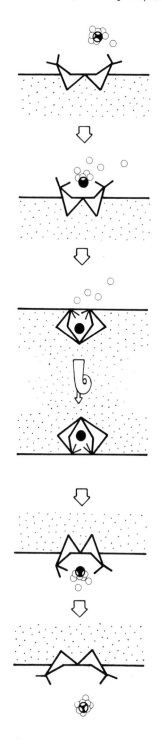

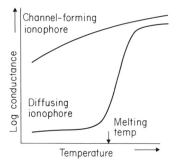

The effectiveness of ionophores in increasing the ion permeability of membranes has led to speculations that analogous compounds might be naturally present in membranes and account for many of the downhill movements of cations. Several relatively low molecular weight molecules with ionophoric properties, both proteins and lipids, have been found in natural membranes; a hydrophobic protein of molecular weight 8000 appears to be a component of the phosphate transport system in mitochondria. Possible mechanisms whereby membrane proteins provide channels with specific recognition properties are discussed on p. 73.

3.8 Mediated permeation: molecular mechanisms

inducible transport

One of the clearest indications that specific proteins are involved in the performance of mediated transport events comes from genetic studies. Some mediated systems are inducible; when a new nutrient is added to a bacterial culture this is often followed, after a brief lag, by the appearance of a transport system for this new substrate. This response can be blocked by inhibitors of protein biosynthesis. Single mutations abolish the activities of these transport systems and studies of such mutants have provided much information on the molecular components of bacterial transport systems. In man, several inherited diseases have been identified in which there is malfunction or loss of specific transport systems (see Chapter 8).

	Wild type (normal)	Mutant deficient in transport of X
Intracellular metabolism of X	+	+
Growth on X	+	−
Inducible transport system for X	+	−

transport in isolated membranes

One of the most useful findings in the study of transport phenomena was the discovery that many isolated membranes, provided that they are prepared in an essentially impermeable state and with appropriate topology (usually a closed spherical profile, but occasionally, as with an empty squid giant axon, a hollow cylinder), can effectively sustain transport processes. Such observations, which have now been made with a variety of resealed emptied cells, isolated organelles and membrane vesicles, show that the membranes possess complete transport systems that only need to be supplied with permeants and, when necessary, the appropriate energy source, for example ATP or an ion gradient. Their use also avoids artefacts due to metabolic conversion of permeant by intact cells. In some cases, the same membranes have been obtained as closed vesicles both of normal topography and inside-out, and these have been particularly useful in the characterization of the orientation of the molecular components of the transport systems and of the presentation of the energy supply.

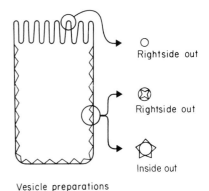

Rightside out

Rightside out

Inside out

Vesicle preparations for transport studies

Since they are enriched in the transport components, isolated membrane preparations are usually the starting material chosen for attempts to identify and isolate these molecules and such attempts are usually most successful if the chosen membrane is especially rich in the system under study. For example, sodium pump proteins form up to 10 per cent of the protein in plasma membrane fractions from mammalian kidney, dogfish salt gland, or the electrogenic tissues of electric fish (but less than 0.1 per cent of the proteins of the human erythrocyte membrane). Other particularly advantageous sources of transport proteins are the sarcoplasmic reticulum of fast skeletal muscle, where 80 per cent or more of the protein is the Ca^{2+} pump, and the purple membrane of *Halobacterium halobium*, in which the only protein is bacteriorhodopsin, a light-driven proton pump. The techniques used for isolating the molecular components of these systems are basically similar to those used for other membrane proteins; in a few cases permeant molecules or their analogues, or transport inhibitors, have been used as affinity ligands in schemes for their purification.

Mediated transport across biological membranes involves specific binding of permeant at one side of the membrane, its translocation to the other side of the membrane, its release and, if the process is driven against an electrochemical gradient, coupling to the system responsible for the required energy linkage. Understanding of the molecular mechanisms involved has been advanced by the identification and isolation of the components involved and their insertion in functional form into model membranes. Identification of the protein component(s) involved in a transport process may be through any characteristic that proves both specific and practicable, such as binding of a permeant or inhibitor, translocation of permeant or some aspect of the energy linkage, for example an ATPase activity. Such studies have revealed that in some transport systems the entire function is achieved by a single polypeptide component, while in others different aspects of the overall transport process are achieved by different polypeptide components.

One important technique for identifying molecular components of permeation systems is through detection of proteins with binding sites whose characteristics match those of the transport system. Such characteristics include specificity for permeants and inhibitors, kinetics of binding, and so on, and care is needed to ensure that the identified binding sites are really those involved in the transport process.

A variety of binding proteins which bind specific permeants can be released from bacteria by osmotic or ionic shock, procedures that release proteins from the space between the

enriched sources

recognition criteria

binding protein

Some binding proteins isolated from bacteria

Galactose	
Arabinose	
Maltose	
Arginine, lysine	*Escherichia coli*
Leucine, isoleucine	
Glutamine	
Cysteine	
Phosphate	
Sulphate	*Salmonella*
Histidine	*Typhimurium*
Tryptophan	*Neurospora crassa*
Phenylalanine	*Commonas* spp.

66

plasma membrane and the cell wall (periplasmic space). Involvement of many of these binding proteins in transport systems seems probable for several reasons. (1) Their binding constants for permeants are similar to those of the transport systems. (2) Transport-negative mutants exist which lack a binding protein but are otherwise normal. (3) Indication of a transport system involves the appearance of the appropriate binding protein. (4) Binding and transport of individual permeants are blocked by antibodies to the appropriate binding proteins. (5) Addition of purified binding proteins to shocked cells that have lost their binding proteins can restore transport activity. Although this evidence clearly implicates these binding proteins in transport processes, the existence of transport-negative mutants that possess the appropriate binding proteins demonstrates that additional protein components must be present for transport to occur.

In many other transport systems, however, permeant is bound directly to intrinsic membrane proteins. One of the best characterized is a membrane-bound binding protein involved in an inducible β-galactoside transport system in *E. coli*. This system transports a variety of β-galactosides, for example lactose, and is inhibited by *N*-ethylmaleimide (NEM). Thiodigalactoside (TDG), which is transported but not metabolized, was used to protect the binding sites of the transport system during extensive reaction of other cell surface proteins with NEM. After the NEM and TDG had been removed, the cells were treated with radioactive NEM with the binding site of the transport system now unprotected. A single protein (the M-protein) was labelled under these conditions, and this protein was only found in bacteria induced for transport. The M-protein, an intrinsic protein, has been solubilized with detergents and purified but further studies of its function were initially limited by the fact that the inhibitor was irreversibly attached. More recently, however, the M-protein has been solubilized in its native form and, when added to membrane vesicles made from lac⁻ mutants, was able to establish transport of β-galactosides. Intrinsic proteins with the same binding affinities as the corresponding transport systems have now been isolated from other membranes.

M-protein

Highly radioactive specific inhibitors have been useful in identifying components of a variety of other transport systems. Often these have been molecules which make a covalent bond and inhibit irreversibly, but sometimes reversible inhibitors of high affinity have been used: the former facilitate the isolation of the identified molecules, but the latter also

inhibitor binding

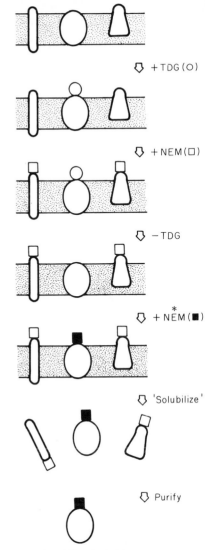

Isolation of β-galactoside permease

allow one to study function after isolation. For example, NEM (covalent) and carboxyatractylate (reversible) bind to the ATP/ADP transport system of the mitochondrial inner membrane, ouabain (reversible) identifies the plasma membrane sodium pump, and DIDS (see p. 62) is a good covalent probe for the anion transport system of the erythrocyte membrane.

translocation

Central to the concept of transport is the translocation of permeant through a membrane. Molecular components responsible for this stage can only be unequivocally identified by their purification and functionally effective insertion into a lipid membrane, but significant progress can also be made by selectively eliminating uninvolved proteins to yield modified membranes that retain transport activities.

anion transport

Facilitated diffusion systems in erythrocyte membranes have been identified by both procedures. An anion transporter was isolated in detergent and used to reconstitute anion transport in lipid vesicles—like the binding protein identified by inhibitor labelling, it was a component of approximate molecular weight 100 000. Treatment with pronase (a proteolytic enzyme) cleaved this molecule to fragments of molecular weight 65 000 and 35 000, both of which were needed for transport, but only the larger, more hydrophobic fragment bound permeants.

bacteriorhodopsin

Probably the simplest energy-linked transport system is the light-driven proton pump, bacteriorhodopsin. After isolation in detergent, this protein (mol. wt 26 000) can be incorporated almost unidirectionally into artificial lipid vesicles where it will, when illuminated, generate an electrochemical gradient of protons ($\Delta\bar{\mu}_{H^+}$). Detergent treatment of brush border membranes from intestinal epithelial cells solubilizes a number of proteins, including those responsible for Na^+/glu-

incorporation into lipid vesicles

cose symport and for Na^+/amino acid symports. Incorporation of these proteins in lipid vesicles confers on the vesicles the ability to catalyse permeant transport driven by an electrochemical gradient of Na^+. Finally, the transport activities of cation transport systems that are driven by ATP hydrolysis at the cytoplasmic surface of the appropriate membranes, including the Ca^{2+} pump of sarcoplasmic reticulum and the Na^+/K^+ pump of the plasma membrane (Chapter 4.6), have been re-established when isolated pump proteins were incorporated into lipid vesicles of appropriate composition. As in the intact membranes, ATP hydrolysis by the Ca^{2+} pump drove Ca^{2+} to the side of the vesicle away from the ATP-hydrolysing site, and ATP hydrolysis by the Na^+/K^+ pump

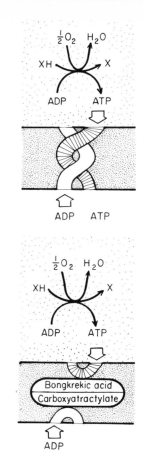

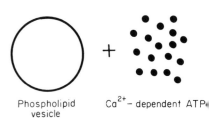

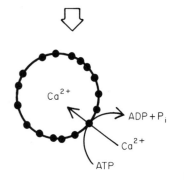

drove Na^+ away from, and K^+ towards, the membrane surface at which hydrolysis occurred.

Definition of the asymmetric nature of the action of the Na^+/K^+ pump was first achieved in emptied squid axons and in resealed erythrocyte ghosts. In the erythrocyte ghosts three Na^+ were transported outwards and two K^+ inwards as a result of the hydrolysis of one ATP molecule at the inner surface of the membrane, but stoichiometries from 1:1 to 3:1 have been reported for other tissues. No other ions are moved and thus the pump is electrogenic (see Chapter 4) whenever the ratio of $Na^+:K^+$ moved is greater than 1:1. Pumping is inhibited by ouabain at the outer surface of the membrane and by vanadate ions at the cytoplasmic surface.

The hydrolysis of ATP by this system suggested that components of the active transport system might be recognized by their expression of ATPase activity, and it is now known that most eukaryote plasma membrane preparations possess both a 'basal' Mg^{2+}-dependent ATPase activity and an additional ATPase activity which is expressed only when both Na^+ and K^+ are present. This Na^+/K^+-dependent ATPase is inhibited by ouabain, and its activity closely parallels the Na^+/K^+-pumping activity of tissues. Its spatial requirements are identical to those of the pump: it interacts with Mg^{2+}, ATP, Na^+ and vanadate at the cytoplasmic surface of the membrane and with K^+ and ouabain at the outer surface. Experimental enhancement of the normal ion gradients across a sealed erythrocyte membrane, to very high $[Na^+]$ outside and very high $[K^+]$ inside, provides an energy supply with which this activity can be driven backwards to synthesize ATP within the ghost. It has, therefore, been concluded that this ATPase activity represents the enzymic expression of the energy supply to the transport of Na^+ and K^+.

Studies with ^{32}P-ATP have demonstrated that the transport and ATPase activities of this system involve a cycle of phosphorylation and dephosphorylation of an aspartyl residue of a tetrapeptide sequence (-thr-ser-asp-lys-) in a participating polypeptide. Cytoplasmic Na^+ stimulates phosphorylation and extracellular K^+ stimulates an ouabain-sensitive dephosphorylation: the net result of this cycle is ATP hydrolysis and the movement of Na^+ outwards and K^+ inwards across the membrane.

Na^+/K^+ ATPase has been isolated from plasma membranes from several sources: the usual techniques have involved removal of extrinsic proteins with chaotropic agents followed by selective extraction of intrinsic proteins with mild detergents.

Marginal notes:

Na^+/K^+ pump

Na^+/K^+-dependent ATPase

phosphorylated intermediate

isolated Na^+/K^+ ATPase

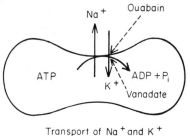

Transport of Na^+ and K^+ in erythrocytes

Na^+/K^+-dependent ATPase

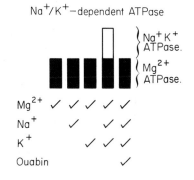

	Na^+/K^+ ATPase	Na^+ transport
Erythrocyte	+	+
Skeletal muscle	++	++
Brain	++++	++++
Kidney cortex	+++++	+++++
Fish electric organ	++++++	++++++

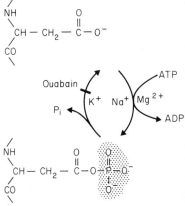

OVERALL REACTION

$$ATP \xrightarrow[Mg^{2+}]{Na^+K^+} ADP + P_i$$

Pure preparations, from whatever source, have similar specific activities and they possess an equal number of each of two types of polypeptide subunit, α-subunits (mol.wt ~100 000) and β-subunits (mol.wt ~40 000).

α- and β-subunits

The α-subunit contains a relatively large proportion of non-polar amino acid residues and a hydrophobic segment has been identified using iodonaphthylazide. It bears one site which is phosphorylated by cytoplasmic ATP and another site which binds extracellular ouabain. Proteolytic and labelling studies indicate that the polypeptide chain of each α-subunit probably spans the membrane at least twice and has a substantial region exposed on the cytoplasmic side of the membrane. The β-subunit is a glycosylated polypeptide: its carbohydrate moiety is exposed at the cell surface. Although the function of the β-subunit is unknown, it seems to be an essential component of the ATPase: attempts to dissociate α- and β-subunits always cause loss of activity and antibodies raised against the β-subunit inhibit the ATPase activity of the complex.

Studies with imidodiesters have shown that the α- and β-subunits can be cross-linked via lysine residues, and the thiol groups of adjacent α-subunits have been catalytically cross-linked using cupric o-phenanthroline. There have been no indications of the proximity of β-subunits. These results have led to suggestions that the structure of the ATPase in the membrane may be that of two αβ pairs which associate by interaction of their α-subunits. In detergent solutions, the smallest active species has a molecular weight of approximately 280 000, suggesting that the native structure may be $βααβ$.

conformational changes during transport

A variety of approaches has indicated that the enzyme (α-subunit) may exist in at least two conformational states, E_1 and E_2, depending upon permeant binding and phosphorylation. Thus, ATP binding causes a change from E_1 to E_2 that can be detected by changes in intrinsic tryptophan fluorescence. ATP binding is also associated with changes in reactivity towards the thiol reagent, N-ethylmaleimide. Phosphorylation of the enzyme causes a 100-fold increase in the affinity for ouabain even though phosphorylation and binding of ouabain occur on opposite sides of the membrane. Binding of Na^+ or K^+ decreases the susceptibility of the α-subunit to tryptic digestion and, in addition, changes the sites of attack: binding of each ion leads to production of different cleavage products. However, if Na^+ and $MgATP^{2-}$ are both present, then the phosphorylated enzyme is cleaved by trypsin at the same point as with K^+ alone. Studies of these conformational changes,

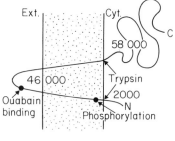

Polypeptide chain of α–subunit of Na^+/K^+-ATPase

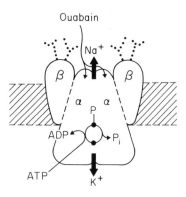

Subunit structure of Na^+/K^+-ATPase

and of a variety of kinetic characteristics of the Na^+/K^+-AT-Pase, have given rise to several detailed mechanistic models for its operation, for example:

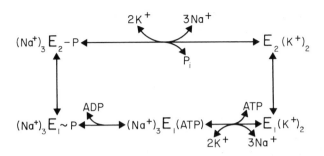

Several other ATPase activities have been identified which are intimately associated with, and probably responsible for, ion-pumping: these include the Ca^{2+}-ATPase of sarcoplasmic reticulum which helps to regulate cytosol $[Ca^{2+}]$ in fast skeletal muscle (see pp. 93–94); the Ca^{2+}-ATPase of erythrocyte membranes (and probably other plasma membranes) which maintains low cytosol $[Ca^{2+}]$; and the H^+/K^+-ATPase of the apical microvilli of gastric parietal cells which provides the acid secretion in the stomach. All require $MgATP^{2-}$ as substrate and their mechanisms involve the phosphorylation and dephosphorylation of large (100 000–150 000) membrane-spanning polypeptide chains.

The site of the phosphorylation of the Ca^{2+}-ATPase of the sarcoplasmic reticulum has been identified as an aspartyl residue in a tetrapeptide sequence identical with that in the Na^+/K^+-ATPase. Ca^{2+} ions stimulate the formation of the phosphorylated protein and Mg^{2+} ions stimulate its dephosphorylation. The Ca^{2+} pump is electrogenic and an anion transport system (for phosphate or oxalate) is required if extensive pumping is to cause appreciable accumulation of Ca^{2+} within the vesicles (see Chapter 4). The membrane-spanning polypeptide (mol.wt ~100 000) is relatively rich in hydrophobic amino acid residues. When it is subjected to limited attack by trypsin, it is split into two fragments. The larger fragment (mol.wt ~55 000) bears the ATP-hydrolysing site and the phosphorylation site has about 50 per cent polar amino acid residues and is easily iodinated by lactoperoxidase at the cytoplasmic surface of the membrane. It therefore seems likely that this fragment represents a fairly polar part of the molecule that is exposed at the cytoplasmic surface and is responsible for coupling ATP hydrolysis to transport. Negatively stained vesicles of the sacroplasmic reticulum show 3.5 nm

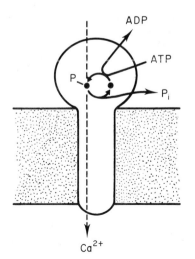

Ca²⁺-ATPases

Sarcoplasmic
reticulum
Ca²⁺-ATPase

projections on their cytoplasmic surface and these are removed by this type of trypsin treatment. The smaller tryptic fragment (mol.wt ~45000) contains a larger proportion of hydrophobic amino acid residues and is less accessible to iodination by lactoperoxidase. It therefore seems to be more deeply buried in the membrane and is probably involved in the translocation of Ca^{2+} into the lumen of the sarcoplasmic reticulum. The intact polypeptide of molecular weight 100 000 spans the sarcoplasmic reticulum membrane; the *N*-terminal sequence is cytoplasmic, and cleavage and amino acid sequence data suggest that the polypeptide chain may cross the membrane several times.

The catalytic component of the Ca^{2+}-ATPase of the erythrocyte membrane is a polypeptide of molecular weight ~140 000 that constitutes about 1 per cent of the total membrane protein. The enzyme shows a high affinity for Ca^{2+}, both for activation of ATPase activity and for ion-pumping, only when it associates with a complex of Ca^{2+} and calmodulin, a small Ca^{2+}-binding protein. It is not known whether or not the calcium ions bound to the calmodulin are passed to the ATPase and transported. The interaction with calmodulin has been exploited by the use of a calmodulin affinity column to purify the ATPase from detergent solution.

A family of group transport systems, in which the enzymic mechanisms involved in coupling to the energy supply are much more complex, are the bacterial phosphoenolpyruvate-linked phosphotransferase systems (introduced on p. 62). The phosphorylation of a particular sugar involves the sequential transfer of the phosphoryl moiety initially to soluble proteins (Enzyme I and HPr) and then to sugar-specific proteins (Enzymes III and II). These latter enzymes are associated with the membrane, and the translocation of the sugar moiety across the membrane occurs concomitantly with its phosphorylation by Enzyme II; this is an intrinsic protein complex, probably spanning the membrane, whose performance depends upon a specific association with phosphatidylglycerol.

Transport proteins translocate permeants across membranes. If a transport protein were to act as a diffusing or rotating carrier then it would have, in the process, to reverse its orientation in the membrane, and any hydrophilic portions that were exposed at either membrane surface would have to be moved through the lipophilic interior. Such events would be energetically unlikely, and they would not be consistent with the maintenance of a generally constant and

calmodulin and Ca^{2+}-binding

sugar phosphorylation (group transport)

carrier mechanisms

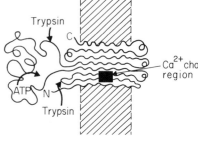

Possible structure of Ca^{2+}-ATPase polypeptide chain

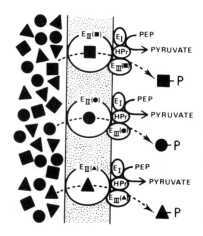

asymmetric topography of membrane proteins. However, these considerations do not necessarily exclude the possibility that some proteins might refold to yield a more complete lipophilic outer surface, allowing diffusion and reorientation. Perhaps, as demonstrated with diffusing ionophores (see p. 64), the most positive identification of a diffusing carrier in membranes would be by its inactivation when membrane lipid is cooled from a liquid-crystalline to a gel phase. No such identifications have been reported for natural membrane transport systems.

channel mechanisms

The other alternative, that of specific hydrophilic pathways through the lipophilic centre of membranes, would call for intrinsic proteins which spanned membranes. This type of mechanism is compatible with the asymmetric functional characteristics of a number of transport systems, for example their sensitivities to different inhibitors at the two membrane surfaces. Several of the proteins involved in mediated permeations have been identified as membrane-spanning proteins, some of them with substantial glycopeptide segments (e.g., the erythrocyte anion exchange protein and the β-subunit of Na^+/K^+-ATPase) which might help to stabilize them in a fixed orientation in the membrane.

Such membrane-spanning molecules almost certainly provide controlled pathways through the lipid barrier, but there is little information on the ways in which this is accomplished. However, each type of permeant presumably passes along a pathway either through a spanning polypeptide or between the polypeptide units of an oligomeric assembly. Individual transport proteins whose native state is an oligomer presumably operate through one of these two alternatives, but whenever a transport protein exists in an active monomeric form in a membrane then presumably the transport pathway is through the spanning polypeptide.

monomeric transporters

One protein which has been shown to be active as a transporter in monomeric form is bacteriorhodopsin (see pp. 30, 82). In this case, the seven adjacent rod-like peptide structures, probably α-helices, that span the membrane most likely form a proton pathway: several polar amino acid residues that seem likely to form components of the pathway that relays the proton through the structure have been identified. Another type of structure, an open polypeptide helix with a lipophilic exterior and a water-filled interior, is formed by the ionophore, gramicidin (see p. 64), but such structures are not yet known in transport proteins. It is known that the Ca^{2+}-ATPase of the sarcoplasmic reticulum, another protein whose

Asymmetries of transport systems.

polypeptide chain traverses the membrane several times, can act as an ATPase in monomeric form, but it is not known whether the monomer is an effective Ca^{2+} pump. Its graded tryptic digestion gives rise to fragments which remain associated with the membrane. One of these (mol.wt 20000) can act as a Ca^{2+} ionophore, but it is not clear whether this represents a Ca^{2+} transport pathway through the original protein. Proteolytic digestion of the erythrocyte anion transporter, another protein whose polypeptide chain spans the membrane more than once, appears to destroy the ion transport pathway without preventing ion binding to the protein.

oligomeric transporters

There have been indications that a variety of transport proteins might exist in oligomeric form. Only in the case of the Na^+/K^+-ATPase and the ATP/ADP transporter of mitochondria, however, are there clear indications that biological function is lost upon dissociation of the oligomers to monomers. In some cases, including Na^+/K^+-ATPase and Ca^{2+}-ATPase, it has been claimed that the transport proteins bind only half as many permeant (or inhibitor) molecules as the number of spanning polypeptides in the oligomer, and this 'half-of-the-sites' reactivity has been interpreted as an indication that the active species is dimeric. However, the evidence for this is only convincing for the mitochondrial ATP/ADP transporter, which binds the inhibitors atractylate and bongkrekic acid at opposite sides of the membrane. In the other cases, uncertainties in the stoichiometry relate to technical factors such as the presence of inactive protein and the validity of the protein assay method.

Only in a few cases, such as the water-filled channels through the outer membrane of gram-negative bacteria, the mitochondrial outer membrane and through gap junctions (Chapter 5), are non-specific transport pathways provided by proteins: usually there is selective permeability to one or a group of closely related solutes. This appears to imply the binding of solute at one side of the membrane, followed by some structural reorganization of the transport protein so as to expose and release the permeant at the opposite face, without at the same time allowing the passage of other molecules of generally similar molecular character (e.g., charge, polarity and size). For those transport proteins that catalyse freely reversible facilitated diffusion processes of low activation energy, the energy barrier separating the two protein conformations seems likely to be small. In the case of active transport processes, however, the energy input, whether derived from phosphorylation and dephosphorylation or from the

energy for conformational change

74

movement of an ion in an electrochemical gradient, presumably serves to drive conformational transitions of the transport proteins over an energy barrier.

lipid
involvement

Studies of inactivation of transport systems in membranes by modification of the lipid environment and their subsequent reactivation by restoration of appropriate lipids have suggested specific lipid requirements for some transport activities—for example, requirement for phosphatidylglycerol to sustain the activity of certain phosphoenolpyruvate-linked phosphotransferases. In the case of Na^+/K^+-ATPase, there is conflicting evidence for, on the one hand, a specific requirement for anionic lipids and, on the other, simply a requirement for a fluid lipid environment. A still more detailed assessment of the influence of lipid environment has been made for the Ca^{2+} transport system where the substitution of a completely artificial lipid environment around the protein molecule has distinguished two requirements: one for the ATPase activity and one for sealing the vesicles to achieve effective Ca^{2+} accumulation. In these experiments, maximum Ca^{2+}-dependent ATPase activity was achieved with a synthetic dioleoylphosphatidylethanolamine (PE), but efficient retention of Ca^{2+} in the vesicles (assessed as a Ca^{2+}-transported:ATP-hydrolysed ratio), in addition, required dioleoylphosphatidylcholine (PC). It is perhaps significant that PC and PE are the principal phospholipids of sarcoplasmic reticulum.

Further Reading

Wilson D.B. (1978) Cellular transport systems. *Ann Rev Biochem* **47**, 933–965.

Bonting S.L. & de Pont J.J.H.H. (eds.) (1981) Membrane Transport. *New Comprehensive Biochemistry*, Volume 2. Elsevier, Amsterdam.

Martonosi A.N. (ed.) (1982) *Membranes and Transport*, Volume 1. Plenum, New York.

Deuticke B. (1977) Properties and structural basis of simple diffusion pathways in the erythrocyte membrane, *Rev. Physiol. Biochem. Pharmacol.* **78**, 1–97.

Baldwin S.A. & Leinhard G.E. (1982) Glucose transport across plasma membranes; facilitated diffusion systems. *Trends Biochem. Sci.* **6**, 208–211.

Sugar Transport across Animal Membranes (a colloquium of small useful reviews on sugar transport). *Biochem. Soc. Trans.* **10**, 5–16.

Szabo G. (1981) Structural aspects of ionophore function. *Federation Proceedings* **40**, 2196–2201.

Jones M.N. & Nickson J.K. (1980) Identifying the monosaccharide transport protein in the human erythrocyte membrane. *FEBS Letters* **115**, 1–8.

Murer H. & Kinne R. (1980) The use of isolated membrane vesicles to study epithelial transport processes. *J. Memb. Biol.* **55**, 81–95.

Hobbs A.S. & Albers R.W. (1980) The structures of proteins involved in active membrane transport. *Ann. Rev. Biophys. Bioeng.* **9**, 259–292.

Kyte J. (1981) Molecular considerations relevant to the mechanism of active transport. *Nature* **292**, 201–204.

Klingenberg M. (1981) Membrane protein oligomeric structure and transport function. *Nature* **290,** 449–454.

Roseman S. *et al.* (1982) (A collection of papers dealing with the bacterial phosphotransferase group transport systems). *J. Biol. Chem.* **257,** 14461–14575.

Bennet J.P., McGill K.A. & Warren G.B. (1980) The role of lipids in the functioning of a membrane protein: the sarcoplasmic reticulum calcium pump. *Current Topics in Membranes and Transport* **14,** 128–165.

See also pp. 212, 213.

4 Generation and utilization of ion gradients

The ultimate source of energy for life is solar radiation of visible or near-visible wavelengths. Most plants and some bacteria utilize the energy of this radiation directly to drive the photosynthesis of organic compounds; such organisms are autotrophic. The metabolism of other plants and bacteria, and of all animals, utilizes organic compounds originating from photosynthesis. Such organisms are heterotrophic and their energy needs are met by oxidative reactions.

redox
potential

Both types of organism possess specialized energy coupling membranes in which electrons at a high negative redox potential are obtained either by photoactivation or from substrate oxidation and are then transferred through a series of redox components of decreasing redox potential. The energy released during this change in potential is coupled to the generation of a transmembrane electrochemical gradient of protons, $\Delta\bar{\mu}_{H^+}$. This can then be used for a variety of purposes (frequently within the same membrane), for example for heat production, to drive bacterial flagellar rotation, to generate transmembrane gradients of inorganic ions or metabolites, to provide a membrane potential, and to synthesize ATP. ATP synthesis represents only a part of the energy conservation in photosynthesis; its other aspect is independent of $\Delta\bar{\mu}_{H^+}$ and is the synthesis of a compound of high negative reduction potential, NADPH.

The redox (oxidation/reduction) potential of any compound is a measure of its ability to reduce or to oxidize other compounds. A high negative redox potential signifies an effective reducing capacity (electron or hydrogen donor) whilst a high positive redox potential is characteristic of an effective oxidizing agent (electron or hydrogen acceptor).

Both ATP and the electrochemical gradients of ions represent energy stores which can be exploited by the cell. This chapter will examine the maintenance of these energy stores and the various purposes for which cells utilize ion gradients.

4.1 Energy coupling membranes

The photosynthetic membranes in plants are the thylakoid membranes of chloroplasts whereas in photosynthetic bacteria they are specialized invaginations of the plasma membrane termed chromatophores. The plasma membrane of bacteria and the inner membrane of mitochondria in eukaryotic cells support heterotrophic metabolism. All of these specialized membranes are relatively highly organized structures which contain high concentrations of redox components, light sensitive pigments (where appropriate), an ATP synthesizing system and often transport systems for various ions and metabolites. Physical proximity is particularly important in sequences of components which involve unstable intermediates; in a membrane this can reduce diffusion paths to a minimum and thereby permit energy transfers, such as those between photosynthetic pigments that are extremely close together. Spectroscopic studies have demonstrated the presence, during electron transfer, of free radicals such as semiquinones that have only a short life in free solution.

photosynthesis in plants

During the process of photosynthesis in plants, light excites a series of lipid-like pigments (carotenoids, phycobilins and chlorophylls a and b). These pigments pass their excitation energy by resonance energy transfer to P_{682}, a complex of a pair of chlorophyll a molecules with protein. This is the photochemical reaction centre for this assembly, termed Photosystem II. As a result of this excitation, electrons in P_{682} are raised to a higher energy level (more negative redox potential) and these then reduce an unidentified compound, possibly a quinone or an iron-sulphur protein. (The electron deficiency in P_{682} is corrected by electron transfer from water, which is split to yield protons and oxygen.) The electrons are then transferred through a series of electron and (electron+proton) redox components of increasingly positive potential, including plastoquinone, cytochrome b_6, cytochrome f and plastocyanin, with the released free energy being sufficient for the generation of a molecule of ATP.

Plastocyanin then donates electrons to another form of protein-associated chlorophyll, P_{700}, which is the photochemical reaction centre for another functional assembly termed Photosystem I; Photosystem I is excited by longer wavelength light than is Photosystem II.

After excitation, the pigments in Photosystem I pass their excitation energy to P_{700}, raising the incoming electrons to a yet more negative redox potential. These are then transferred to an unknown acceptor (possibly an iron–sulphur protein), onwards to ferredoxin (another iron–sulphur protein) and finally to a flavoprotein which utilizes them to reduce $NADP^+$.

Careful detergent dissection of chloroplast membranes has yielded separate preparations selectively enriched in Photosystems I and II; each of these preparations contain a distinc-

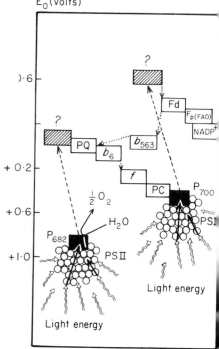

Chlorophyll a

Energy transfer in photosynthesis
E_0 (volts)

tive population of chlorophylls, accessory pigments, proteins and lipids. Some of these proteins, which have been isolated separately, are associated with several molecules of chlorophyll *a*; these associations are probably responsible for the shifts of the absorption peak (e.g., to 678, 682, 700 nm) away from the 633 nm absorption peak of chlorophyll *a*.

bacterial photosynthesis

In bacteria, the photosynthetic pigments show a wide species variation, but all species utilize bacteriochlorophyll in place of the chlorophyll *a* of plants. In the overall photosynthetic process a photosystem donates excitation energy to a photochemical reaction centre, P_{870}, containing a pair of bacteriochlorophyll molecules. Both plants and bacteria carry out cyclic photophosphorylation in which the high potential electrons resulting from photoactivation are returned to the photochemical reaction centre for reactivation. In plants this cycle involves the electron transfer components involved in the non-cyclic process together with an intermediate cytochrome *b* (see diagram, p. 78). Since the same electrons are recycled, there is no requirement for primary electron donors. The fall in potential in the electron transport sequence, in both plants and bacteria, is sufficient to support the generation of a molecule of ATP. Bacteria are also capable of non-cyclic electron flow in which electrons are raised to a high negative potential and, via ferredoxin and a flavoprotein, ultimately generate NADH or H_2. The electrons are originally derived from electron donors (e.g., H_2S, $Na_2S_2O_3$, acetate or succinate, according to the species) via an electron transfer sequence which is, as yet, little understood.

cyclic photophosphorylation

The inner membrane of the mitochondrion and the plasma membranes of aerobic bacteria contain components which carry out the oxidation of substrates of high negative redox potential using oxygen as the ultimate acceptor of electrons; anaerobic bacteria utilize other compounds, for example NO_3^- or SO_4^{2-}, as terminal electron acceptors. In carrying out these oxidations, these membranes employ an electron transfer chain consisting of a series of electron transferring components, some of which also transfer protons, of increasingly positive redox potential.

electron transfer chains

The functional sequences of these components in mitochondria, in some bacteria, and also in the photosynthetic membranes mentioned above, have been analysed by the use of substrates and acceptors of known redox potential, by the use of specific inhibitors and by specialized spectroscopic techniques. Some of the individual redox components have been purified, but often with modified properties; others have

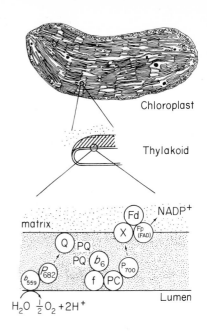

Chloroplast

Thylakoid

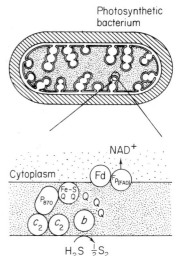

Photosynthetic bacterium

been detected only in functioning membranes, with their properties being dictated by their functional inter-relationships with other components. Although in many cases the overall sequences are known, the exact positions of some components, for example the *b*-type cytochromes and various iron–sulphur proteins in mitochondrial electron transfer, are still uncertain.

Careful detergent dissection of mitochondrial membranes has resulted in the isolation of several functional sequences of components; these are the electron transfer complexes NADH-Q reductase, succinate-Q reductase, QH$_2$-cytochrome *c* reductase and cytochrome *c* oxidase. Kinetic analysis of electron transfer in membranes containing different amounts of lipids shows that electron transfer between components within each complex is little affected by alterations in membrane lipid content whereas electron transfer between complexes is slowed by increasing the amount of lipid in the membrane, thereby increasing the diffusion distance between the complexes.

In the mitochondrial electron transfer chain, the electrons are originally derived from NADH (standard redox potential -0.32 V) or another substrate of more positive redox potential (e.g., succinate, *sn*-3-glycerophosphate, fatty acyl-CoA) and then passed to flavoproteins. This is followed by electron transfer to other components of the sequence (iron–sulphur proteins, quinones, cytochromes), until, with the reduction of oxygen by cytochrome oxidase, a redox potential of $+0.82$ V is achieved.

The change in redox potential between NADH and oxygen is 1.14 V, and this represents a free energy change of about 220 kJ/mol NADH. This free energy change supports the establishment of an electrochemical gradient of protons (proton motive force) $\Delta\bar{\mu}_{H^+}$ and is more than sufficient to support the observed generation of 3 mol of ATP from ADP (3×31 kJ) by the overall process termed oxidative phosphorylation.

By using specific substrates, acceptors and inhibitors, it can be demonstrated that the passage of electrons through NADH-Q reductase, QH$_2$-cytochrome *c* reductase or cytochrome *c* oxidase results in a free energy change of sufficient magnitude to support the generation of ATP; the complexes are therefore energy-conserving sites.

The components of the electron transfer complexes and of the ATP-synthesizing apparatus are asymmetrically distributed in membranes. Information on these distributions has come from a variety of approaches. One of the most useful of

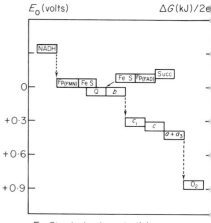

Mitochondrial electron transfer

E_0 = Standard redox potential

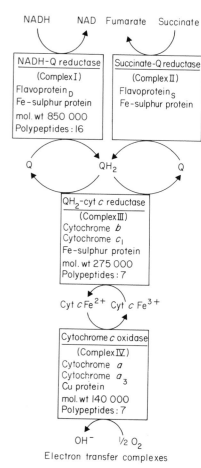

Electron transfer complexes

these is the preparation of vesicles of normal or reversed orientation whose behaviour is then compared to that of the original organelle. Such techniques have been used to establish the topography of components in mitochondrial inner membranes, in bacterial plasma membranes and in photosynthetic membranes.

	Digitonin or phospholipase c (and intact mitochondria) *Outside-out*	Sonication *Inside-out*
NADH dehydrogenase	– latent	– non-latent
Succinate dehydrogenase (SDH)	– latent	– non-latent
Quenching of EPR signal of SDH Fe–S protein	– not so readily	– readily
Release of cytochrome c	– by salt	– by detergent; not by salt
Antibody to cytochrome c	– inhibits respiration	– no effect
Antibody to cytochrome c_1	– inhibits respiration	– no effect
Quenching of EPR signal of cyt c_1 Fe–S protein	– readily	– not so readily
Inhibition of respiration (at cyt a_3) by azide	– not so readily	– readily
Addition of reduced cyt c	– rapid oxidation; supports phosphorylation	– slow oxidation; non-phosphorylation
Antibody to F_1 – ATPase	– no effect	– inhibits phosphorylation

4.2 Generation of $\Delta\bar{\mu}_{H^+}$

Operation of the electron transfer chains in energy coupling membranes causes these membranes to act as proton pumps. This can be seen during electron transfer in intact mitochondria, chloroplasts or bacteria (or sealed vesicles derived from them) suspended, at high concentration, in a very lightly buffered medium of non-permeant ions, when there is a slight acidification on one side of the proton-impermeable membrane and an alkalinization on the other; these changes can be detected by sensitive pH meters. The driving force for this pumping of protons is derived from the change in free energy of electrons as they traverse the gradient of redox potential.

Two types of hypothesis have been advanced to explain how this proton-pumping is achieved. One proposes that the pumping of protons could be the result of conformational change in a membrane-spanning redox component (or some associated molecule(s)) during the redox event. Such a

Mitochondria

Bacteria

Photosynthetic bacteria

Light

Chloroplasts

proton-pump mechanism could operate with a high H^+/e^- stoichiometry and would not require the obligatory involvement of a hydrogen-transferring redox component during the redox event. Thus, cytochrome c oxidase is an electron transfer complex that spans the membrane and functions in a region of the mitochondrial electron transfer chain in which hydrogen-transfer components have not been identified: it can pump protons when inserted into lipid vesicles.

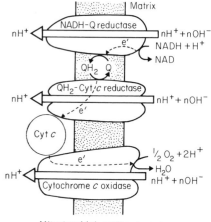

Mitochondrial proton pumps

The second possibility is that of 'loops' of electron-transfer reactions arranged spatially so that protons are moved across the membrane as a result of electron plus proton (i.e., hydrogen) transfer, with the electrons returning to the original side of the membrane by electron transfer. Redox reactions involving flavoproteins and quinones are dehydrogenations and are therefore candidates for the hydrogen transfer arms of such loops.

Some parts of electron transfer chains (including several of the simpler chains in some bacteria) do not contain obvious hydrogen-transferring components and the loop hypothesis is clearly unsatisfactory as a model for these. Moreover, the stoichiometry of proton movement by hydrogen transfer would be expected to be $1H^+/1e^-$ or $2H^+/2e^-$ at each energy-conserving site, whereas stoichiometries of 3 or 4 $H^+/2e^-$ at each energy-conserving site have been observed in mitochondria; in other words, a total of $>9H^+$ for each O atom reduced during oxidation of NADH-linked substrates.

Proton pumps are not restricted to redox components since bacteriorhodopsin, the only protein in the purple patches in the plasma membrane of *Halobacterium halobium*, is a proton-pumping component driven by light. (Redox components are present in other regions of the plasma membrane but not in the purple patches.) When *Halobacterium* is illuminated, the purple form of bacteriorhodopsin (λ_{max} 570 nm), which contains *cis*-retinal, is converted to a bleached form (λ_{max} 412 nm) containing *trans*-retinal, and protons are abstracted from the cytoplasm. The bleached form then reverts within a few milliseconds to the purple form and protons are released to the external medium. Although it is known that bacteriorhodopsin spans the membrane with seven rod-like sequences (Chapter 2) and that it can catalyse light-driven proton-pumping even in an artificial lipid membrane (Chapter 3), it is not clear how this pumping is achieved. Another molecule that is capable of proton-pumping in the absence of redox carriers is the ubiquitous 'coupling ATPase' responsible for coupling proton movements to ATP synthesis (Section 4.5).

Pumping of H^+ through membranes in the absence of any other ion movement is electrogenic, that is, it establishes a charge difference across the membrane (a membrane potential, $\Delta\Psi$). This membrane potential and the chemical concentration gradient of protons, taken together, constitute an electrochemical gradient of protons (also called an electrochemical potential difference, proton motive force, pmf, Δp or $\Delta\bar{\mu}_{H^+}$). Energy from electron-transfer reactions, incident light or ATP hydrolysis (Section 4.4) is thereby conserved in the form of an electrochemical gradient. Storage of energy in this form depends upon the impermeability to protons of these membranes: the magnitude of $\Delta\bar{\mu}_{H^+}$ achieved is due to the balance between proton-pumping and the proton leak through the membrane. Neither $\Delta\bar{\mu}_{H^+}$ nor any phenomenon generated by it (e.g., ATP synthesis, establishment of ion gradients), can be observed in damaged organelles or vesicles, in membranes in which the lipid layer is disorganized (e.g., by detergents) or in membranes rendered specifically permeable to protons by incorporation of an 'uncoupling agent' (see p. 84).

The contribution to $\Delta\bar{\mu}_{H^+}$ of ΔpH and $\Delta\Psi$ can be measured by a variety of techniques. Changes in pH in the medium can be measured with sensitive pH meters or with coloured or fluorescent acid–base indicators, but the best estimates of ΔpH probably come from studies of the distribution, at equilibrium, of tracer quantities of the anions of weak acids (e.g., acetate, 5,5-dimethyl oxazolidine-2,4-dione). A higher proportion of the non-permeant anion exists on the more alkaline side of the membrane and equilibrium across the membrane is achieved through diffusion of the more lipophilic protonated species (i.e., the undissociated acid). At equilibrium, the vesicles or organelles are separated by centrifugation and the concentration gradient of the anionic species is determined: this is equal and opposite to the gradient of H^+. Similar determinations can be made with weak bases, for example methylamine, which are lipophilic in the non-protonated form, but in this case the concentration gradient of H^+ is equal to, and in the same direction as, that of the protonated cation. ΔpH can also be estimated using ^{31}P-NMR spectroscopy, a non-perturbing technique based upon the different resonances of HPO_3^{2-} and $H_2PO_3^{-}$, the latter form being present in a higher relative concentration on the more acid side of the membrane.

Membrane potential, $\Delta\Psi$, can be assessed from the distribution, at equilibrium, of trace amounts of lipophilic

electrochemical gradients of protons (margin note)

measurement of ΔpH (margin note)

measurement of $\Delta\Psi$ (margin note)

Components of $\Delta\bar{\mu}_{H^+}$

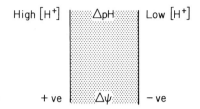

$\Delta\Psi$ is the overall membrane potential. In energy coupling membranes $\Delta\Psi$ is almost entirely electrogenic in origin, i.e. $\Delta\psi \simeq \Delta\psi_e$.

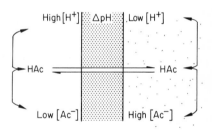

$$\Delta pH = -\log_{10}\frac{[H^+]\,in}{[H^+]\,out}$$
$$= -\log_{10}\frac{[CH_3NH_3^+]\,in}{[CH_3NH_3^+]\,out}$$

Note that for any particular $[H^+]$ gradient the sign ($\pm$) is opposite to that of

$$\frac{[H^+]\,in}{[H^+]\,out}$$

83

cations, for example triphenylmethyl phosphonium, or lipophilic anions, for example SCN^-, or of an ion carried by a uniport. The uniport may be natural or induced by an ionophore, e.g. movement of ^{86}Rb through valinomycin-treated membranes. The movement of these ions to equilibrium is electrophoretic. At equilibrium the distribution of the ion gives a measure of $\Delta\Psi$ (i.e., a gradient of $10\times$ for a monovalent ion indicates a $\Delta\Psi$ of 58 mV). Other reporters of $\Delta\Psi$ include electrochromic shifts; these are spectral or fluorescent responses to $\Delta\Psi$ of lipophilic membrane chromophores such as carotenoids.

electrophoretic ion movement

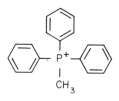

Triphenylmethyl phosphonium

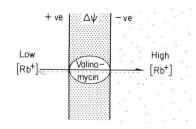

$\Delta\bar{\mu}_{H^+}$ cannot be completely dissipated even by large quantities of ions which respond only to one of its components. However, there are compounds which can dissipate $\Delta\bar{\mu}_{H^+}$ completely because they collapse both Δ pH and $\Delta\Psi$. These compounds are lipophilic weak acids (able to collapse Δ pH) which also possess a lipophilic anion (able to collapse $\Delta\Psi$). These compounds, known as uncoupling agents (or energy 'uncouplers'), are typified by dinitrophenol and FCCP (carbonyl cyanide *m*-trifluorophenyl hydrazone). A combination of K^+ with nigericin and valinomycin has a similar uncoupling effect: Δ pH is dissipated by electroneutral nigericin-catalysed H^+/K^+ antiport, and the dissipation of the resulting K^+ gradient by an electrophoretic valinomycin-catalysed K^+ uniport abolishes $\Delta\Psi$. In the presence of uncoupling agents, dissipation of $\Delta\bar{\mu}_{H^+}$ is continuous and equilibrium is therefore never achieved: continued energy input is required to sustain a $\Delta\bar{\mu}_{H^+}$.

uncoupling agents

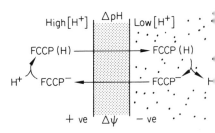

The magnitude of $\Delta\bar{\mu}_{H^+}$ and the relative contributions to it of $\Delta\Psi$ and Δ pH are, for any given membrane, partly dependent upon the membrane and partly dependent on the precise environment on either side of the membrane. Thus, in addition to its proton pump(s), the membrane may have an

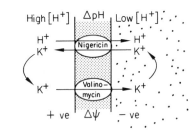

Magnitudes of contributions to $\Delta\bar{\mu}_{H^+}$ (in mV)

	$\Delta\Psi$	58Δ pH	$\Delta\bar{\mu}_{H^+}$
Mitochondria	~-170	$\sim+50$	~-220
Chloroplasts	~ 0	$\sim+220$	~-220
Chromatophores (*R. rubrum*)	~-90	$\sim+110$	~-200
E. coli	~-130	$\sim+30$	~-160

$$\Delta\bar{\mu}_{H^+} = \Delta\psi - 2.3\frac{RT}{zF}\Delta\text{ pH}$$

$$= \Delta\psi - 58\,\Delta\text{pH}$$

in mV for a one-electron change.

magnitude of $\Delta\bar{\mu}_{H^+}$

appreciable proton permeability and may also have transport systems for other ions (these can contribute to $\Delta\Psi$ but not to Δ pH). Important environmental influences are the pH of the medium and the presence of ions to which the membrane is permeable. In membrane vesicles the internal ionic composition can be controlled but this control is more difficult to achieve in intact organelles *in vitro*.

When proton transport occurs in membrane vesicles suspended in a neutral solution of non-permeant ions, then $\Delta\bar{\mu}_{H^+}$ is due mainly to $\Delta\Psi$. This is also the situation in mitochondria oxidizing an NAD-linked substrate: these mitochondria can generate a $\Delta\bar{\mu}_{H^+}$ of about 220 mV (negative inside), of which about 80 per cent is due to $\Delta\Psi$. In contrast, some illuminated chloroplasts pump protons to an approximately similar $\Delta\bar{\mu}_{H^+}$ but this is principally expressed in the form Δ pH: the pH difference across the thylakoid membrane can be as much as 3 pH units, with the interior of the thylakoid becoming acidic. Here, the pumping of protons is accompanied by a mediated influx of chloride ions. $\Delta\bar{\mu}_{H^+}$, values of about 180–240 mV (negative inside) also occur across the membranes of several respiring bacteria: $\Delta\Psi$ is usually dominant but in some species Δ pH is appreciable (up to about 2 pH units).

The effect of environmental pH on $\Delta\bar{\mu}_{H^+}$ is more on the pH component than on $\Delta\Psi$. While both intracellular and extracellular pH probably remain fairly constant in multicellular organisms, some bacteria flourish in substantially acidic or alkaline environments.

$\Delta\bar{\mu}_{H^+}$ *in E. coli (mV)*

Extracellular pH	$\Delta\Psi$	$58\,\Delta$ pH	$\Delta\bar{\mu}_{H^+}$
6.0	~−100	~+105	~−205
7.0	~−130	~+ 30	~−160
8.0	~−150	~ 0	~−150

4.3 Utilization of $\Delta\bar{\mu}_{H^+}$ to drive ion and metabolite movements

Once a $\Delta\bar{\mu}_{H^+}$ has been established, a membrane is 'energized' and useful work can be achieved by the coupling of processes such as solute movements or ATP synthesis to the dissipation of either or both of the components of $\Delta\bar{\mu}_{H^+}$. In isolated vesicles or organelles suspended in a medium of limited volume, processes which draw on only one component of $\Delta\bar{\mu}_{H^+}$ rapidly reach equilibrium with this component. In cells, however, processes driven by dissipation of $\Delta\Psi$, Δ pH or both are often themselves harnessed to drive further processes: in such open systems there is a balance between the flow of energy into $\Delta\bar{\mu}_{H^+}$ and its withdrawal ultimately to supply many of the energy requirements of the cell.

One important use of $\Delta\bar{\mu}_{H^+}$ is to drive the translocation of ions and metabolites against concentration gradients, as in the accumulation of nutrients by bacteria and the control of entry and exit of metabolites in mitochondria. Sometimes one or both components of $\Delta\bar{\mu}_{H^+}$ are directly harnessed to drive such

generation of concentration gradients

85

mediated movements and in other situations successions of energetically linked mediated transport systems may use $\Delta\bar{\mu}_{H^+}$ as their ultimate energy supply. This is an effective way of energizing transport processes since, in principle, a $\Delta\bar{\mu}_{H^+}$ of 240 mV can, by the electrophoretic movement of one mol of protons, generate a concentration gradient of $\sim10^4$ for a univalent ion. In most organisms the required $\Delta\bar{\mu}_{H^+}$ is generated by substrate oxidation. In many facultative anaerobes, however, a sufficient $\Delta\bar{\mu}_{H^+}$ has to be generated through hydrolysis by the H^+-translocating ATPase (Section 4.5) of ATP that has been generated by substrate-level phosphorylation.

bacterial transport system

Bacteria such as *E. coli* move solutes across their membranes through the action of a great diversity of mediated transport systems, with some of them driven by phosphenol-pyruvate (Chapter 3.8) and others by ATP; these systems can be recognized by their sensitivity to inhibitors of glycolysis and by their susceptibility to osmotic shock in the cold (which releases extrinsic permeant-binding proteins from the plasma membrane). These high-affinity transport systems are effective at very low environmental substrate concentrations. Many other transport processes employ only intrinsic membrane proteins, operate at normal environmental substrate concentrations and high maximum rates and draw their energy directly from $\Delta\bar{\mu}_{H^+}$.

With molecules that are either unionized or electrically neutral (including β-galactosides, galactose, arabinose, proline, serine, glycine, leucine and cystine), the preferred mechanism appears to be an electrophoretically mediated symport of the permeant and a proton, with energy being obtained from both Δ pH and $\Delta\Psi$.

Ions, however, are handled in two different ways. Electroneutral H^+symports (for anions) or H^+antiports (for cations) are driven by withdrawal of energy from Δ pH, while electrophoretic uniports are driven in appropriate directions by $\Delta\Psi$. Anions carried by symports in *E. coli* include glutamate, glucose-6-phosphate, gluconate, glucuronate and phosphate. An important Na^+/H^+ antiport in *E. coli* maintains low internal Na^+ concentration in the face of high environmental levels, and cations moved by electrophoretic uniport in this organism include K^+ and several basic amino acids, for example lysine.

In the green alga, *Chlorella,* glucose is transported into the cell via a H^+symport with a stoichiometry of 1 H^+:1 glucose. Chloroplasts have a uniport that mediates Cl^- movement into the lumen of the thylakoid. This uniport is responsible for

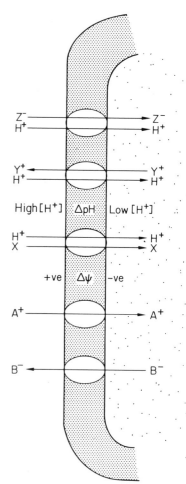

Transport systems driven by $\Delta\bar{\mu}_{H^+}$

collapsing $\Delta\Psi$ and thereby prescribes the large ΔpH (3 pH units) across the thylakoid membrane.

4.4 Transport systems in mitochondrial metabolism

Mitochondria from most sources possess mediated systems for the movement of adenine nucleotides, inorganic phosphate (P_i), Ca^{2+} and primary respiratory substrates, and some mitochondria possess additional mediated permeation systems which allow them to establish wider metabolic links with the cytosol. These movements are driven either directly or indirectly by the components of $\Delta\bar{\mu}_{H^+}$ and specific inhibitors have been important in the identification of these systems.

Movement of ATP out of the mitochondrion replenishes the energy store of the cytosol while inward movement of ADP provides substrate for ATP generation. These movements are effected by an ATP/ADP antiport which is inhibited by atractylate. At physiological pH there is a difference in charge between the two adenine nucleotides, i.e., ATP^{4-} and ADP^{3-}, and thus the antiport is electrophoretic and driven by mitochondrial $\Delta\Psi$. Inorganic phosphate, the other substrate necessary for the generation of ATP, is moved into the mitochondria by an electroneutral process in response to ΔpH; the mechanism is either an $HPO_4^{2-}/2H^+$ symport or, more probably, an $HPO_4^{2-}/2OH^+$ electroneutral antiport utilizing the gradient of hydroxyl ions which exists in the opposite direction to ΔpH. Pyruvate entry into some mitochondria also appears to be an OH^--linked antiport. The movement of Ca^{2+} into mitochondria is electrophoretically driven by $\Delta\Psi$ and is a Ca^{2+} uniport; this transport system has a very high affinity for Ca^{2+} and in many cells probably helps to maintain low cytosolic Ca^{2+} levels.

Although some ion gradients across the mitochondrial inner membrane are set up and maintained by the direct involvement of $\Delta\bar{\mu}_{H^+}$, other metabolites move in and out of the mitochondrion utilizing the energy in these secondary ion gradients, particularly that of phosphate. Thus, many mitochondria possess mediated transport systems bringing about electroneutral antiport of P_i with dicarboxylate anions, especially malate and succinate.

Malate, in its turn, can participate in antiports with other anions, for example α-ketoglutarate and tricarboxylates such as citrate. The exit of citrate from the mitochondrion requires the opposite movement of malate. In the cytosol the citrate is

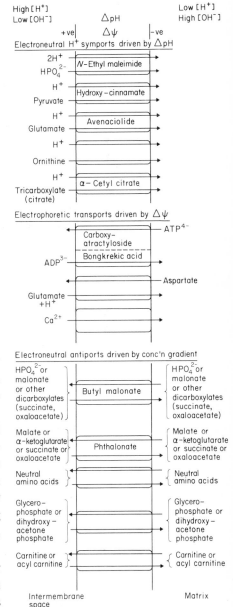

cleaved to yield oxaloacetate and acetyl CoA, thus supplying acetyl CoA to the cytosol for processes such as fatty acid and cholesterol biosynthesis: acetyl CoA cannot itself cross the mitochondrial inner membrane.

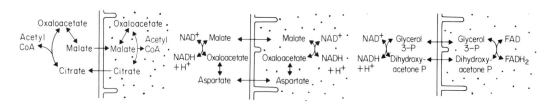

Movement of malate across the mitochondrial membrane is important in mitochondrial physiology. NADH is unable to cross the mitochondrial membrane, so the movement of malate forms part of a 'shuttle' that moves reducing equivalents between extramitochondrial and intramitochondrial pools of NADH. In some types of mitochondria this reducing equivalent shuttle is replaced by one involving movements of sn-3 glycerolphosphate and dihydroxyacetone phosphate.

Mitochondrial metabolism in blowfly flight muscle, which is almost entirely geared to ATP production, is supported only by transport systems for primary fuels, and these mitochondria are impermeable to intermediates of the tricarboxylic acid cycle. In contrast, mammalian liver and kidney mitochondria possess a much wider range of transport systems, allowing for much more metabolic interchange with the cytosol, for example in relation to fatty acid biosynthesis and amino acid metabolism.

4.5 Utilization of $\Delta\bar{\mu}_{H^+}$ to support the generation of ATP

The equilibrium of the reaction describing ATP synthesis,

$$ADP^{3-} + H_2PO_4^- \rightleftharpoons ATP^{4-} + H_2O$$

lies far to the left; i.e., the synthesis of ATP is endergonic. Thus, energy has to be supplied continuously if cellular ATP levels are to be maintained.

In most cells the provision of energy for synthesis of ATP is probably the most important function of the $\Delta\bar{\mu}_{H^+}$ across their energy-coupling membranes. In appropriate membranes, ATP synthesis follows redox reactions, illumination or the artificial imposition of a $\Delta\bar{\mu}_{H^+}$, Δ pH or $\Delta\Psi$. Thus, chloroplasts

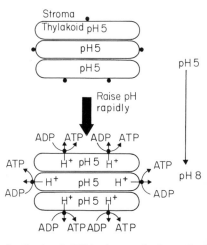

Synthesis of ATP by imposed pH gradient in chloroplasts

normally synthesize ATP when exposed to light but can also synthesize it when exposed to a rapidly imposed pH gradient. Mitochondria or submitochondrial particles normally synthesize ATP when carrying out redox reactions. In the presence of valinomycin, submitochondrial particles phosphorylate ADP when rapidly transferred to a medium of lower pH (to set up a Δ pH) and higher $[K^+]$ (to set up a $\Delta\Psi$ as a K^+ diffusion potential). The time sequences of such experiments have been followed using rapid reaction techniques and have shown that $\Delta\bar{\mu}_{H^+}$ can be generated rapidly enough to precede ATP formation. An even more direct indication of the link between $\Delta\bar{\mu}_{H^+}$ and ATP synthesis is provided by experiments in which individual proton pumps, for example bacteriorhodopsin, or artificial systems generating $\Delta\bar{\mu}_{H^+}$, for example acid-loaded vesicles transferred to an alkaline medium (to provide ΔpH) containing K^+ in the presence of valinomycin (to provide $\Delta\Psi$), have been shown to support ATP generation when incorporated in lipid bilayers containing only the coupling ATPase (see p. 90).

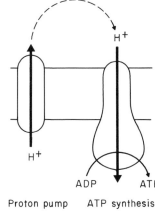

Proton pump   ATP synthesis

The energy for the synthesis of a molecule of ATP appears to be derived from the translocation of protons down $\Delta\bar{\mu}_{H^+}$. This reaction may be written

$$ADP^{3-} + H_2PO_4^- + nH_I^+ \rightleftharpoons ATP_{4-} + H_2O + nH_{II}^+$$

where H_I^+ and H_{II}^+, respectively, represent protons before and after they have crossed the membrane down their electrochemical gradient, and n represents the number of protons involved.

The free energy change for this reaction can be expressed as

$$\Delta Gp = nF \Delta\bar{\mu}_{H^+}$$

where ΔGp is the phosphorylation potential (free energy of hydrolysis of a molecule of ATP under the conditions of the experiment). Experimentally determined values of $\Delta\bar{\mu}_{H^+}$ in various systems all indicate that n values in excess of two are necessary to support ATP synthesis. Present estimates, for example in submitochondrial particles, in chloroplasts and in bacteria, indicate that the value is probably $3H^+$ translocated for each ATP synthesized. In the case of mitochondria, a further H^+ is required to support the translocation of adenine nucleotides and phosphate.

The synthesis of ATP is catalysed by an enzyme; in the forward direction it is termed ATP synthase, while in the reverse direction it is an ATPase (specifically, proton-translocating Mg^{2+}-ATPase). This enzyme can utilize the energy released by the movement of protons down $\Delta\bar{\mu}_{H^+}$ to energize the synthesis of ATP. The structure and properties of this enzyme are essentially similar in all species that have been examined, and it is located in the energy-coupling membranes responsible for generating the $\Delta\bar{\mu}_{H^+}$ upon which its activity is dependent. Synthesis and hydrolysis of ATP by this enzyme, when in its native form in a membrane, are susceptible to specific inhibitors, for example oligomycin, dicyclohexylcarbodiimide and aurovertin.

When negatively stained, energy-coupling membranes are examined by electron microscopy, they exhibit 8 nm 'knobs' associated only with that surface which, in energized membranes, is exposed to a lower H^+ activity i.e., towards the matrix in mitochondria or chloroplasts and towards the cytoplasm in bacteria. Treatments that remove these particles (i.e., low ionic strength, urea, intense sonication) abolish the membrane's ability to synthesize or hydrolyse ATP, and the catalytic unit of the ATP synthase, usually known as F_1-ATPase or F_1, can be isolated from the supernatants after such treatment. This material hydrolyses ATP in an aurovertin-sensitive manner, but does not synthesize ATP or show inhibition by oligomycin or dicyclohexylcarbodiimide. If, however, it is reassociated with the F_1-depleted membranes, then its $\Delta\bar{\mu}_{H^+}$-driven ATP-synthetic ability and its oligomycin sensitivity are restored, indicating that an essential component of the ATPase synthase (termed F_0 or CF_0) remained tightly associated with the membrane. Both F_1 and F_0 have been purified from a variety of sources and it has been shown that they can catalyse ATP synthesis if present together in the membrane of a lipid vesicle across which a $\Delta\bar{\mu}_{H^+}$ is applied, for example by illuminated bacteriorhodopsin or functioning electron transfer complexes. Vesicles whose membranes contain only F_0+F_1 can generate ATP even when $\Delta\bar{\mu}_{H^+}$ is imposed by a totally artificial system. In order to synthesize ATP, a $\Delta\bar{\mu}_{H^+}$ greater than 200 mV is required. The ATP synthase is reversible, since these vesicles generate a $\Delta\bar{\mu}_{H^+}$ when supplied with MgATP.

Although ATP synthase has been purified from several sources, that from thermophilic bacteria has proved to be the most amenable to molecular characterization. It has only eight polypeptide subunits (several of the extra polypeptides in preparation from other sources are suspected of being contaminants), and these eight polypeptides are more stable than

F_1-ATPase

F_0 component

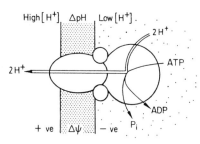

those from other organisms due to their more extensive salt bridging. This has allowed the synthase to be associated and reassociated without loss of activity.

The F_1 component has a molecular weight of about 380000 and contains five different polypeptides, possibly with a stoichiometry of $\alpha_3\beta_3\gamma\,\delta\,\epsilon$. The δ- and ϵ-subunits can be removed without loss of ATPase activity but all of the subunits are required for H^+ translocation and ATP synthesis. None of the isolated polypeptides can hydrolyse ATP but both the α- and β-subunits bind nucleotides: the β-subunit is probably the catalytic centre and contains a protonated tyrosyl residue at the ATP binding site. Antibodies to either the α- or β-subunits inhibit the ATPase activity of the F_1 complex, whereas antibodies to γ, δ or ϵ are ineffective.

The δ- and ϵ-subunits form the connection between the F_1-ATPase and the F_0 complex in the membrane. They bind to a polypeptide of F_0, of molecular weight 13500, and the δ-subunit also binds to the α-subunit of the ATPase.

In addition to providing the 'stalk', which attaches F_1 to F_0, the δ- and ϵ-subunits (together with the γ-subunit) are involved in controlling (gating) the passage of protons across the membrane through the F_0 complex. Membranes depleted of F_1 show abnormally high H^+ permeability which can be prevented by adding back intact F_1, or subunits γ, δ and ϵ of F_1, or either oligomycin or dicyclohexylcarbodiimide (DCCD). The membrane complex to which these bind (F_0) forms the transmembrane channel through which protons travel during ATP synthesis by attached F_1.

Composition of ATP synthase

	Mol.wt	No. of copies
F_1 component		
α (ATP binding, catalytic)	54000	3
β (ATP binding, regulatory)	51000	3
γ (Gating, regulatory)	30000	1
δ (Connecting, gating)	21000	1
ϵ (Connecting, gating)	16000	1
F_0 component		
Oligomycin-sensitivity conferring protein	19000	1
F_1-binding protein	13500	2
DCCD-binding protein	7200	6

The F_0 complex has a molecular weight of about 90000 and is composed of three polypeptides, probably in a stoichiometry of 1:2:6. All three are necessary for the coupling of proton movement across the membrane to ATP synthesis. The polypeptide of molecular weight 19000 is, in eukaryotes, the site of inhibition by oligomycin, but its function in ATP synthesis is not known. The polypeptide of molecular weight 13500 binds the F_1-ATPase to the F_0 complex (see above). It also interacts with hexameric arrays of the smallest polypeptide, which probably forms the transmembrane proton channel. This polypeptide, which binds DCCD and is very lipophilic, is composed largely (~80 per cent) of amino acids with apolar side-chains; it is soluble in chloroform:methanol and is probably almost completely buried in the hydrocarbon core of the membrane. There are only eight ionizable residues in the polypeptide, and one of these (Glu^{56}) has a γ-carboxyl with unusual characteristics for a protein γ-carboxyl group: it is protonated, with a pK_a of 6.8 (rather than pH 4.3) and reacts with DCCD. This carboxyl is therefore a strong candidate for involvement in the transmembrane proton channel.

Electrophoretic movement of protons through the ATP synthase causes conformational changes in F_1 that make an —SH group more susceptible to reaction with N-ethylmaleimide, alters the affinities for ADP and ATP binding and increases the number of hydrogen atoms that are exchangeable with tritiated water. The exact mechanism by which the ATP synthase couples proton movement to ATP synthesis (or hydrolysis) is not understood but it does not involve a phosphoprotein intermediate and thus seems quite different from the mechanism employed by the Ca^{2+} and Na^+/K^+ pumps of the plasma membrane (Chapter 3).

Since energy-coupling membranes are energized under most physiological circumstances, the F_1+F_0 complex normally acts as an ATP synthase. H^+-translocating ATPase activity is appropriate in anaerobic bacteria which derive their ATP from substrate-level phosphorylation. They utilize the H^+-translocating ATPase to establish and maintain a $\Delta\bar{\mu}_{H^+}$ across the plasma membrane in order to drive their ion and metabolic transport systems (see Section 4.3).

An H^+-translocating ATPase is also found in the membrane of the chromaffin granule in adrenal medullary cells. The catalytic component is oriented towards the cytosol and utilizes cytosolic ATP to produce a $\Delta\bar{\mu}_{H^+}$ across the membrane (positive inside): the $\Delta\bar{\mu}_{H^+}$ created is utilized to drive transport systems for the accumulation of materials stored within the chromaffin granule (see Chapter 6.3).

Bacterial transport driven by
H^+- translocating ATPase (ATP synthase)

4.6 The use of ATP to establish ion gradients

ATP forms the major chemical energy currency of cells and carries energy from the energy-coupling membranes to other intracellular compartments, where one of its most important uses is to drive membrane ion pumps. These transport ATPases differ from the H^+-translocating ATPase in that their reaction mechanisms appear generally to involve a cycle of phosphorylation and dephosphorylation of the transport protein (Chapter 3). Under normal physiological conditions they work in the direction of ATP hydrolysis and the generation of ion gradients, but under artificial conditions in which abnormally high gradients are imposed their reactions can be reversed so as to synthesize ATP.

When the Ca^{2+} ion concentration in the cytosol of a skeletal muscle cell rises to about 10^{-5} M, the actomyosin system contracts, and it is fully relaxed when cytoplasmic $[Ca^{2+}]$ is reduced below about 10^{-5} M. Control of these Ca^{2+} concentrations is largely achieved by the sarcoplasmic reticulum; this possesses a powerful Ca^{2+}-transport ATPase which allows it to reduce the surrounding Ca^{2+} concentration to $<10^{-7}$ M. For each ATP hydrolysed, two Ca^{2+} ions are transported into the sarcoplasmic reticulum, provided that a permeant anion is available, probably phosphate or, *in vitro,* oxalate. There appears to be some movement of Mg^{2+} in the opposite direction to Ca^{2+}, but the requirement for a permeant counter-ion suggests that Ca^{2+} entry is either by electroneutral symport with phosphate or is electrogenic, with the resulting membrane potential being collapsed by an independent uniport of phosphate. Anion accumulation occurs even with highly purified ATPase preparations, suggesting it may be an activity of the ATPase molecule. In both the resting cell and in isolated membrane vesicles the rate of Ca^{2+} accumulation exceeds its outward leakage by at least a factor of 100.

Release of the stored Ca^{2+} and initiation of muscle contraction is triggered by the arrival of a nerve impulse at the neuromuscular junction. The resulting action potential (see Section 4.8) propagates over the muscle surface and through tubular invaginations of the plasma membrane (sarcolemma) which make specialized contacts (at T-junctions) with the sarcoplasmic reticulum. This then provokes a release of most of the accumulated Ca^{2+} in about a millisecond, a process that requires a transient 100000-fold increase in membrane permeability to Ca^{2+}: most of this release appears to occur through channels distinct from the Ca^{2+}-ATPase. The

sarcoplasmic reticulum Ca^{2+}-transport ATPase

Ca^{2+} and muscle contraction

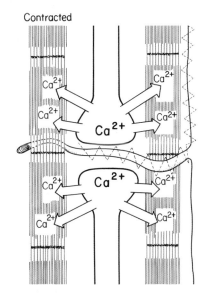

Ca^{2+} movements in muscle contraction

93

mechanism of this release is little understood and it has yet to be reproduced in isolated membrane vesicles.

Other eukaryote cells also maintain intracellular Ca^{2+} ion concentrations of 10^{-7} M or lower in the face of an extracellular concentration of about 10^{-3} M. The maintenance of this gradient is probably largely the responsibility of the Ca^{2+}-pump ATPase found in the plasma membrane of many cells. This activity can be distinguished from other ATPases by its inhibitor specificity: it is inhibited by thiol reagents and by ethacrynic acid but is insensitive to ruthenium red (an inhibitor of mitochondrial Ca^{2+} transport) and ouabain, which inhibits Na^+/K^+-ATPase. Maintenance of a low intracellular Ca^{2+} concentration appears to be essential for the normal functioning of some cellular enzymes. In addition, the existence of a substantial gradient of Ca^{2+} concentration allows changes in membrane Ca^{2+} permeability to be utilized as a cellular signalling device, either by controlling intracellular Ca^{2+} levels (Chapter 5.5) or by changing the electrical properties of membranes (Section 4.8).

The other major ion gradients at cell surfaces are the Na^+ and K^+ gradients set up in opposite directions by Na^+/K^+-ATPase. In some tissues pumping of these two ions appears to be stoichiometrically equivalent (i.e., electroneutral) whilst in others it appears to be electrogenic, with stoichiometries of up to $3Na^+:1K^+$. The high cytoplasmic K^+ concentrations achieved by this pump seem to be necessary for certain intracellular enzyme reactions, for example in the biosynthesis of proteins. In addition, the ion gradients are essential for the occurrence of many bioelectric phenomena (Section 4.8) and to supply the energy for the active accumulation of other molecules, in both prokaryotic and eukaryotic cells.

4.7 The use of ion gradients to drive movements of other permeants

In most prokaryotic cells $[Na^+]$ is kept low by the action of a Na^+/H^+ antiport; depending on the organism, the $\Delta\bar{\mu}_{H^+}$ required to drive the system is supplied by substrate oxidation, by ATP hydrolysis, or by light-driven proton-pumping. The high intracellular $[K^+]$ is the result of a $[K^+]$ uniport driven by the membrane potential (negative inside). In eukaryotic cells, low intracellular $[Na^+]$ is maintained by Na^+/K^+-ATPase; in multicellular organisms, Na^+ is usually the principal extracellular cation. Thus, there exists across the plasma mem-

plasma membrane
Ca^{2+}-pump

cell surface
Na^+ gradient

94

brane in both eukaryotes and most prokaryotes a considerable gradient of $[Na^+]$ in one direction (low $[Na^+]$ inside) and of $[K^+]$ in the other.

Both the $[Na^+]$ gradient and $\Delta\Psi$, the two components of $\Delta\bar{\mu}_{H^+}$, can supply energy for the generation and maintenance of gradients of metabolites across the plasma membrane. A series of Na^+-linked transport systems utilize the $\Delta\bar{\mu}_{H^+}$ in an analogous way to the H^+-linked systems in energy-coupling membranes which utilize $\Delta\bar{\mu}_{H^+}$. The continuous dissipation of one or both components of $\Delta\bar{\mu}_{H^+}$ by these is counter-balanced by the operation of the Na^+/K^+-pump in eukaryotes or Na^+/H^+ antiport in prokaryotes. Some of these Na^+-linked mediated transport systems, like that for phosphate in intestinal epithelial cells, catalyse the electroneutral symport of an anion and Na^+ in response to the $[Na^+]$ gradient. An Na^+/H^+ electroneutral antiport responsive to the $[Na^+]$ gradient has been found in mammalian intestine.

Other transport systems move Na^+ in symport with neutral or non-ionized compounds and respond, in the presence of Na^+, to $\Delta\Psi$. Systems of this type are abundant and include the transport of several amino acids and sugars into a wide variety of bacteria, the transport of neutral amino acids into many mammalian cells (e.g., adipose, liver, fibroblasts, ascites, kidney, intestine), and the transport of several sugars across the brush-border surfaces of intestinal and kidney epithelial cells.

In many cells these Na^+-linked systems act simply to bring metabolites into the cells to sustain metabolism, but in absorbing epithelia they also contribute to the transcellular movement of absorbed materials. The Na^+-linked symports are located at the absorptive (luminal) surface of the cell, and in the basolateral plasma membrane there are Na^+-independent transport systems which facilitate the exit of the absorbed material down the concentration gradient. The glucose transport systems of the brush-border membrane and the basolateral membrane differ both in their sensitivity to Na^+ and to inhibitors: phlorizin inhibits the brush-border system more effectively than phloretin but phloretin is more effective against the basolateral membrane system. The gradient of Na^+ across the cell surface in these cells is maintained by a ouabain-sensitive Na^+/K^+-pump located largely or solely in the basolateral plasma membrane.

Electrogenic Na^+ transport, by Na^+/K^+-ATPase and sometimes by a separate ouabain-insensitive Na^+-pump, is also used to drive the movement of water across epithelial layers in absorbing (intestine and kidney) tissues. In such

Na+-linked transport systems

intestinal glucose transport

water transport in epithelia

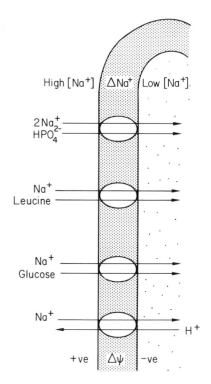

Na^+-linked transport systems

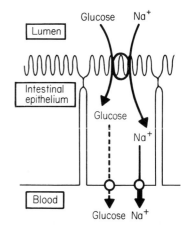

95

tissues, sheets of epithelial cells are sealed together at tight junctions, but away from these junctions adjacent cells may separate to form substantial intercellular spaces within which localized hydrostatic and osmotic gradients are generated by secretion of NaCl. In the intestinal epithelium, these intercellular spaces form elongated channels closed off from the lumen of the intestine by tight junctions. Movement of water through the epithelium is probably driven by the electrogenic pumping of Na^+, accompanied by electrophoretic uniport of Cl^-, into the intercellular space. The resulting local hypertonicity draws water from the cells (and ultimately from the intestinal lumen), dilates the intercellular space and drives secreted salt solution towards the base of the cells. The net result is to draw water from one extracellular fluid and to release it as a salt solution to another extracellular fluid.

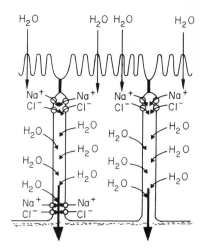

In tissues that secrete isotonic fluids (e.g., exocrine pancreas, salivary glands), the cells appear to be arranged loosely in a tube around a central lumen; the tight junctions between the cells appear to be relatively permeable, thus allowing the slightly hypertonic NaCl solution formed at the lateral surface to diffuse into the lumen. By contrast, tissues that secrete a hypertonic solution (e.g., the salt glands of birds) possess a very large amount of extensively folded lateral membrane (bearing a high density of the sodium pump and chloride uniport) and a tiny lumen. The concentrated NaCl solution probably passes through the leaky tight junction without substantial dilution from intracellular water.

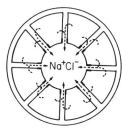

isotonic secretion

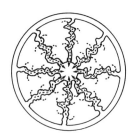

hypertonic secretion

4.8 Membrane potentials and their variation at the plasma membrane of eukaryote cells

The realization that membrane potentials and ion gradients are essential to energy coupling and active transport processes is relatively recent, but membrane potentials that occur at the plasma membranes of large eukaryote cells were described many years earlier. When a glass microelectrode (filled with 3 M-KCl to minimize diffusion potentials) is inserted into such a cell (the membrane spontaneously reforms an insulating seal around the electrode) then a $\Delta\Psi$ of between 40 mV and 100 mV (negative inside) is usually observed: this is termed a resting potential.

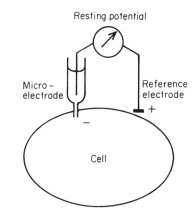

The resting potential is a consequence both of the existence of ion gradients across the membrane, chiefly of Na^+ (high outside), K^+ (high inside), and Cl^- (high outside), and of the selective permeability properties of the membrane. Under such circumstances, differential rates of diffusion of the ions back down their electrochemical gradients can give rise to a membrane potential (a diffusion potential, $\Delta\Psi_d$), since such ion movements will effect a net transfer of charge across the membrane and thus generate electrical imbalance. In the general case of a solution of monovalent ions (A^+ and B^-):

Nernst equation

$$\Delta\Psi_d = -\frac{RT}{zF}\frac{u-v}{u+v}\ln\frac{C_2}{C_1}$$

R = universal gas constant
T = absolute temperature
z = valency
F = the Faraday

Mobilities of individual ionic species across membranes are expressed in terms of permeability coefficients (P): these are usually derived experimentally from measurements of the fluxes of radioactive ions across the membranes. Thus, the diffusion potential at a plasma membrane is approximately described by:

For NaCl solutions of concentrations C_1 and C_2
u is mobility of A^+
v is mobility of B^+

Goldman–Hodgkin–Katz equation

$$\Delta\Psi_d = -\frac{RT}{zF}\ln\frac{P_{K^+}[K^+]_{in}+P_{Na^+}[Na^+]_{in}+P_{Cl^-}[Cl^-]_{out}}{P_{K^+}[K^+]_{out}+P_{Na^+}[Na^+]_{out}+P_{Cl^+}[Cl^-]_{in}}$$

The contributions of individual ions to the resting potential were largely elucidated by using the large diameter 'giant' nerve axon of the squid; this can be emptied of cytoplasm and internally perfused with modified ionic media as required. Its passive permeability to all three major ions is relatively low, but that to K^+ is much greater than to Na^+ or Cl^-. As a result, the dominant passive ion movement is outward K^+ leakage, and this generates an internally negative K^+ diffusion potential that largely accounts for the recorded resting potential:

$$\Delta\Psi_d = -\frac{RT}{F}\ln\frac{[K^+]_{in}}{[K^+]_{out}}$$

If the external K^+ is raised to be equal to the cytosolic K^+, no net K^+ flux occurs and the K^+ diffusion potential is eliminated. By contrast, changing the extracellular concentration of the almost non-permeant Na^+ ion (e.g., by replacement with choline$^+$) has little effect on the resting potential. The higher permeability of the membrane to K^+ ions than to Na^+ ions is probably due to the smaller size of hydrated K^+ ions. Such K^+ diffusion potentials largely account for the resting potentials of a variety of animal cells. The precision of this conclusion is, however, subject to some uncertainties arising from possible differences in ion activities in the bulk phase

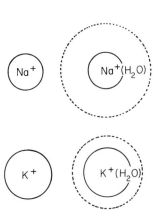

and at the membrane surface and from difficulties in the experimental determination of very reliable permeability coefficients.

In some cells, there are appreciable discrepancies between the resting potentials and the K^+ diffusion potentials, and in these it seems likely that an additional, and occasionally dominant, contribution to the resting potential ($\Delta\Psi_e$) may arise from electrogenic ion-pumping. As mentioned in Section 4.6, the ratio of $Na^+:K^+$ pumping by the Na^+/K^+-pump is frequently greater than $1:1$, and this can contribute substantially to the membrane potential in cells where passive ion permeabilities are low; this is the case in the membranes of some *Aplysia* neurones and also in membranes of the cochlea.

Microelectrodes can be used not only to record the electrical characteristics of membranes but also to inject ionic currents so as to perturb the electrical state of the membrane. Injection of a current of negative ions increases the membrane potential (i.e., hyperpolarizes the membrane). Such hyperpolarization can be considerable, but eventually the imposed $\Delta\Psi$ overcomes the electrical resistance of the membrane and electrical breakdown (i.e., a short-circuit) occurs; this is usually at about 200 mV, or about 500 kV/cm (assuming the presence of an electrically resistive lipophilic barrier of ~5 nm thickness). If a positive ion current is introduced, the membrane potential is reduced—the membrane is depolarized. If a second microelectrode is inserted into the cell close by, the extent to which the imposed change in membrane potential is transmitted along the membrane to this electrode can be measured. The form of the attenuated electrical change detected by this electrode provides information on the electrical properties of the intervening membrane (e.g., its capacitance and resistance).

excitable cells

In some cells, which are termed excitable, depolarization initiates a sudden spontaneous additional depolarization. This happens if the positive, depolarizing current that is injected into an excitable cell such as nerve or muscle is sufficient to reduce the existing negative membrane potential to below a certain critical 'threshold' value, when the membrane suddenly shows a dramatic reversal of potential caused by a rapid influx of positive ions. This reversal of potential occurs within about 0.5 msec and is then rapidly reversed by the outward flow of a positive ion current that restores the membrane potential to its normal resting value. This rapid reversal and restoration of the membrane potential is known as an action potential (or spike potential) and is not attenuated as it propagates along

action potential

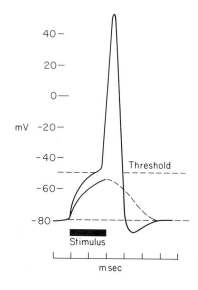

the membrane; sometimes, as in a nerve axon, it may travel for very long distances without changing its form. This rapid propagation of the action potential occurs because an action potential at one point produces local currents that are sufficient to depolarize adjacent membrane to below the threshold at which it then displays an action potential.

Immediate restimulation of an excitable cell by depolarization fails to evoke another action potential, but after a brief period (the refractory period) the cell returns to a state where another, identical, action potential is evoked by depolarization. The refractory period ensures that action potentials propagate unidirectionally away from the site at which they are initiated.

Attempts to account for action potentials in terms of the movements of particular ions have mainly employed three techniques. In a few cells, notably the giant axon of the squid (see also p. 97), direct measurements have been made of the associated fluxes of radioactively labelled ions; such studies, of course, cannot resolve events within the time-scale of an action potential. Second, the changes in the evoked potential that occur when the external (and in the squid axon, internal) ionic environments are changed have been defined. Third, the ionic environment can be varied at a membrane whose potential is held constant by the injection of a current that is controlled by a feedback circuit: this is the voltage–clamp technique. When an excitable membrane is rapidly depolarized to, and held at, a subthreshold potential, then a series of ionic currents are observed. First, there is a rapid but transient inflow of positive current, and this is followed by an outward ion current that continues for as long as the membrane is kept depolarized by the voltage clamp. Most action potentials are only observed if physiological Na^+ concentrations are present outside the cell, and removal of extracellular Na^+ during voltage clamp abolishes the initial inward ionic current; the rapid reversal of potential that initiates the action potential is therefore due to a very rapid increase in membrane permeability to Na^+. Similar experiments revealed that the major ion flow contributing to the outward ion current that repolarizes the cell during the falling phase of the action potential is K^+ efflux. The magnitudes of the ionic currents during an action potential are relatively small ($3-4 \times 10^{-12}$ mol/cm^2): these have a negligible effect upon overall cellular ion gradients, which are easily maintained by the Na^+- and K^+-pumps of the membrane.

voltage–clamp technique

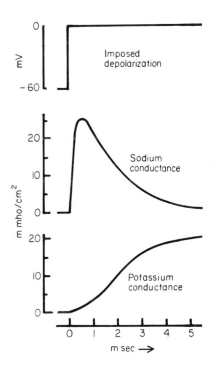

99

At a molecular level, the action potential results from the very rapid opening in sequence of plasma membrane ion permeability channels (graphically referred to as 'gates') relatively specific for Na^+ and K^+; these 'gates' also possess an inherent ability to spontaneously close during the latter part of the action potential. When an individual Na^+ gate is opened during an action potential it allows the passage of about 10^6 ions/sec. This is a rate that appears incompatible with a diffusing carrier and it therefore seems that the Na^+ 'gate' is a continuous, but controlled, channel through the membrane. The channel must be associated with some form of charged groupings which are moved under the influence of membrane depolarization and which form the sensors that couple membrane depolarization to the opening of ion channels. Electrophysiological studies have directly indicated the existence of two movable charged groupings per Na^+ channel in nerve membrane: the very small 'gating current' generated by the movement of these is only detectable under conditions in which movements of mobile ions across membranes have been largely abolished. In nerve, the potential-controlled Na^+ channels are readily identified and labelled by their interaction with externally applied tetrodotoxin or saxitoxin, both of which prevent potential-sensitive Na^+ movements but still allow the opening of the K^+ channel under voltage-clamp conditions. Other groups of lipid-soluble neurotoxins (e.g., veratridine) and polypeptide neurotoxins from scorpion and sea anemone interact with different sites on the Na^+ channel, both shifting the threshold voltage for channel-opening and preventing its closure. The availability of these toxins has facilitated the identification of the channel constituents and their isolation for more detailed studies. The major polypeptide of the channel (α-subunit) in nerve tissue has a molecular weight of $\sim 270\,000$ and is associated with one or two smaller β-subunits (mol.wt. $\sim 38\,000$). Ion movement through the distinct potential-sensitive K^+ channels can be inhibited by tetraethylammonium ions applied to the cytoplasmic surface of the membrane (e.g., in squid axon).

Action potentials are not always reflections only of Na^+ and K^+ fluxes. Even in the squid axon there is a very small inward current of Ca^{2+} ions that occurs during the latter part of the action potential (when the dominant ion movement is outward K flow); the Ca^{2+} moves through potential-sensitive Ca^{2+} gates that are sensitive to the specific inhibitors methoxyverapamil and nifedipine. There are also excitable cells in which the dominant depolarizing ion current during

Tetrodotoxin

the transmission of an action potential is carried by Ca^{2+} ions, for example barnacle muscle, *Paramecium* and some insect and molluscan neurones. Potential-sensitive Ca^{2+} entry is essential for the release of neurotransmitters when an action potential arrives at a synapse (see p. 120).

The velocity at which an impulse is propagated along a membrane is determined by the rate at which the electrical capacitance ahead of the action potential is discharged to a subthreshold level: this is determined both by the membrane's intrinsic capacitance and the electrical resistance of the cytoplasm and extracellular medium. In simple nerve axons the velocity of propagation is inversely proportional to the square root of the diameter. Thus, some invertebrates use 'giant axons', with diameters up to 1 mm, to carry nerve impulses to muscles involved in rapid escape responses (e.g., the mantle of the squid). In the more complex nervous systems of vertebrates, the current-carrying properties of small nerve fibres are improved by investing axons with an additional layer

insulation
by myelin

of insulating material, a myelin sheath (see Chapter 1). This is a multilayered spiral of membrane that is provided by satellite (Schwann or oligodendroglial) cells and which increases the electrical resistance (i.e., reduces ion fluxes) and reduces the effective capacitance of the conducting axon membrane about 200-fold. As a result, the primary propagation of the action potential only occurs in the small ($\sim$1 μm) regions of axon surface exposed between adjacent myelinated segments (the nodes of Ranvier)—the action potential effectively jumps from node to node. This provides both metabolic economy and a rapidity of transmission similar to that in large unmyelinated axons. The specialization of the nodes of Ranvier is reflected in their possession of a high density of potential-sensitive ion channels; in various nerves, Na^+ 'gates' vary between about 2.5/μm^2 and 5000/μm^2, with the highest densities at the nodes of myelinated nerves.

Changes in membrane potential (i.e., in ion permeabilities) at the plasma membrane are not only characteristic of excitable cells; smaller variations occur in many other cells in response to stimuli such as hormones and neurotransmitters (see Chapter 5). In addition, changes in membrane potential, whether they are action potentials or less dramatic variations,

electrical coupling
via gap
junctions

are often not confined to a single cell. As discussed elsewhere (Chapter 5), the aqueous cytoplasmic compartments of many types of cell are connected by gap junctions through which small solutes, including ions, diffuse freely. As a result, an electrical change in one cell may be transmitted directly to its

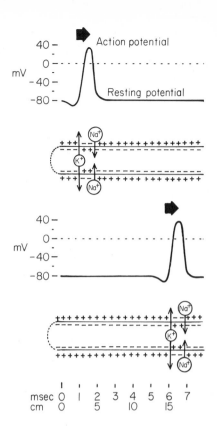

101

neighbour in an unattenuated form. For example, all of the cells of a single acinus of the exocrine pancreas form a single electrically coupled unit, but they are electrically unconnected to the cells of adjacent acini.

Although plasma membranes generally show a low Na^+ permeability, many cells possess Na^+-linked symport systems for solutes such as sugars and amino acids, and the action of such transport systems supports an electrogenic Na^+ flow into cells. Thus, the addition to cells of a solute transportable by one of these mechanisms causes an immediate membrane depolarization; electrophysiological studies therefore offer an easily accessible experimental approach to the characterization of these Na^+-linked transport systems. If such transport systems were to be present in cells impermeable to K^+, then their action would be opposed by the $\Delta\Psi$ which they would create through unidirectional Na^+ movement. The relative permeability of many plasma membranes to K^+, and hence the normal existence of K^+ diffusion potentials, may thus be essential for the effective functioning of these transport systems.

Further Reading

Nicholls D.G. (1982) *Bioenergetics: an Introduction to the Chemiosmotic Theory*. Academic Press, London.

Miller K.R. (1979) The photosynthetic membrane. *Scientific American* Oct., 100–111.

Anderson J.M. & Anderson B. (1982) The architecture of photosynthetic membranes: lateral and transverse organization. *Trends in Biochem. Sci.* **7,** 288–292.

Brunori M. & Wilson M.T. (1982) Cytochrome oxidase. *Trends in Biochem. Sci.* **7,** 295–299.

Hackenbrock C.R. (1981) Lateral diffusion and electron transfer in the mitochondrial inner membrane. *Trends in Biochem. Sci.* **6,** 151–154.

Boyer P.D., Chance B., Ernster L., Mitchell P., Racker E. & Slater E. (1977) *Ann. Rev. Biochem.* **46,** 955–1026.

Filligame R.H. (1980) The proton-translocating pumps of oxidative phosphorylation. *Ann. Rev. Biochem.* **49,** 1079–1113.

Stockenius W. (1976) The purple membrane of salt-loving bacteria. *Scientific American* June, 38–46.

Ferguson S.J. & Sorgato M.C. (1982) The relationship of proton electrochemical gradients to energy transduction processes. *Ann. Rev. Biochem.* **51,** 185–217.

Kagawa Y., Ohta S., Yoshida M. & Sone N. (1980) Functions of subunits of H^+-ATPase. *Annals New York Acad. Sci.* **358,** 103–117.

Martonosi A.N. (ed.) (1982) *Membranes and Transport,* Volume 1. Plenum, New York.

LaNoue K. & Schoolworth A.C. (1979) Metabolite transport in mitochondria. *Ann. Rev. Biochem.* **48,** 871–922.

Crane R.K. (1977) The gradient hypothesis and other models of carrier mediated transport. *Rev. Physiol. Biochem. Pharmacol.* **78,** 99–159.

Murer H. & Kinne R. (1980) The use of isolated membrane vesicles to study epithelial transport processes. *J. Memb. Biol.* **55,** 81–95.

Lanyi J.K. (1979) The role of Na^+ in transport processes of bacterial membranes. *Biochim. Biophys. Acta* **559,** 377–397.

Dibona D.R. & Mills J.W. (1979) Distribution of Na^+-pump sites in transporting epithelia. *Fed. Proc.* **36,** 134–143.

Schultz S.G. (1974) Principles of electrophysiology and their application to epithelial tissues. In *MTP International Review of Science.* Physiology Series One, Volume 4, Gasterointestinal Physiology. Butterworth, London.

Keynes R.D. (1979) Ion channels in the nerve cell membrane. *Scientific American* March, 96–107.

Catterall W.A. (1982) The emerging molecular view of the sodium channel. *Trends in Neurosciences* **5,** 303–310.

Miles F.A. (1979) *Excitable Cells.* Heinemann, New York.

Reuter H. (1983) Calcium channel modulation by neurotransmitters, enzymes and drugs. *Nature* **301,** 569–574.

See also pp. 212, 213.

5 Recognition, response and communication

Cells interact with an environment over which they can exert only limited control. They therefore possess mechanisms for recognizing and responding to a wide variety of changes in the environment. Detection of and response to most of these changes is achieved by components of the plasma membrane. Some of these responses are to physical factors such as light, pressure or an electric field but the majority are to chemical ligands which may be either soluble (e.g., neurotransmitters, hormones, chemotactic attractants) or attached to the surfaces of other cells (e.g., antigens).

5.1 Phototaxis and chemotaxis

Photosynthetic microorganisms show positive phototaxis (i.e., migration towards a source of light). In the extremely halophilic bacterium *Halobacterium halobium* this migration is towards green light, and it shows the same action spectrum as does photosynthesis mediated by bacteriorhodopsin, the light-trapping proton pump of the plasma membrane. The control of phototaxis under these conditions is achieved by the cell sensing changes in plasma membrane $\Delta\bar{\mu}_{H^+}$ that are produced by variations in illumination. In the same organism, membrane carotenoids appear to provide the sensor for negative phototaxis to avoid excess blue or ultraviolet light.

Among the most primitive forms of response to the chemical environment are the positive chemotaxis of whole organisms towards a food source or otherwise favourable environment, and their negative chemotaxis away from adverse conditions. This has been studied in great detail in bacteria, where the specific 'receptors' that recognize chemotactic attractants are in some cases the same periplasmic proteins that bind solutes destined for transport into the cells (Chapter 3.8). For example, mutants which lack the periplasmic binding protein for β-galactosides neither transport them nor respond to them chemotactically. However, the coupling of binding to chemotaxis does not involve transport. Transport-negative mutants that possess the binding proteins and are still capable of chemotaxis show enhanced methylation of particular intrinsic membrane proteins that appear to be essential to the control of chemotaxis; in the case of maltose-induced chemotaxis in *E. coli* this protein has a molecular weight of 62 000. Mutants lacking these proteins are incapable of chemotaxis.

An independent set of chemotaxis-negative mutants are transport-negative with regard to the phosphoenolpyruvate-linked phosphotransferase group transport system (Chapter 3.8). Here, however, mutants of any part of the system (HPr, Enzymes I, II or III) display neither chemotaxis nor transport, probably because chemotaxis requires binding of the attractant to the phosphorylated form of the appropriate Enzyme II.

slime mould aggregation

In social amoebae (slime moulds) the free-living single-celled forms show chemotaxis up concentration gradients of an attractant released by cells in zones of high cell density and limited food supply; this effect brings about the aggregation of the free-living cells that has to occur before differentiation into the multicellular spore-forming stage of the life cycle. Two such attractants have been identified: *Dictyostelium* spp. use cyclic AMP (see p. 122) whereas *Polysphondylium* spp. use glorin (a modified dipeptide, see diagram). Thus, these two organisms, which coexist in soil, can successfully locate their own kind and form monospecific spore-forming structures. Migration up chemical concentration gradients also occurs with whole multicellular organisms. Many insects locate mates by migrating along gradients of volatile 'pheromones', and sometimes the receptor cells on the antennae of the males can show a detectable electrophysiological response even to a single molecule of pheromone, for example the response of the moth *Bombyx mori* to bombykol. Similarly, the sensory recognition by taste or smell of molecular groupings, for example as sweetness or bitterness, depends on the presence of specific chemoreceptors on the exposed microvilli of the receptor cells in taste buds and olfactory epithelia.

pheromones

Examples of chemotaxis by the free-living differentiated cells of higher animals include the migration of macrophages and polymorphonuclear leucocytes towards sites of infection. Amongst the most potent attractants for polymorphonuclear leucocytes are small formylated peptides (e.g., *f*met–leu–phe); these are active below 10^{-10} M. It is probable that the receptors for these ligands allow the cells to locate invading

leucocyte chemotaxis

Glorin

Bombykol

105

bacteria by migrating up gradients of the signal peptides that are released during bacterial protein secretion (see Chapter 6): bacterial signal peptides terminate with a formyl methionine residue, whereas the terminal amino acid residue in equivalent eukaryote peptides is a methionine. Attractants (e.g., the small peptides C3a and C5a) are also generated during the interactions between bacteria, circulating immunoglobulins and the complement system of the plasma. Activated polymorphonuclear leucocytes generate arachidonate metabolites, especially leukotrienes, that attract more leucocytes to sites of inflammation.

Spatial gradients of solutes may also be essential in governing the migration of cells, growth of cellular processes or differential development of spatially separated cells during the generation of complex three-dimensional patterns of different types of cells in developing organisms or tissues. For example, a head-to-foot gradient of a small neuropeptide regulator appears to be involved in the longitudinal differentiation of *Hydra*, and it is widely thought that similar principles will apply to the generation of more complex spatial patterns such as those in brain.

5.2 Cell–cell recognition and immune responses

Tissue differentiation in animals relies upon the abilities of different cell types to recognize themselves and each other. A simple model for this process may be offered by the self-recognition shown by dispersed sponge cells during formation of cellular aggregates from mixed dispersions, a process in which cell-surface glycoproteins appear to be key participants. When more complex systems such as dispersed embryonic retinal or cerebellar cell mixtures are used in such experiments they show both the reassociation of like cells and also the generation of spatial organizations similar to those in the original tissues. Such cells seem to carry surface components involved in self-recognition and adhesion (e.g., cell adhesion molecule (CAM), an embryonic retinal glycoprotein of mol. wt 140 000) and in morphogenesis.

Glycoproteins are also responsible for the specific interactions between unlike mating types in the sexual interactions of algae and of protozoa, and discrimination between different strains in the sexual interactions of yeast and of bacteria seem to involve sex-specific cell-surface mannoproteins.

The immune system identifies and eliminates materials that appear foreign; these are usually either bacteria or host cells

Head activator neuropeptide

pyroglu – pro – pro – gly – gly – ser – lys – val – ile – leu – phe

Self-recognition in dispersed sponge cells

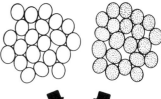
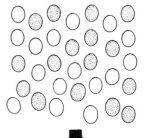

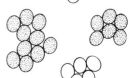

106

whose antigenic appearance has been altered (e.g., by viral infection), but it may sometimes be a piece of tissue taken from a genetically different individual of the same species (i.e., an allogeneic graft). Both the antigenic determinants by which foreign cellular material is recognized and the receptors of the cells of the immune system which achieve this recognition are exposed and accessible at the cell surface.

Plasma cells, which secrete soluble immunoglobulins (antibodies) of a variety of types, arise by the proliferation and differentiation of B-lymphocytes in response to challenge by the antigens for which they bear receptors. These B cell receptors are themselves immunoglobulins, mainly of the IgM and IgD classes, and they are externally located components of the plasma membrane. For any cell, the identical antigen specificity of all of its immunoglobulins, whether secreted or membrane-bound, is achieved by their possession of identical variable (V) regions. The difference between the membrane bound and soluble forms arises from the possession by membrane immunoglobulin of alternative C-terminal sequences consisting of a membrane-spanning lipophilic sequence and, at least in the case of IgM, a basic terminal tripeptide. However, triggering of these receptors on B cells by antigen is not adequate to provoke both their proliferation and differentiation. In some species, for example, cross-linking of receptors by anti-immunoglobulin antisera triggers division, but not differentiation to functional plasma cells. For a full response the B-lymphocytes must interact both with antigen and, depending on the particular antigen, with either antigen-activated T-lymphocytes of the T_{helper} subclass or with a 'non-specific' B-cell mitogen such as the lipid A moiety of bacterial lipopolysaccharide. After activation, some of the activated B-lymphocytes do not differentiate into plasma cells but become immunological 'memory' cells. These cells, which equip an animal to rapidly respond to a later antigen challenge, may simultaneously carry as many as three different types of membrane-bound antibody (IgM, IgD, IgG), all with identical antigen recognition sites and all functional as antigen receptors.

Mature T-lymphocytes of the $T_{cytotoxic}$ subclass, on the other hand, are cells that destroy immunologically changed (e.g., virus-infected) syngeneic cells (or the cells of tissue grafts that are antigenically similar, but not identical). The antigen receptors of T cells are glycoproteins which are probably unrelated to immunoglobulins. The maturation of $T_{cytotoxic}$ cells is complex (see p. 108). T_{helper} cells recognize an an-

Immunoglobulins

Immunoglobulins of several classes (IgG, IgM, etc.) are made by lymphocytes and plasma cells. Intracellular gene splicing determines the synthesis of both soluble and membrane-bound forms. Immunoglobulin molecules consist either of two 'heavy chains' and two 'light chains' or of a multiple of this basic tetrameric structure. The heavy chains are of several types: α (present in IgA), δ (IgD), ε (IgE), γ (IgG), or μ (IgM). Each pair of heavy chains is associated with a pair of κ or λ light chains. A single lymphocyte/plasma cell can make more than one class of immunoglobulin, but all of its immunoglobulins bear the same antigen-binding site (idiotype).

Maturation of B cells to plasma cells

↓ Type II MHC antigens
Membrane-bound (Y Y) and free (Y)
immunoglobulins

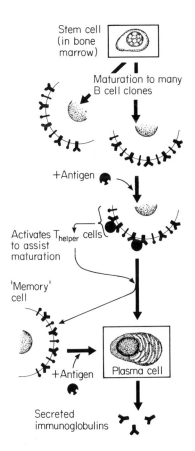

Stem cell
(in bone
marrow)

Maturation to many
B cell clones

+Antigen

Activates T_{helper} cells
to assist
maturation

'Memory'
cell

+Antigen

Plasma cell

Secreted
immunoglobulins

tigenic pattern of 'altered self' on the surface of antigenically activated macrophage, this pattern being a combination of 'self' type II MHC antigens (see below) and 'non-self' antigen (e.g., a viral glycoprotein). In response, they secrete interleukin II (mol.wt 35000), a growth factor for $T_{cytotoxic}$ cells. Interleukin II production is potentiated by antigen-activated $T_{inducer}$ cells. Quiescent $T_{cytotoxic}$ cell precursors have no receptors for interleukin II. However, these receptors are induced by exposure to antigen and the cells first proliferate in response to interleukin II secreted by the T_{helper} cells and then differentiate in response to an uncharacterized maturation factor.

T cell development

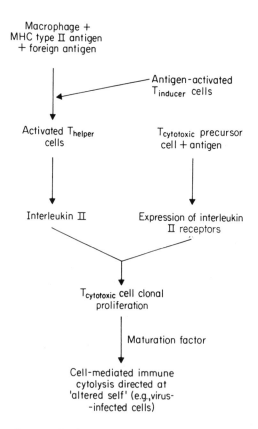

major histocompatability antigens

type I MHC antigens

The antigens of the major histocompatibility complex (MHC antigens) are of two major subtypes. Type I MHC antigens, typified by HLA-A, HLA-B and HLA-C in man and by H2-D and H2-K in mice, are two-chain glycoproteins that show striking sequence homologies with membrane-bound immunoglobulin. About 80 per cent of each heavy chain

108

(mol.wt 45000) is exposed at the cell surface, a small hydrophilic segment is at the cytoplasmic face of the membrane, and the remainder forms a membrane-spanning lipophilic sequence. The light chains of all type I MHC antigens are β_2-microglobulin polypeptides: these have a molecular weight of 12500, are associated with the externally exposed portion of the heavy chains and show close sequence homology with a single domain of an immunoglobulin. MHC antigens of this class are implicated in the response of $T_{cytotoxic}$ lymphocytes to allogeneic tissue grafts.

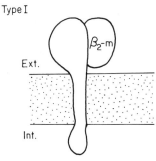

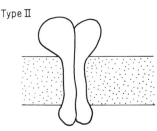

type II MHC
antigens

Type II MHC antigens, typified by HLA-D antigens in man and by I_a antigens in mice, are the products of the genes of the so-called immune response complex. These, again, are two-chain membrane glycoproteins, with each molecule consisting of 27000 and 33000 molecular weight subunits. They are the antigens that are recognized, in addition to the invading foreign antigen, by the T_{helper} and $T_{inducer}$ cells that are needed for full expression of the responses to antigens of B cells and $T_{cytotoxic}$ cells.

The antigen receptors on lymphocytes are synthesized and displayed at their surfaces by the lymphocytes themselves; other cells of the immune system derive responsiveness to antigen challenge from circulating antibodies that become adsorbed on to specific surface membrane receptors that recognize the F_c regions of the heavy chains of the various circulating immunoglobulin classes. On mast cells and basophils, both of which secrete histamine and other anaphylactic mediators, each F_c receptor binds a single bivalent IgE molecule. The IgE receptor is a glycoprotein of molecular weight 80000 which consists of an exposed glycopeptide of molecular weight 50000 (38000 peptide + 14000 carbohydrate) and a non-covalently attached and less accessible peptide of molecular weight 30000. It has an equilibrium dissociation constant for IgE of 10^{-11} M, and there are 10^5–10^6 receptors per mast cell. Although the normal mode of triggering of histamine secretion is for a multivalent antigen to cross-link the receptor-bound IgE molecules, and hence the receptors, it has recently become clear that secretion can be evoked by any procedure which functionally cross-links the IgE receptors, whether or not IgE is bound. Examples include the cross-linking of bound IgE molecules either chemically or by concanavalin A (a lectin) and the cross-linking of unoccupied IgE receptors by a bivalent antireceptor antibody.

IgE (F_c)
receptors

mast cells

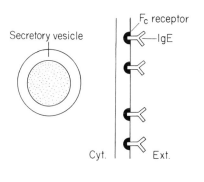

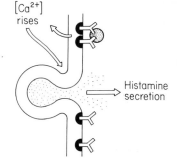

Antigen–induced histamine secretion

IgG (F_c)
receptors

Macrophages and polymorphonuclear leucocytes also bear receptors that bind immunoglobulins, principally IgG, through their F_c regions. These receptors are largely responsible for a process known as opsonization, whereby bacteria become coated with antibody and are much more rapidly phagocytized and killed than are bacteria that have not been exposed to serum (Chapter 6).

5.3 The nervous and endocrine systems

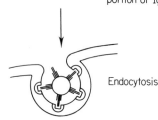

Endocytosis of opsonized bacterium by polymorphonuclear leucocyte or macrophage

Opsonized (IgG-coated) bacterium

Plasma membrane bearing receptors for the Fc portion of IgG heavy chain

Endocytosis

neurotransmission

Integration of the individual activities of the cells and tissues of a multicellular organism into a pattern that is spatially and temporally coherent requires continuous transmission of information throughout the organism. When this information is travelling very rapidly between widely spaced but discrete sites the messages are usually carried electrically by nerves, with chemical neurotransmitters only needed to pass them across the synapses that form the relays either between two nerve cells or between nerve cells and either sensory receptor cells or effector cells. Hormones, in contrast to neurotransmitters, are released from endocrine glands into the bloodstream, and this carries them to their target cells. The actions of some are directed to particular organs by the special design of the local circulation, for example carriage to the anterior pituitary of the hypothalamic hormones that control pituitary secretion. However, most hormones become disseminated throughout the systemic circulation where they control the activities of all tissues whose cells possess appropriate receptors; some hormones thus exert influence over most tissues (e.g., adrenaline) while the effects of others are limited to few sites. In addition, many cells liberate active ligands (e.g., histamine, prostaglandins) that reach appreciable concentrations only in their immediate environment and thus exert control over nearby cells.

hormones

electrical and biochemical responses

The most important effects of neurotransmitters on nerve cells are the rapid changes that they cause in the electrical properties (i.e., ion permeabilities) of their plasma membranes. These permeability changes are also essential to the effects of neurotransmitters on some peripheral tissues (e.g., skeletal muscle, see below), but in other tissues electrical changes are not a mandatory requirement for the evocation of responses such as contraction and secretion. Hormones often produce electrical responses in target cells, but their actions, many of which are slower than those of neurotransmitters, are usually interpreted largely in terms of the biochemical mechanisms that they control. This polarization of views has tended to lead to neural and hormonal communication being

110

regarded as separate processes, with chemically different signals, different time scales and different mechanisms. In recent years, however, it has become apparent that the signals and mechanisms of response in the nervous and endocrine systems show great similarities. For example, histamine is a neurotransmitter but is also a local mediator of tissue inflammation when released from mast cells; many small peptides classically regarded only as hormones appear also to be neurotransmitters (e.g., pancreozymin, angiotensin, vasopressin); and peripheral tissues use the same receptors to respond both to noradrenaline, a neurotransmitter, and to the hormone adrenaline.

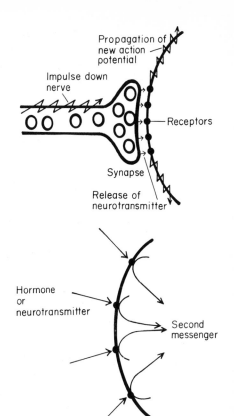

cell surface receptors

As far as is known, all neurotransmitters produce responses as a result of their interactions with receptors located on cell surfaces. The same is true of most hormones. Notable exceptions are steroid and thyroid hormones (thyroxine and triiodothyronine) which enter target cells and react inside with soluble receptors. However, even these may exert some effects through interaction with membrane receptors. Some polypeptide hormones form very stable complexes with their receptors; these then enter the target cells by endocytosis (see Chapter 6). It is possible that some relatively long-term aspects of cellular control are a function of such internalization of hormone–receptor complexes.

stimulus–response coupling

Many responses of cells to the binding of ligands at cell-surface receptors are rapid, and they occur without the extracellular messenger gaining entry to the cells. The receptor systems in the membranes, therefore, must express at least two functions: the recognition and binding of an extracellular ligand and the translation of the received message into some change in membrane function. The latter may be either a change in the ionic permeability characteristics of the membrane or the activation of some membrane-bound enzyme. Each type of receptor is coupled to one, or occasionally more than one, such effector system. Mammalian cells are normally exposed to an environment that contains a complex mixture of ligands to which they are responsive, some of which produce similar effects; for example, acetylcholine and pancreozymin both stimulate pancreatic exocrine secretion. Other ligands will produce either quite different or opposed effects. For

integrated responses to multiple stimuli

example, inhibitory and stimulatory neurotransmitters produce, respectively, hyperpolarization and depolarization of neurones, and adrenaline stimulates and insulin inhibits lipolysis (triacylglycerol breakdown) in adipose cells. Often, the receptors responsive to several of the extracellular stimuli

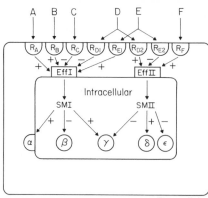

Many extracellular signals (A–F) activate receptors (R_A–R_F) that either stimulate or inhibit the activity of effector systems (Eff I, Eff II). Each effector system controls the intracellular concentration of a second messenger (SM I, SM II) that has several intracellular targets (α–ϵ)

will be coupled to the same effector system, so that the many receptor systems of the plasma membrane serve to translate the information brought by a large number of extracellular ligands into a simplified language, consisting of a smaller number of intracellular messenger molecules ('second messengers') which can exert control over intracellular processes. Although it seems likely that there are several second messengers, only adenosine-3′,5′-cyclic monophosphate (cyclic AMP) and Ca^{2+} have so far been identified with certainty.

5.4 Synaptic transmission

Synapses vary greatly in morphology. At many, there are specific contacts between the participating cells, as indicated both by electron microscopy and by the fact that synaptic junctions, consisting of the apposed presynaptic and postsynaptic membranes, can survive quite severe disruptive procedures, for example in preparation for subcellular fractionation. However, a separation of at least 15 nm is usually maintained between the trilamellar images of the two membranes. Sometimes synaptic contacts are much less morphologically precise. In smooth muscles, for example, noradrenaline is released from a series of beadlike swellings (varicosities) along sympathetic nerve fibres that course amongst the muscle fibres; noradrenaline causes direct activation only of the fibres nearest to its point of release.

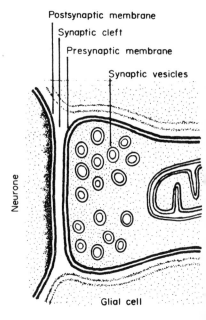

Postsynaptic membrane
Synaptic cleft
Presynaptic membrane
Synaptic vesicles
Neurone
Glial cell

'second messengers'

synaptic structures

Action potentials are usually transmitted rapidly along nerves as a consequence of the presence of potential-sensitive Na^+ gates (see Chapter 4). However, the plasma membranes of nerve terminals possess potential-sensitive Ca^{2+} gates, so that the arrival of an action potential causes a rise in cytosol Ca^{2+} concentration within the terminal. This, in turn, causes the release of neurotransmitter into the synaptic cleft, almost certainly by exocytosis (see Chapter 6). Each neuron releases its own characteristic neurotransmitter or mixture of neurotransmitters (e.g., 5-hydroxytryptamine and substance P from some spinal neurones). These diffuse across the synaptic cleft and interact with receptors on the plasma membrane of the target cell. Processes for terminating the activity of a neurotransmitter include its destruction, for example the hydrolysis of acetylcholine by acetylcholinesterase, or its reabsorption by nerve endings and/or adjacent cells, for example the reabsorption of catecholamines and amino acids.

Acetylcholine

Adrenaline

Noradrenaline

Catecholamines

Some accepted and probable neurotransmitters

Acetylcholine
Noradrenaline
Dopamine
5-hydroxytryptamine
Histamine
γ-aminobutyrate (GABA)
Glutamate
Glycine
ATP
Substance P
Enkephalin } small peptides
TRH
Other peptide ligands

Within the nervous system individual neurones typically receive 1000–10000 separate synaptic inputs from something like 1000 other neurones with each neurone releasing its own characteristic neurotransmitter(s). The majority of synapses are between terminals at the ends of axons and the dendrites of other neurones, but there are also synaptic contacts between axon and cell body, axon and axon, and dendrite and dendrite. Some of the neurotransmitters are excitatory, in that they depolarize the cells, while others hyperpolarize neurones and are thus inhibitory. Depolarizing stimuli tend, as in nerve axons, to increase the frequency of action potentials, but neuronal cell bodies and dendrites possess a much greater variety of controlled ion channels (particularly for Na^+, K^+, Cl^- and Ca^{2+}), some responding in milliseconds

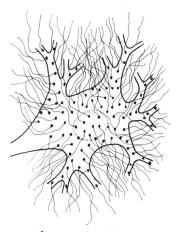

A neuronal cell body

113

and others in seconds, so they can display a much richer repertoire of subtle change in membrane potential and in firing
pattern. Some of these ion channels are directly responsive to
receptor activation (e.g., Na^+ channels associated with excitatory nicotinic acetylcholine receptors and Cl^- channels
activated by inhibitory glycine receptors), others are opened
or closed in response to changes in membrane potential, and
yet others are controlled by changes in intracellular concentrations of second messengers (e.g., Ca^{2+}-activated channels
for various ions, see p. 59). As a consequence of their varied
patterns of synaptic input and complements of ion conductance mechanisms, individual neurones thus display distinctive patterns of electrical activity; these are dramatically illustrated by the quite different firing patterns of several of the
individually identifiable neurones of small molluscan ganglia.
Although postsynaptic target cells bear the majority of the receptors for neurotransmitters, it is now clear that many
neurotransmitters also exert a feedback control that moder-
ates their continued release from stimulated nerve terminals.
This is achieved through presynaptic receptors (often called
autoreceptors) on the nerve terminals; for acetylcholine the
inhibition of continued release is mediated by muscarinic receptors, and noradrenaline output is restrained by α_2-adrener-
gic receptors (see diagram).

The phenomenon of neurotransmission has been studied
in greatest detail at the specialized junctions between motor
neurons and voluntary (skeletal) muscle cells. At such
neuromuscular neuromuscular junctions, the tip of the nerve axon divides
junctions into several terminal fibres of small diameter which are
accommodated in closely fitting grooves in a small,
specialized region (the endplate region) of the surface of the
muscle cell. In the regions of contact with the nerve terminals, the membrane of the muscle cell (sarcolemma) forms
complex convolutions. The postsynaptic, nicotinic acetylcholine receptors occupy the peaks of these membrane convolutions, closest to the presynaptic release sites, and the
acetylcholinesterase that destroys the transmitter lines
troughs into which acetylcholine will then diffuse.

Neurotransmitters are stored in presynaptic nerve termi-
synaptic nals in small membrane vesicles; for acetylcholine at the
vesicles mammalian neuromuscular junction these are 30–60 nm in
diameter. When an action potential arrives at the nerve terminal this triggers the release of neurotransmitter into the
synaptic cleft or neuromuscular junction, probably by
exocytosis (Chapter 6). There is then a delay (about 0.7 m sec in

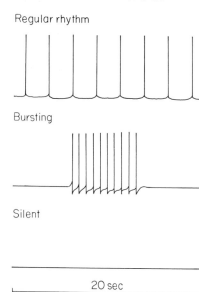

Electrical activity patterns
of different neurones

Regular rhythm

Bursting

Silent

|——— 20 sec ———|

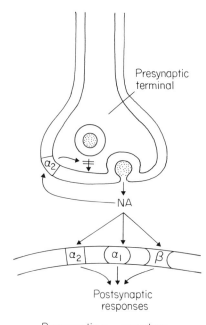

Presynaptic
terminal

NA

Postsynaptic
responses

Presynaptic α_2-receptors
control noradrenaline (NA) release

114

the neuromuscular junction) before any change is detected in the membrane potential of the postsynaptic cell. If the neurotransmitter-induced depolarization reaches the appropriate threshold value, an action potential is generated which travels over the whole surface of the stimulated muscle cell. Direct application of acetylcholine to the endplate region of skeletal muscle cells by micropipette has indicated that 10^{-15}–10^{-16} mol of acetylcholine is sufficient to excite a single muscle fibre.

Even in the absence of an action potential at a nerve ending small spontaneous fluctuations are seen in the membrane potential of postsynaptic cells: at motor endplates these 'miniature endplate potentials' are usually multiples of about 0.4 mV. They have been attributed to the irregular spontaneous release of quanta (10^{-18}–10^{-19} mol) of acetylcholine into the junction from the nerve terminal; each quantum may represent the discharge of one vesicle.

miniature endplate potentials

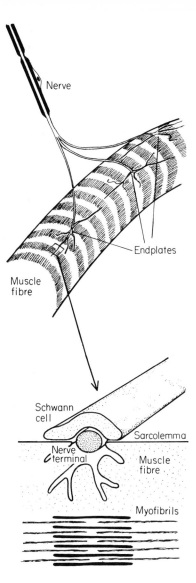

5.5 Receptors: pharmacological classification and identification by ligand binding

The presence of a particular type of functional receptor in a tissue is initially inferred from the fact that a particular ligand either evokes a cellular response or it inhibits a response evoked by another ligand. Some hormones and neurotransmitters, however, evoke a spectrum of different responses in various target tissues, with individual responses showing differing sensitivities to ligands that either mimic (agonists) or inhibit (antagonists) the effect of the natural signal. From this came the idea that not all of the responses of cells to a single hormone or neurotransmitter are necessarily controlled by activation of the same receptors.

multiple receptor types for single ligands

The responses of postsynaptic neurones in sympathetic ganglia and of skeletal muscle cells to acetylcholine are very rapid, involving the opening within 1 m sec of receptor-controlled Na^+ channels in the postsynaptic membrane; the resulting depolarization, provided that it reaches the appropriate threshold value, initiates action potentials that propagate the neurotransmitter signal to distant regions of the cell surface (and, in skeletal muscle, down the T-tubule system to cause activation of the sarcoplasmic reticulum, see p. 93). These responses are blocked by tubocurarine (a constituent of curare, an arrow poison) and by certain polypeptide neurotoxins from snake venoms (e.g., α-bungarotoxin);

115

they are mediated through activation of nicotinic cholinergic receptors. By contrast, the responses to acetylcholine of most of the organs innervated by the cholinergic parasympathetic nervous system are much slower, with no detectable response for at least 100 m sec, and are blocked by a different family of antagonists, for example atropine. These responses are mediated by muscarinic cholinergic receptors, whose most important effects upon cells appear to be to raise cytoplasmic Ca^{2+} concentrations and to depress cyclic AMP levels. In some cells both types of cholinergic receptors coexist; in the postsynaptic neurones of sympathetic ganglia, nicotinic receptors mediate the fast transmission of information through the ganglion, but the responsiveness of the neurones is also modulated by muscarinic evocation of a slow excitatory postsynaptic potential.

Similar situations exist for other ligands such as histamine, 5-hydroxytryptamine and opiate peptides. They interact with more than one class of receptor and each receptor class shows distinctive ligand selectivity, employs a distinctive mechanism and evokes distinctive responses. In many cases, the special therapeutic qualities of receptor-directed drugs

are a result of selective interaction with a particular receptor population (see Chapter 8). The complex potentialities for cell control that arise from the evolution of closely related intercellular messengers and of multiple receptor types is well illustrated by the catecholamines. Adrenaline is a circulating hormone, noradrenaline a central and peripheral neurotransmitter, and dopamine a central neurotransmitter; there are at least two types of dopamine receptor and at least four types of receptor (designated α_1, α_2, β_1 and β_2) which respond to adrenaline and noradrenaline.

Since two or more types of receptor responsive to a single stimulus often coexist in a single cell, an essential step in the analysis of the mechanisms involved in cellular responses to stimuli is to define which receptor type is responsible for the control of each evoked cellular event.

Each class of receptor was originally characterized in terms of its responsiveness to particular agonists and antagonists. Recently, however, radioactive ligands of very high specific radioactivity have been used as selectively bound ligands for detecting, characterizing and isolating the intrinsic membrane proteins which these receptors comprise. Most polypeptide hormones show receptor binding affinities in the $10^{-11}-10^{-8}$ M range and dissociate from their receptors relatively slowly. In such cases, the preferred radioactive ligand

Ligands that act at receptors

Hormones and neurotransmitters activate the appropriate cellular receptors: they are *agonists*. Other agonists include natural products (morphine at opiate receptors) and synthetic drugs (salbutamol at β_2-adrenergic receptors). Molecules that both bind to receptors without evoking any response and prevent the binding of agonists are termed *antagonists*. These may be natural (e.g., atropine) or synthetic (e.g., propranolol). *Partial agonists* are molecules that are capable of evoking a less than maximal response but which also inhibit cellular responses to more efficacious agonists.

d - Tubocurarine

Atropine

Antagonists used in identification of receptor subclasses

Receptor	Antagonist
Nicotinic cholinergic	Tubocurare, α-bungarotoxin
Muscarinic cholinergic	Atropine, scopolamine
α_1-adrenergic	Phenoxybenzamine, prazosin
α_2-adrenergic	Yohimbine
β-adrenergic	Propranolol, pindolol
H_1-histamine	Mepyramine
H_2-histamine	Cimetidine, ranitidine

for receptor characterization is a labelled form of the hormone that retains full biological activity (e.g., insulin substituted with a single ^{125}I atom). The affinities of small neurotransmitters for their receptors are usually much lower (10^{-7}–10^{-5} M) and their dissociation rapid, properties that are difficult to accommodate in convenient assays of ligand binding. For these receptors, therefore, the labelled ligand is usually an antagonist of high affinity which dissociates from the receptor only slowly or is bound essentially irreversibly. Many clinically important, receptor-directed drugs and some natural toxins fall into the former category. α-Bungarotoxin, a polypeptide neurotoxin from a snake venom, is typical of the latter. The interaction of an unlabelled ligand with a receptor is assayed in terms of its ability to compete with a labelled ligand for the receptor sites. Such binding studies have confirmed that the various hypothetical receptors that were proposed as a result of studies of pharmacological activities are indeed different species of membrane-bound, ligand-binding sites—for example, such techniques distinguish between α_1-, α_2-, β_1- and β_2-adrenergic receptors.

competitive binding assays

Receptors are intrinsic membrane proteins and their solubilization and isolation normally require detergents. Identification of the isolated protein depends upon its ligand-binding properties. In one approach, which yields functionally inactivated receptors, a ligand is covalently attached to the receptor whilst it is still in the intact cell: examples include alkylation of the nicotinic cholinergic receptor by 4-(N-maleimido) benzyltrimethylammonium (MBTA), the attachment of azido derivatives of hormones (e.g., azidoinsulin) which can undergo photoactivation, and the use of a bivalent cross-linking reagent to covalently stabilize insulin–receptor complexes. Such studies provide the most unambiguous route to receptor identification, but functional studies aimed at the reconstitution of the activity of isolated receptors call for isolation of the unmodified receptor. This is achieved either by affinity chromatography (using a column containing a pharmacologically active ligand which forms receptor complexes of moderate affinity that dissociate relatively rapidly) or by selective immunoadsorption or immunoprecipitation with an antireceptor antibody. In a limited number of cases, receptor isolation is facilitated by the availability of tissues containing remarkably high concentrations of receptors, for example the nicotinic acetylcholine receptors of the electroplaques of *Torpedo* sp. (electric rays), but most receptors are

receptor isolation

covalent labelling

affinity chromatography

Isolation of receptor-antagonist complex

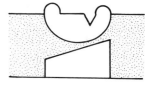

 +Labelled antagonist

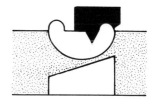

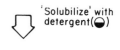 'Solubilize' with detergent(○)

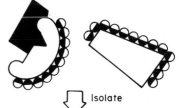

Isolate

117

present in very small concentrations and the purifications needed are more than 10000-fold.

5.6 The nicotinic acetylcholine receptor

postsynaptic
receptor arrays

The high concentration of nicotinic receptors in electro-plaques arises because these organs are evolutionary derivatives of skeletal muscle that retain relatively little other than the neuromuscular junction. As in the mammalian neuromuscular junction, the postsynaptic membrane closest to the nerve terminal consists of a closely packed hexagonal array of receptors, as demonstrated both by freeze–fracture electron microscopy and by x-ray diffraction. α-Bungaro-toxin binds to such membranes at densities of up to 30000 molecules/μm^2, with about three bungarotoxin molecules bound to each receptor molecule. Affinity chromatography allows isolation of the nicotinic receptors, completely separated from acetylcholinesterase, in two forms of molecular weights 275000 and 550000, the heavier form being a disulphide-linked dimer of the lighter. Each unit of molecular weight 275000 consists of four types of polypeptide subunits: these have molecular weights of 40000 (α), 50000 (β), 60000 (γ) and 66000 (δ), and are present in a stoichiometry of 2:1:1:1. The disulphide bridge between two such complexes is between the 66000 molecular weight subunits. The amino acid sequences of the subunits show striking sequence homologies, suggesting that they evolved by gene duplication. All subunits are glycopeptides whose heterosaccharides include mannose, glucose and galactose residues, bind lectins and face the extracellular space. All subunits span the post-synaptic membrane: the amino acid sequence of each contains four probable membrane-spanning sequences. The resulting complex has a diameter of about 8.5 nm and protrudes about 5 nm and 1.5 nm beyond the membrane surface on the external and cytoplasmic surfaces, respectively. The receptor-rich membranes also contain a peripheral polypeptide of molecular weight 43000 that is present at the cytoplasmic surface in amounts approximately equimolar with the 40000 molecular weight subunit of the receptor and is removed at alkaline pH ($\geqslant 11$). Removal and replacement of this component leads to dispersion and reformation of the closely packed receptor arrays characteristic of the post-synaptic membrane, suggesting that it is responsible for the maintenance of this ordered membrane lattice.

transmembrane
receptor subunits

The activation of the nicotinic receptor causes the opening, for approximately 1 m sec, of a 'gated' cation channel

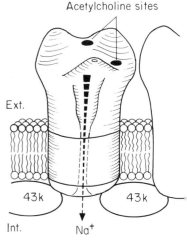

Nicotinic acetylcholine receptor

that allows the passage of about 10^4 small ions, mainly Na^+. These responses can be antagonized by classical nicotinic antagonists that competitively inhibit the interaction of acetylcholine with its binding sites and by certain amine local anaesthetics or histrionicotoxin (a frog skin toxin), both of which seem to interfere with the mechanism responsible for increased ion conductance. The acetylcholine binding sites have been identified using labelled MBTA (p. 117): they are on the two α-subunits. Binding studies with labelled histrionicotoxin suggest that the δ-subunit polypeptide is implicated in control of ion conductance.

functional states
of nicotinic
receptor

Pharmacological, physiological and physical studies of the nicotinic receptor (in intact tissue, in membrane fragments, or in isolation) demonstrate that it exists in at least three interconvertible forms. Addition of agonist converts the receptor from a closed resting (R) state to an activated (A) state in which the ion conductance channel is open; both of these have relatively low affinities for agonist (approximately 10^{-5}–10^{-4} M). Continued presence of agonist, especially at high concentrations, converts most of the receptors to their very high affinity, desensitized (D) form. Direct evidence for these molecular transitions has been obtained from rapid reaction studies using the fluorescent agonist dansyl-C_6-choline. Recent studies have shown that isolated nicotinic receptors can be incorporated into appropriate lipid bilayer structures in a form in which they reproduce the agonist-stimulated changes in conductance and dansyl-C_6-choline fluorescence relatively faithfully: the time-resolution of the conductance measurements demanded that these were done in single planar bilayers.

Nicotinic receptors have also been isolated from the electroplaques of *Electroplax* (an electric eel), and from mammalian brain and skeletal muscle. In general terms, the receptors from all sites appear structurally and functionally similar (see also p. 208).

5.7 Receptors that elevate cytosolic Ca^{2+} concentration

cell surface
[Ca^{2+}] gradient

Ca^{2+} differs from other cellular cations in that its concentration gradient at the cell surface is very large, from around 1 mM outside to 0.01–1 μM inside; taking into account the resting potential of the cell, this represents an electrochemical gradient of approximately 10^6-fold. This very large gradient is sustained, at the expense of metabolic energy, by

119

at least two distinct plasma membrane Ca^{2+} pumps, a calmodulin-dependent Ca^{2+}-ATPase (Chapter 3) and a $Ca^{2+}/3Na^+$ antiport. As a consequence of this maintained gradient, the mobilization of a very small amount of Ca^{2+} into the cytosol compartment of cells, whether from membranes or as a result of Ca^{2+} flow through membranes whose permeability is increased (e.g., the sarcoplasmic reticulum, p. 93), can cause changes in cytosol Ca^{2+} concentration sufficient to activate the many cellular responses that are responsive to Ca^{2+} in the micromolar range. Such processes include contraction, exocytosis (see Chapter 6), and the activation of certain types of surface membrane ion channels (Chapter 3).

touch response
of *Paramecium*

Changes in cytosol $[Ca^{2+}]$ appear to be important in cells responding both to primary external stimuli (e.g., light, touch) and to chemical signals such as hormones, neurotransmitters and antigens. An excellent example of the former, and one amenable to genetic manipulation, is the touch response of *Paramecium*. When this ciliated, unicellular animal swims into an obstacle it immediately reverses its ciliary beat and swims backwards. This response, which is mediated through a rise in cytosol $[Ca^{2+}]$, is brought about by the opening of touch-sensitive Ca^{2+} channels in the membrane of the cilia at the front end of the organism, with the consequent depolarization activating potential-sensitive Ca^{2+} channels over the remainder of the surface: the response can be mimicked by depolarizing the cells by immersion in KCl. The Ca^{2+} channels appear to be absent from so-called *pawn* mutants (they always go forwards!) which are insensitive to both touch and depolarization.

identification of
Ca^{2+}-mediated
responses

Chemosensitive Ca^{2+}-mobilizing receptors are usually identified in two ways. Responses, especially sustained responses, to stimulation of these receptors are greatly diminished either by removal of Ca^{2+} from the external medium during stimulation or by stimulating the cells in the presence of ions which inhibit fluxes through Ca^{2+} channels or compete at membrane Ca^{2+}-binding sites (e.g., La^{3+}, Mn^{2+}). In addition, the receptors can be bypassed and the responses elicited directly by admitting Ca^{2+} to cells either with an ionophore such as A23187 or ionomycin (Chapter 3), or with a microelectrode. A particularly valuable technique is to follow transient changes in cytosol $[Ca^{2+}]$ in stimulated cells by monitoring the optical properties of Ca^{2+}-sensitive molecules introduced into cells: these include aequorin, a jellyfish protein that is made luminescent by submicromolar Ca^{2+}, and quin-2, a fluorescent Ca^{2+}-chelator.

Some receptors whose activation causes Ca²⁺ mobilization

Receptor	Target tissue (examples)
Muscarinic cholinergic	Salivary glands, pancreas (exocrine)
α_1-adrenergic	Smooth muscle, liver
H_1-histamine	Smooth muscle, brain
Pancreozymin	Pancreas (exocrine)
Substance P	Salivary glands, smooth muscle
V_1-vasopressin	Smooth muscle, liver
Angiotensin	Smooth muscle, liver
LHRH (GnRH)	Anterior pituitary
Appropriate antigens	Mast cells
Chemotactic attractants	Polymorphonuclear leucocytes

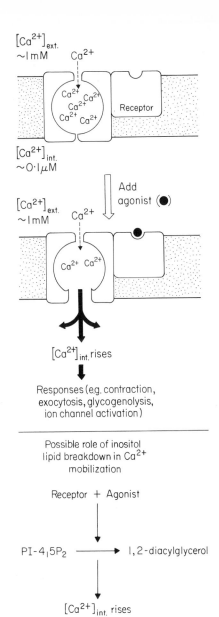

source of mobilized Ca²⁺

The mechanism(s) by which receptor activation causes Ca^{2+} mobilization in stimulated cells is not well understood. In many cells, it seems likely that the major sources of the rise in cytosol $[Ca^{2+}]$ are release of Ca^{2+} from a pool bound to the plasma membrane (and mobilized within a few seconds) and a sustained inflow of Ca^{2+} through cell surface Ca^{2+} channels that are controlled by receptor activation. However, it also remains possible that in some cells a substantial amount of Ca^{2+} is liberated from pools sequestered within intracellular organelles, maybe mitochondria and/or endoplasmic reticulum. One general feature of all Ca^{2+}-mobilizing receptors is that they stimulate the breakdown of an inositol phospholipid (probably phosphatidylinositol 4,5-bisphosphate). This response, however, differs from the majority of other cell responses by its independence of changes in the intracellular $[Ca^{2+}]$ and by the fact that its full evocation depends upon the activation of all the relevant receptors (Section 5.11). These observations led to the suggestion that breakdown of phosphatidylinositol 4,5-bisphosphate might somehow be involved in the coupling between activation of Ca^{2+}-mobilizing receptors and the mobilization of Ca^{2+} from and through the plasma membrane.

role of inositol phospholipid breakdown

termination of Ca²⁺-mediated responses

The termination of cell responses that are brought about by an increase in cytosol $[Ca^{2+}]$ involves several factors. Ca^{2+} channels opened by depolarization or by receptor activation stay open only for a brief period. Continued exposure to Ca^{2+} of intracellular targets, such as plasma membrane K^+ channels, may lead to their desensitization. Finally, Ca^{2+} is rapidly pumped out of the cytosol compartment of cells both by the plasma membrane pumps and by pumps in intracellular membranes (mitochondria and endoplasmic reticulum). The relative contributions of these to the rapid termination of a response vary from cell to cell, but ulti-

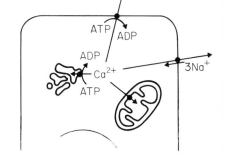

121

mately any net influx of Ca^{2+} must be matched by a net efflux driven by the Ca^{2+} pump(s) at the plasma membrane.

5.8 Receptors that control adenylate cyclase activity

stimulation and inhibition of adenylate cyclase

A second family of receptors that all share a single second messenger within the cell are those that control the activity of adenylate cyclase and hence the synthesis of cyclic AMP. Recently, this group has been distinguished into two families of receptors, one group being stimulatory and the other inhibitory. It has now been established, from several lines of evidence, that control of adenylate cyclase by extracellular ligands involves at least three separate plasma membrane proteins; a receptor that recognizes and responds to the ligand, the catalytic adenylate cyclase, and one of the two guanine nucleotide-binding proteins (G-proteins, also known as G, N or G/F) which serve to communicate between receptors and cyclase. These components can be separated and analysed. Although each type of receptor is a different macromolecule, all receptors appear to control the activity of the same population of adenylate cyclase molecules. Coupling between receptors and adenylate cyclase is achieved by stimulatory (G_s) and inhibitory (G_i) G-proteins. The G-proteins and adenylate cyclase are intrinsic plasma membrane proteins that face the cell interior: the G_s-protein has a molecular weight of 130000, with subunits of molecular weights 52000 and 35000 and adenylate cyclase is rather larger (mol.wt approximately 200000).

role of GTP

The key role of the G-proteins was first revealed by the demonstration that GTP is an essential cofactor for the control of adenylate cyclase by receptors both in isolated plasma membranes and in intact cells. It was then shown that AC^- mutants of S49 lymphoma cells, which lack functional G_s-protein, show adenylate cyclase activity only in the presence of $MnATP^{2-}$, an unphysiological substrate. Membranes from such cells do not show cyclase activation either in the presence of receptor-directed stimuli or in the presence of artificial stimuli that act directly upon the G_s-protein (F^- ion, cholera toxin or p(NG)ppG, a non-hydrolysable GTP analogue), but full responsiveness can be restored simply by the addition of a G_s-protein preparation from wild-type cells. A second class of mutants, designated UNC (uncoupled), possesses a modified G_s-protein that is capable of conferring sensitivity to F^-, cholera toxin and p(NH)ppG, but cannot mediate responsiveness to hormone activation.

Some receptors whose activation stimulates or inhibits adenylate cyclase

Receptor	Target tissue (examples)
Stimulatory	
β-adrenergic	Many
Glucagon	Liver, adipose
ACTH	Adrenal cortex, adipose
TSH	Thyroid
Lutropin (LH, ICSH)	Corpus luteum, testis
Prostacyclin	Platelets
H_2-histamine	Gastric mucosa
Inhibitory	
Opiates	Neurones
Adenosine	Heart
$α_2$-adrenergic	Platelets
Muscarinic cholinergic	Heart, neurones

122

A firm indication that the activation of adenylate cyclase by hormones does not require the existence of long-lasting ternary complexes of receptor, G_s-protein and cyclase came from the demonstration that fully responsive heterokaryons are produced by the fusion of cells containing activatory receptors (e.g., β-adrenergic receptors) and no cyclase with other cells containing cyclase but no receptors: the separate components from the two fused cells rapidly become functionally coupled. In an extension of these experiments, it has been shown that activated receptors can, in a guanyl nucleotide-dependent manner, produce an activated form of the G_s-protein and that this can, in its turn, bring about activation of adenylate cyclase. Studies involving systematic variation of the viscosity of the lipid bilayer in which the various components coexist have demonstrated that cyclase activation by stimulated receptors is a diffusion-limited process: activation is a direct function of the frequency of collisions between laterally diffusing components.

When adenylate cyclase is activated by a receptor in a GTP-dependent manner the activation is transient, being rapidly reversed once the stimulus is removed. If, however, a non-hydrolysable GTP analogue such as p(NH)ppG is substituted, activation becomes quasi-irreversible—it is only reversed by subsequent incubation in the presence of hormone and either GTP or GDP. This is because the G_s-protein possesses GTPase activity, and it only retains the ability to activate adenylate cyclase for as long as GTP (or p(NH)ppG) is the bound ligand.

These observations can all be accommodated by a relatively simple model for the control of adenylate cyclase, in which interaction with an activatory receptor opens up the guanyl nucleotide binding site of the G_s-protein, facilitating guanyl nucleotide exchange, and interaction with an inhibitory receptor enhances the GTPase activity of the G_i-protein. Thus, in an unstimulated cell most of the G-proteins will, as a result of their GTPase activity, possess bound GDP: they will tend to leave adenylate cyclase inactive. Stimulation of an activatory receptor leads to formation of a complex with the G_s-protein, and the bound GDP is exchanged for GTP. The activated G_s-protein then diffuses laterally in the membrane, activating adenylate cyclase molecules which it encounters, until hydrolysis of its bound GTP by its intrinsic GTPase causes it to revert to the non-activatory state. If activation occurs in the presence of p(NH)ppG rather than GTP then activation is persistent: the non-hydrolysable GTP analogue

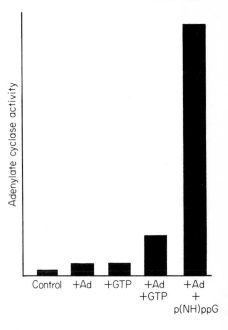

Potentiation of adenylate cyclase
activation by guanine nucleotides

123

will hold the G_s-protein in the active state until it encounters a combination of a normal guanyl nucleotide and an activated receptor that stimulates guanyl nucleotide exchange. Persistent activation by cholera toxin is achieved by irreversible inhibition of the GTPase activity (see p. 203). In the presence of switched-on inhibitory receptors, the lifetime of the GTP-associated form of the G_i-protein is reduced as a result of enhancement of its GTPase activity, meaning that these GTP-associated G_i-proteins can compete with activated G_s-proteins and thus attenuate the activation of adenylate cyclase by activatory ligands.

see p. 203

Ca^{2+}/cAMP
inter-relationships

An additional factor which modulates cyclic AMP levels in cells is the cytoplasmic Ca^{2+} concentration. However, these effects vary from tissue to tissue. In some cells (e.g., turkey erythrocytes) a rise in cytoplasmic Ca^{2+} inhibits the activation of adenylate cyclase by hormones, but in others (e.g., brain, islets of Langerhans), adenylate cyclase is subject to a calmodulin-dependent activation by Ca^{2+}. Another way in which Ca^{2+} controls cyclic AMP levels is through the activity of cyclic AMP phosphodiesterase, an enzyme that exists in several forms. One widespread form of this enzyme is activated by Ca^{2+} in a calmodulin-dependent manner, while a second, plasma membrane-bound, species is activated as a result of an insulin-stimulated phosphorylation reaction. Both serve as illustrations of the extent to which the individual biochemical events controlled by different hormone receptors may interact with one another in spatially and temporally complex patterns.

5.9 The insulin receptor

effects of
insulin

Insulin provokes a wide variety of responses in its target tissues, primarily skeletal muscle, adipose tissue and liver. These include rapid enhancement of glucose transport (not in liver), increased glycogen and lipid synthesis and much longer-term effects on gene expression: all of these appear to be mediated through the interaction of insulin with a single receptor population.

isolation

Even in the most favourable situations, such as the adipocyte, the receptor represents no more than 0.01 per cent of the plasma membrane protein. Despite this, substantial purification of the detergent-solubilized receptor on insulin affinity columns showed that it is a rod-shaped glycoprotein with a molecular weight of approximately 300 000. More recently, covalent insulin–receptor complexes have been iden-

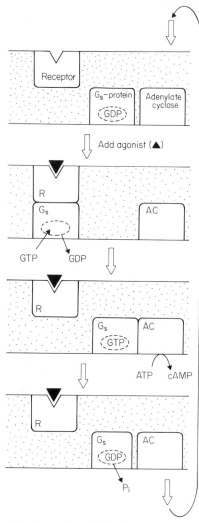

Activation and inactivation of adenylate cyclase

tified and isolated after the application of photoactivatable ^{125}I-derivatives (with azide groups on residue 1 or 29 of the B chain) and after cross-linking of the hormone–receptor complex with disuccinimidyl suberate. In addition, the receptor has been isolated by immunoprecipitation from detergent solution, using anti-insulin receptor antibodies from patients with acanthocytosis nigricans, an autoimmune condition (see pp. 208–209).

structure

The isolated receptor consists of four disulphide-linked glycosylated polypeptide chains, two α-subunits (mol.wt 125 000) and two β-subunits (mol.wt 90 000). The molecule is symmetrical, with two disulphide-linked αβ pairs themselves linked by a disulphide bridge between their larger α-subunits; this is an arrangement reminiscent of immunoglobulins, which act as cell surface receptors on B-lymphocytes (p. 106). The disulphide bridge between the αβ pairs is much more susceptible to reduction than are those linking α-to β-subunits. The binding properties of the isolated receptor are not substantially changed by enzymatic removal of phospholipids or sialic acid, despite the fact that electrophoretic studies suggest that sialic acid is a component of the heterosaccharides attached to both the α- and β-chains. The β-subunit is particularly sensitive to proteolytic cleavage by elastase, with the release of a 40 000 molecular weight fragment; this apparently does not change either the binding affinity (3 nM) or the biological activity of the receptor. Indeed, the receptor in intact cells appears to be a mixture of intact and proteolytically nicked forms.

insulin second messenger

Despite intensive efforts, the second messenger of the insulin receptor is still unidentified. Recent work has suggested, however, that insulin-stimulated muscle and adipose cells, and also adipocyte plasma membranes, generate a putative mediator molecule that can mimic the effects of insulin even in broken cells: this appears to be a (glyco)-peptide of molecular weight approximately 1500. As with cyclic AMP and Ca^{2+}, many of the effects of insulin appear to be brought about by control over the phosphorylation or dephosphorylation of cell proteins (e.g., cyclic nucleotide phosphodiesterase, p. 124), but it is not known whether protein phosphorylation is involved in insulin-stimulated enhancement of glucose entry into stimulated cells. This energy-dependent response, in which the V_{max} for glucose entry may rise tenfold without any accompanying change in the affinity of the transport system, is achieved largely by the rapid and reversible integration into the adipocyte plasma

control of glucose transport

Insulin-stimulated glucose transport in adipocytes

Ext.   Int.

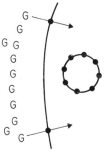

+ Insulin

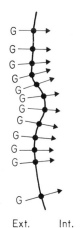

Ext.   Int.

membrane of glucose transporters that were previously
sequestered within the cell, possibly in Golgi membranes.

5.10 Other methods of stimulus–response coupling

Despite the knowledge summarized above, there are still
many receptors whose associated mechanisms for stimulus–
response coupling are either less well understood or unknown.

control of ion permeabilities

Some of these undoubtedly exert fairly direct control over
membrane ion permeabilities: glutamate is an excitatory
transmitter that, like nicotinic cholinergic stimuli (p. 118),
activates fast Na^+ channels. The inhibitory transmitters
glycine (strychnine-inhibited) and γ-aminobutyrate (antagonized by bicuculline or picrotoxin) open rapidly responsive Cl^- channels: Cl^- inflow hyperpolarizes the cells. Some
inhibitory muscarinic acetylcholine receptors act by increasing membrane K^+ conductance. Indeed, a wide variety of
ligands that control cells through interactions at the plasma
membrane cause changes in membrane ion fluxes, either
primarily or in response to changes in intracellular messengers such as Ca^{2+} or cyclic AMP; the effects upon cell function of these permeability changes and of the resulting
changes in membrane potentials are poorly understood.

prostaglandins and leukotrienes

Although the majority of ligands that interact with cell-
surface receptors are polar molecules, especially peptides or
small amine derivatives, a limited number are lipid derivatives. Many of these are derived from arachidonate, a
polyunsaturated fatty acid (see p. 35) of membrane lipids,
either via the action of a cyclo-oxygenase (yielding a variety
of prostaglandins) or of lipo-oxygenase (leading to the
leukotrienes, amongst them slow-reacting anaphylactic
agents). The various prostanoids (prostaglandins and leukotrienes) appear to act on cells at least partially through the
mechanisms discussed above—stimulation and inhibition of
adenylate cyclase or mobilization of Ca^{2+}. In addition, their
production and release is a frequent response of stimulated
cells, particularly cells stimulated by Ca^{2+}-mobilizing
ligands. The total rate of prostaglandin production is con-

liberation of arachidonate

trolled largely by the availability in cells of free arachidonate,
and the pattern of products is dictated by the particular enzyme complement of the stimulated cell. Since almost all of
the arachidonate of cells is esterified at the 2-position of
membrane phospholipids, cell activation must stimulate en-

Arachidonic acid $(C_{20:4})$

Some prostanoid metabolites

Prostaglandin $F_{2\alpha}$
(contracts smooth muscle)

Thromboxane A_2
(aggregates platelets)

Prostaglandin I_2 (prostacyclin)
(inhibits platelet aggregation)

Leukotriene B_4
(chemotactic attractant for
polymorphonuclear leucocytes)

zymes that liberate this fatty acid. These reactions include Ca^{2+}-activated phospholipase A_2 activity and a sequence of reactions that consists of a removal of the headgroup from arachidonate-rich inositol lipid (p. 121), followed by the hydrolysis of the liberated diacylglycerol by lipase(s).

cyclic GMP

Cyclic GMP is a normal constituent of cells, albeit at lower concentrations than cyclic AMP: cells possess both guanylate cyclase and phosphodiesterases that rapidly hydrolyse cyclic GMP. Like cyclic AMP, cyclic GMP shows rapid changes in concentration in response to many cellular stimuli; in particular, its concentration is usually transiently raised in cells exposed to Ca^{2+}-mobilizing stimuli. This has provoked widespread discussion of a possible second messenger function for this nucleotide. This, however, remains unproven: changes in cyclic GMP levels seem often simply to be consequences of changes in cytosol $[Ca^{2+}]$, and cyclic GMP derivatives usually do not mimic the effects of physiological stimuli.

Photoreception by retinal rods

The retinal rod photoreceptor is a cell in which the physiological response to stimulation is a hyperpolarization controlled by changes in the cytoplasmic concentrations of both Ca^{2+} and cyclic GMP. The 'outer segment' of the rod cell is packed with flattened membrane vesicles ('discs'), and the photoreceptor glycoprotein, rhodopsin, constitutes about 95 per cent of the intrinsic protein of the disc membrane. This protein has a molecular weight of 38000, and its polypeptide chain includes seven membrane-spanning α-helices. Its 11-*cis*-retinal chromophore is attached to a lysine residue midway along one of these lipophilic α-helices and is oriented in the plane of the membrane (i.e., it is aligned so as to be maximally exposed to incident light arriving perpendicular to the plane of the disc membranes). Associated with the cytoplasmic surface of the disc membrane is a complex of extrinsic proteins that includes a guanyl nucleotide-binding protein, 'transducin', with subunits of 37000 and 36000 molecular weight, and a very active cyclic GMP phosphodiesterase, with subunits of 88000, 84000 and 13000 molecular weight.

On illumination, rhodopsin is bleached to give all-*trans*-retinal and opsin, and the cyclic GMP concentration of the rod then declines at a rate that represents hydrolysis of 10000 cyclic GMP molecules per second for each bleached rhodopsin molecule. It appears that the illuminated rhodopsin causes exchange of GDP for GTP on transducin and that the GTP-activated transducin then switches on many molecules of cyclic GMP phosphodiesterase before being inactivated by

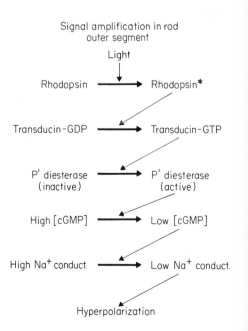

Signal amplification in rod outer segment

Light

Rhodopsin ⟶ Rhodopsin*

Transducin-GDP ⟶ Transducin-GTP

P' diesterase (inactive) ⟶ P' diesterase (active)

High [cGMP] ⟶ Low [cGMP]

High Na⁺ conduct. ⟶ Low Na⁺ conduct.

Hyperpolarization

127

the control of adenylate cyclase by G_s- and G_i-proteins (pp. 122–124), except that in the rod it is control of the phosphodiesterase rather than of cyclase which plays the major part in causing changes in cellular cyclic nucleotide levels. Illumination of rods also causes a rapid rise in cytosol $[Ca^{2+}]$. The rise in cytosol $[Ca^{2+}]$ and fall in cytosol [cyclic GMP] both tend to reduce the Na^+ conductance of the plasma membrane of the outer segment and the firing rate of the synapse at the base of the cell to below their normal high values.

5.11 Responses of different tissues and modulation of receptor sensitivity

tissue sensitivity

The concentrations of hormones and neurotransmitters that are encountered by receptors are often so low as to occupy only a minute fraction of the available receptors on sensitive target tissues. For example, the concentration of adrenaline in blood plasma is usually between 10^{-9} and 10^{-7} M, whereas the dissociation constant of β-adrenergic receptors assessed by binding assays is about 10^{-5} M. The existence of similar large populations of receptors, in excess of the minimum numbers needed to give maximum cell responses (usually referred to as 'spare receptors' or a 'receptor reserve'), has also been demonstrated for several other receptors, for example H_1-histamine and muscarinic cholinergic receptors. It seems likely that the function of such 'spare receptors' is to confer high sensitivity to stimulation on tissues exposed to limited concentrations of agonists.

'spare receptors'

The concentration of occupied receptors [AR] is given by

$$[AR] = \frac{[A] \times ([R_o] - [AR])}{K_A}$$

receptor occupancy

When the hormone concentration is well below its dissociation constant, i.e. $K_A \gg [A]$, then

$$[AR] = \frac{[R_o] \times [A]}{K_A}$$

Thus, under conditions of low receptor occupation, the concentration of occupied receptors is proportional to the total concentration of receptors, and the relative sensitivities of different tissues to the same circulating stimulus will be determined by the relative sizes of their receptor populations.

Physiological responses to concentrations of agonists that activate only a small fraction of the receptor population are

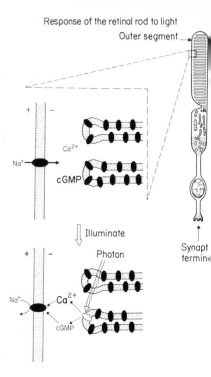

Response of the retinal rod to light

Outer segment

Illuminate

Photon

Synapt termin

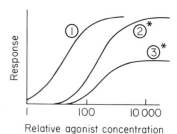

Relative agonist concentration

Receptors available	Response
1 All	Maximum at low [Agonist]
2 Few*	Maximum only if high [Agonist]
3 Very few*	Submaximal even if [Agonist] high

*After partial receptor blockade with a covalent antagonist

achieved through the amplification that is involved in the enzymic and ion 'gating' processes responsible for producing changes in intracellular second messengers. For example, substantial stimulation of amylase secretion from the parotid gland can be achieved by the rise of [cyclic AMP] triggered by activation of less than 1 per cent of the β-adrenergic receptors, and full contraction of ileum smooth muscle can be triggered by the increase in cytosol $[Ca^{2+}]$ that is brought about by achieving less than 1 per cent of its muscarinic cholinergic receptors.

Not only do different tissues show different sensitivities to particular agonists, but also the sensitivity of a single tissue may show both short-term and long-term variations. Sometimes these changes are a reflection of long-term changes in gene expression, as during the appearance of a characteristic receptor complement on each type of cell during embryonic and postnatal development, but more often they are responses to changes in the extracellular concentrations of stimulating ligands. These changes in sensitivity seem to serve as adaptive mechanisms whereby cells can adjust their responsiveness to suit the prevailing hormonal environment: prolonged or intense stimulation produces subsensitivity (also termed desensitization or tachyphylaxis), whereas a substained withdrawal of stimulation tends to lead to supersensitivity to a stimulus when it is reintroduced. Subsensitivity can, in principle, be caused either by decreased functional efficiency or by physical loss of any component in the pathway from receptor occupation to final cellular response, and many such variations in mechanism have been recorded. A receptor may remain at the cell surface, but be converted to a desensitized state, for example the nicotinic receptor (p. 119). Alternatively, it may aggregate into patches and be removed from the cell surface by endocytosis (p. 154). Such effects produce a subsensitivity that is specific to a particular receptor, but prolonged stimulation sometimes causes a cell also to show subsensitivity when it is stimulated through another receptor that employs the same effector mechanism.

Such cross-desensitization, which has been observed both with Ca^{2+}-mobilizing receptors and adenylate cyclase-coupled receptors, indicates a decreased responsiveness later in the stimulus–response sequence.

A natural example of receptor regulation occurs in the rat pineal gland, which is more actively stimulated by the sympathetic nervous system during the dark part of the diurnal cycle than when the animals are in the light. By contrast, the number of functional β-adrenergic receptors is higher in the light period than during the dark period. The variation in the receptor population does not require protein synthesis, suggesting some form of reversible control over the function of existing receptor molecules.

5.12 Intercellular metabolic and electrical coupling

cell–cell exchange of small molecules

Rather than being functionally isolated, the cytoplasmic compartments of adjacent cells in most animal tissues freely exchange small molecules and ions: major exceptions are free-living blood cells, lymphocytes, skeletal muscle cells (already large syncytia formed by fusion of many myoblasts) and many, though not all, nerve cells. The pathways through which cells thus exchange ions, metabolites and other small molecules are water-filled channels which traverse gap junctions (see p. 5); vertebrate gap junctions allow free exchange of molecules of molecular weight up to approximately 1000, while those of arthopods let through slightly larger molecules (mol. wts ≤1500).

gap junction structure

Mild detergent treatment of cells or of plasma membrane preparations has yielded fractions that are enriched with respect to junctional channels. These are hexagonally packed, making them amenable to structural analysis by x-ray diffraction and by image analysis of electron micrographs of negatively stained samples and of samples embedded in ice. Each cylindrical channel consists of two apposed hexameric arrays of (protein) subunits, one from each cell. These link across the extracellular gap, yielding a water-filled channel 20 nm long and 2 nm wide. Two channel configurations have been recognized in these studies, possibly related to the 'open' and 'closed' forms of these channels in intact cells. Freeze–fracture electron microscopy reveals the gap junctions in intact cells as groups of closely packed intramembrane particles: junctions vary in area from groups of a few particles to large areas containing several thousand. Metabolic turnover of the major protein component of the liver gap junction is much more rapid than that of the majority of plasma membrane (glyco)proteins ($T_{1/2}$ of 5 h, as compared with 20–80 h for most components).

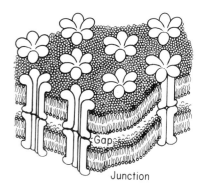

Gap
Junction

electrical cell–cell coupling

The most sensitive methods for demonstrating junctional communication are electrophysiological. If ions diffuse freely between cells, then an imposed change in membrane potential in one cell is reproduced in an essentially unattenuated form in any other cell to which it is electrically coupled. Such coupling synchronizes the contraction of individual muscle fibres in cardiac and smooth muscle. Ion conductances through gap junctions are about 10^4-fold greater than through the remainder of the plasma membrane, with each channel having a conductance similar to that of an open Na^+ channel in nerve (about 10^{-10} mho). Electrophysiological techniques readily demonstrate the free diffusion of ions amongst large groups of cells, for example the several hundred cells of a pancreatic acinus.

metabolic
cooperation

Almost all important metabolic intermediates and intracellular messengers are molecules small enough to diffuse freely between cells that are coupled through gap junctions, but nucleic acids, proteins and other large molecules are confined to their parent cell. One consequence of this arrangement is metabolic cooperation, a process whereby enzymic synthesis of a metabolite on one cell supplies that metabolite to a coupled cell that is incapable of its synthesis. As an example, cells incubated in a medium containing aminopterin cannot synthesize nucleosides *de novo*, but survive if offered xanthine and thymidine as alternative precursors. Their growth is prevented by mutations that inactivate either thymidine kinase (TK^-) or hypoxanthine:guanine phosphoribosyltransferase ($HGPRT^-$). However, when they are cultured together in an aminopterin-containing medium the two crippled mutant cells form gap junctions and exchange the missing metabolites; both then grow normally. A similar pattern exists *in vivo* in the heterozygous mothers of children with Lesch–Nyhan syndrome; although some of their skin fibroblasts completely lack HGPRT, these cells are metabolically supported by their neighbours, thus preventing the emergence of pathological changes.

gap junction
formation

Permeable gap junctions start to form within minutes after the mixing of competent cells, and compatibility extends across a wide evolutionary span; for example, human cells couple not only with other mammalian cells but also with at least some fish and amphibian cells. Vertebrate cells do not, however, seem capable of making hybrid junctions with the slightly larger channels of arthropods.

Ca^{2+} closure
of gap
junctions

Little is known of the control of junctional permeability, with the exception of the observation that junctions remain open only if cytosolic $[Ca^{2+}]$ is maintained below approximately 10 μм. The fall in junctional permeability that occurs at high cytosolic $[Ca^{2+}]$ reverses when the Ca^{2+} level returns to normal. A decreased diffusion of fluorescein (a fluorescent dye of mol.wt 332) between cells is observed at concen-

131

trations of Ca^{2+} too small to appreciably reduce electrical coupling, suggesting either a reduction in the number of open channels or a reduced effective channel diameter under such circumstances. These changes can be brought about either by microinjection of Ca^{2+} or by exposure of cells to Ca^{2+}-mobilizing hormones and neurotransmitters, suggesting that it may be a normal occurrence in cells responding to such stimuli. Since an immediate consequence of any significant damage to a cell is likely to be a dramatic rise in cytosolic $[Ca^{2+}]$, one important function of the abolition of gap junction permeability by this ion may be to insulate healthy cells from dead or damaged neighbours.

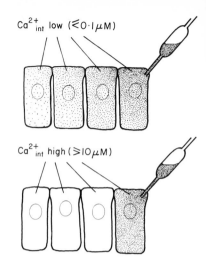

Ca^{2+}_{int} low $(\leqslant 0.1 \mu M)$

Ca^{2+}_{int} high $(\geqslant 10 \mu M)$

Further Reading

Lamble J.W. (ed.) (1981) *Towards Understanding Receptors* and (1982) *More about Receptors*. (Compilations of brief reviews mainly published in *Trends Pharmacol. Sci.* 1979–1982) Elsevier/North Holland, Amsterdam.

The Brain. (1979) (Thematic development from synaptic junctions through to disorders of brain function—originally published as an issue of *Scientific American*.) W.H. Freeman, San Francisco.

Schulster D. & Levitski A. (eds.) (1980) *Cellular Receptors for Hormones and Neurotransmitters.* John Wiley & Sons, Chichester.

Koshland D.G. (1983) The bacterium as a model neuron. *Trends Neurochem. Sci.* **6**, 133–137.

Bonner J.T. (1983) Chemical signals of social amoebae. *Scientific American* April, 106–112.

Edelman G.M. (1983) Cell adhesion molecules. *Science* **219**, 450–457.

Raff M.C. (1976) Cell surface immunology. *Scientific American* May, 30–39.

Howie S. & McBride W.H. (1982) Cellular interactions in thymus-dependent antibody responses, *Immunol. Today* **3**, 273–278.

Jensenius J.C. & Williams A.F. (1982) The T cell antigen receptor-paradigm lost, *Nature* **300**, 583–588.

Glassy M.C. (1982) A chemical and biological profile of HLA-DR (Ia-like) antigens. *Trends Biochem. Sci.* **7**, 286–288.

Owen M.J. & Crumpton M.J. (1980) Biochemistry of major human histocompatibility antigens. *Immunol. Today* **1**, 117–121.

Polak J.A. & Bloom S.R. (1983) Regulatory peptides: key factors in the control of bodily functions. *Brit. Med. J.* **286**, 1461–1466.

Hokfelt T., Johansson O., Ljundahl A., Lundberg J.M. & Schultzberg M. (1980) Peptidergic neurones. *Nature* **284**, 515–521.

Archer R. (1982) Evolution of neuropeptides. *Trends Neurochem. Sci.* **4**, 225–229.

Kaplan J. (1981) Polypeptide-binding membrane receptors: analysis and classification. *Science* **212**, 14–20.

Llinas R. (1982) Calcium in synaptic transmission. *Scientific American* October, 38–47.

Lester H.A. (1977) The response to acetylcholine. *Scientific American* February, 106–118.

Kistler J., Stroud R.M., Klymkowsky M.W., Lalancette R.A. & Fairclough R.H. (1982) Structure and function of an acetylcholine receptor, *Biophys. J.* **37**, 371–383.

Adams P. (1982) Voltage-dependent conductances of vertebrate neurones. *Trends Neurochem. Sci.* **5**, 116–119.

Kandel E.R. & Schwartz J.H. (1982) Molecular biology of learning: modulation of transmitter release. *Science* **218**, 433–443.

Rasmussen H. (1981) *Calcium and cAMP as Synarchic Messengers.* Wiley-Interscience, New York.

Limbird L.E. (1981) Activation and attenuation of adenylate cyclase: the role of GTP-binding proteins as macromolecular messengers in receptor–cyclase coupling. *Biochem. J.* **195**, 1–13.

Johnson G.L., Kaslow H.R., Farfel Z. & Bourne H.R. (1980) Genetic analysis of hormone-sensitive adenylate cyclase. *Adv. Cyclic Nucleotide Res.* **13**, 1–38.

Michell R.H., Kirk C.J., Jones L.M., Downes C.P. & Creba J.A. (1981) The stimulation of inositol lipid metabolism that accompanies calcium mobilization in stimulated cells; defined characteristics and answered questions. *Phil. Trans. Roy. Soc. Lond.* **B 296**, 123–137.

Barrett G.J. (1981) Calcium transport across cell membranes: progress towards molecular mechanisms. *Trends Biochem. Sci.* **6**, 322–325.

Cohen P. (1982) The role of protein phosphorylation in neural and hormonal control of cellular activity. *Nature,* **296**, 613–620.

Czech M.P., Massague J. & Pilch P.F. (1981) The insulin receptor: structural features. *Trends Biochem. Sci.* **6**, 222–225.

Dratz E.A. & Hargrave P.A. (1983) The structure of rhodopsin and the rod outer segment disc membrane. *Trends Biochem. Sci.* **8**, 128–131.

O'Brien D.F. (1982) The chemistry of vision. *Science* **218**, 961–966.

Houslay M.D. (1981) Membrane phosphorylation: a crucial role in the action of insulin, EGF and pp60[src]. *Bioscience Rept.* **1**, 19–34.

Lazo P.S., Barros F., de la Pena P. & Ramos S. (1981) Ion gradients as candidates for transmembrane signalling. *Trends Biochem. Sci.* **6**, 83–86.

Lewis R.A. & Austen K.F. (1981) Mediation of local homeostasis and inflammation by leukotrienes and other mast cell-dependent compounds, *Nature* **293**, 103–108.

Mackey D. (1982) Dose–response curves and mechanisms of drug action. *Trends Pharmacol. Sci.* **12**, 496–499.

Pitts J.D. (1980) The role of junctional communication in animal cells. *In Vitro.* **16**, 1049–1056.

Lowenstein W.R. (1981) Junctional intercellular communication: the cell-to-cell membrane channel. *Physiol. Rev.* **61**, 829–913.

See also pp. 212, 213.

6 Secretion, endocytosis and lysosomes

Membranes are generally impermeable to macromolecules and most polar molecules, and the majority of these molecules are synthesized in the cytosol compartment of cells. Despite this, many of these molecules (e.g., proteins, mucopolysaccharides and neurotransmitters) are commonly found outside cells. In addition, such molecules often find their way into membrane-bounded compartments inside cells (e.g., molecules awaiting secretion, or the internal enzymes of lysosomes or mitochondria). Others, like phagocytosed bacteria or pinocytosed proteins, come into cells from the exterior. Cells must therefore possess specific mechanisms that allow selected macromolecules to pass through these membrane barriers.

secretion by prokaryotes

In prokaryotes, the molecules that are destined for the exterior can be passed directly through the plasma membrane during or after their synthesis. Examples include materials to be incorporated into the cell wall or outer membrane (see p. 7), to be retained in the periplasmic space or to be released to the external environment.

compartmentation in eukaryotes

Eukaryote cells face much greater problems, since they include many intracellular compartments, each of which has a unique complement of proteins and other large and/or polar molecules. The contents of some of these compartments are destined either for secretion or to be selectively added to materials obtained by endocytosis.

The synthesis and segregation of these materials will be considered in this chapter. The manufacture, sorting and delivery of the lipids and proteins of the various membranes of the cell, which involves many similar processes, are discussed in Chapter 7.

6.1 Coordinated polypeptide synthesis and transit through membranes: the signal hypothesis

Eukaryote cells that specialize in secretion, for example exocrine pancreatic cells, often possess a large amount of ribosome-studded endoplasmic reticulum (rough ER), suggesting that this might have some key role in the synthesis and segregation of proteins destined for secretion. This is confirmed by the observation that vesicles of rough ER isolated from secretory cells can incorporate amino acids into secretory proteins and that the synthesized proteins are found inside the membrane vesicles. Thus, the polypeptides are simultaneously synthesized and translocated across the membrane with which the ribosomes are associated. In the cell, this means that secretory proteins synthesized on ribosomes attached to the endoplasmic reticulum are automatically segregated within the cisternae of the endoplasmic reticulum.

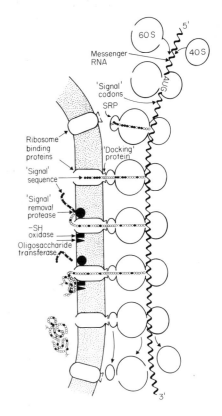

More recently, methods have been developed in which it is possible to reconstitute such protein-synthesizing systems *in vitro* from an appropriate messenger RNA (e.g., that for proinsulin isolated from pancreatic β- cells), ribosomes, ribosome-free endoplasmic reticulum membrane vesicles and the necessary cofactors. These studies have revealed that the translation of a secretory protein starts with an *N*-terminal 'signal' sequence. This dictates that the polypeptide is synthesized at and into the endoplasmic reticulum and is proteolytically discarded before synthesis of the polypeptide is completed (see diagram). These signal sequences are from 15–30 amino acids long and tend to share three common features: a few polar *N*-terminal residues, an unbroken sequence of 9–18 hydrophobic amino acid residues and a small side-chain (usually glycine, alanine or serine) adjacent to the proteolytic cleavage site.

During the translation of polypeptides on free ribosomes, the 28 amino acids most recently incorporated are protected from proteolytic attack, but when membrane-bound ribosomes are used a 49-residue sequence is protected from proteolytic attack at the non-cytoplasmic surface of the polysome–membrane complex. Thus, it seems likely that a sequence of about 20 residues is traversing the endoplasmic reticulum or the bacterial plasma membrane at any moment during synthesis.

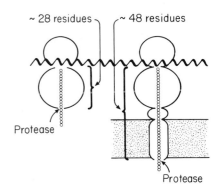

Proteolysis of nascent polypeptide chains on free and membrane-bound ribosomes

The interaction of the signal sequence with the endoplasmic reticulum membrane involves several proteins. When the growing polypeptide chain has reached 70–80 residues and the signal sequence has emerged from the ribosome, further synthesis is interrupted by the association of a ribonucleoprotein 'signal recognition particle' (mol.wt 250 000), which has been identified both in salt extracts of endoplasmic reticulum vesicles and in the cytosol. Linking with the endo-plasmic reticulum is then effected through a membrane-associated 'docking protein' (mol.wt 72000), which also releases the block on synthesis imposed by the signal recognition particle. The route through the membrane is assumed to be provided by additional intrinsic proteins, possibly those already identified as 'ribophorins', and the signal peptidase responsible for the removal of the signal peptide must be closely associated with the exit from the transmembrane channel on the non-cytoplasmic surface.

6.2 Early covalent modifications of secretory polypeptides

Membrane-bound ribosomes synthesize polypeptides and transfer them through a membrane, but unmodified polypeptide chains rarely leave eukaryote cells as secretions. Most often, the initial polypeptide product is covalently modified before its release. These modifications include removal of signal peptides, addition of heterosaccharide chains, insertion of disulphide bridges and proteolytic fragmentation; several such processes are often applied to a single molecule. In addition, many materials released by the process of exocytotic secretion, for example amine neurotransmitters, are not proteins or even derivatives of polypeptides, and these must be packaged along with the secretory proteins before the mixed contents of secretory storage vesicles are released to the exterior (see table on p. 139 and Section 6.3).

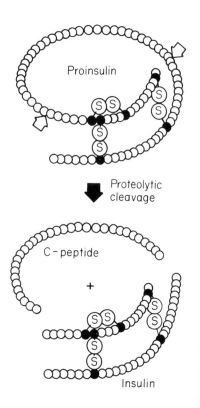

Proinsulin

Proteolytic
cleavage

C-peptide

+

Insulin

signal peptide
removal

The first covalent modification to a secretory polypeptide is usually the proteolytic removal of its signal peptide. Two additional modifications that are initiated whilst secretory polypeptides are still being synthesized through the mem-brane are the introduction of intrachain disulphide bridges and the attachment of N-linked 'core' heterosaccharide chains. The former process is catalysed by a disulphide ex-change enzyme at the luminal surface of the endoplasmic re-ticulum membrane which presumably 'traps' favoured con-figurations of the emerging and folding polypeptide. In the case of insulin, all three disulphide bridges are initially formed as intrachain bridges within the proinsulin molecule; proteolytic removal at the Golgi of an internal peptide se-quence later generates the active, secreted two-chain struc-ture with its two interchain disulphide bridges (see margin). Intrachain disulphide bridging is also a dominant element in the stabilization of many small secretory proteins that func-

disulphide bridge
formation

tion in adverse environments (e.g., pancreatic proteases, nucleases and phospholipase A_2) and of the individual folding domains of immunoglobulins (both heavy and light chains).

Both cell-surface and secreted glycoproteins commonly display two different types of heterosaccharide side-chains, with one type *N*-linked to asparagine residues and the other *O*-linked to serine or threonine residues. Only the synthesis of the larger, *N*-linked chains found on asparagine residues in the amino acid sequence -asparagine-*X*-threonine- or -asparagine-*X*-serine- is initiated at the endoplasmic reticulum. First, a 'core' heterosaccharide is assembled whilst attached to the amphiphilic polyisoprenoid lipid, dolichol pyrophosphate. During this process some of the sugars are donated by

Dolichol phosphate

$$CH_3-\overset{\overset{\textstyle CH_3}{|}}{C}=CH-CH_2-(CH_2-\overset{\overset{\textstyle CH_3}{|}}{C}=CH-CH_2)_n-CH_2-\overset{\overset{\textstyle CH_3}{|}}{CH}-CH_2-O-\overset{\overset{\textstyle O}{||}}{\underset{\underset{\textstyle O^-}{|}}{P}}-O^-$$

n = 15 – 23

water-soluble nucleotide-linked precursors, but the final mannoses and glucoses are donated by membrane-bound dolichol phosphate-linked sugars (see diagram). A valuable tool in attempts to understand the function of the heterosaccharide components of glycoproteins, both membrane-bound and secreted, is tunicamycin, a nucleoside antibiotic that inhibits *N*-glycosylation by blocking transfer of the first *N*-acetylglucosamine residue to dolichol pyrophosphate.

Although the core heterosaccharide that is initially transferred to growing polypeptide chains always contains three glucose residues and nine mannose residues, the *N*-linked heterosaccharides found in various mature glycoproteins contain no glucose and only two to five mannoses (see p. 39). The removal of the three glucoses and sometimes of some mannose residues occurs at the endoplasmic reticulum (one or two glucoses even while the polypeptide chain is still growing), to be followed in the Golgi complex by removal of further mannoses and the addition of those sugars needed to give the heterosaccharide structure characteristic of the particular glycoprotein. The route by which the glycosylating enzymes are supplied with nucleotide-sugar and dolichol-phosphate-sugar cofactors, both in the lumen of the endoplasmic reticulum and within the Golgi cisternae, may be either through appropriate membrane permeation mechanisms or

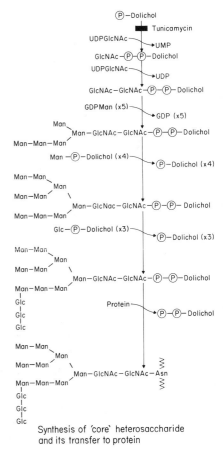

Synthesis of 'core' heterosaccharide and its transfer to protein

addition of heterosaccharides

glycosidases and glycosyl transferases

by the presence of enzymes that generate the cofactors within the organelles.

A particularly extensive repertoire of early post-translational modifications is undergone by procollagen as it is synthesized at the endoplasmic reticulum of fibroblasts. Not only does it lose its signal peptide and receive *N*-linked heterosaccharide groups and intrachain disulphide bonds, but it is also subjected to three distinct types of hydroxylation and trimerizes into a triple helical structure that includes interchain disulphide bridges. The three hydroxylases are all mixed-function oxidases that are located in the endoplasmic reticulum and employ O_2, Fe^{2+} ion, ascorbate and α-keto-glutarate in their activity: the α-ketoglutarate becomes decarboxylated to succinate. These enzymes achieve 3- and 4-hydroxylation of proline residues and the formation of collagen-specific hydroxylysine residues; the latter then serve as sites for addition of *O*-linked galactose or disaccharide (Gal–Glc–*O*–Lys).

Transit of naked or slightly modified polypeptides from the endoplasmic reticulum to the Golgi complex is an energy-dependent process involving membrane structures known as transitional elements; the actual vesicular shuttles are probably clathrin-coated vesicles (see p. 154).

(margin note) hydroxylation of procollagen

6.3 Processing and packaging of secretory products in the Golgi complex and condensing vacuoles

Eukaryote cells that are markedly differentiated for secretion by the process of exocytosis usually show three striking structural features: (1) a well-developed rough endoplasmic reticulum; (2) one or more conspicuous Golgi complexes; and (3) many membrane-bounded vesicles that are located close to those parts of the cell surface through which secretion is directed. These vesicles are often filled with electron-dense material, in which case they may be termed 'granules'. A common chronology of events in which secretory materials traverse these three cell compartments in sequence is now well-established, primarily as a result of studies in which the progress of pulse-labelled secretory products through the cell was followed by electron microscopical autoradiography and by analytical subcellular fractionation. The table below lists a selection of materials that are synthesized, packaged and secreted by this type of route.

(margin note) morphology of secretory cells

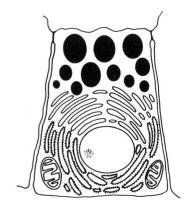

Examples of materials packaged in membrane-bounded vesicles and released from cells by exocytosis

	Secretion contains	Release evoked by
Exocrine secretions		
Parotid salivary gland	α-amylase, ribonuclease, deoxyribonuclease, peroxidase, Ca^{2+}	Adrenaline and noradrenaline (through α_1- and β-receptors), acetylcholine (muscarinic receptors) and substance P
Pancreatic acinar cells	As zymogens: trypsinogen, chymotrypsinogen, procarboxypeptidases A and B, proelastase, phospholipase A zymogen. Active: lipase, RNAase, DNAse, amylase, trypsin inhibitor. Sulphated polyanions	Pancreozymin, acetylcholine (muscarinic receptors) or substance P
Intestinal goblet cell	Mucus	Continuous
Neurotransmitters (localized action at synaptic junctions)		
Sympathetic nerve, e.g. splenic	Noradrenaline, with nucleoside triphosphates and proteins (chromogranins A and B)	Action potentials
Endocrine secretions acting throughout body		
Anterior pituitary (6 different cell types)	Thyrotrophin (TSH), corticotrophin (ACTH), somatotrophin (GH), follitrophin (FSH), lutrophin (LH), prolactin, melanotrophin (MSH)	Hypothalmic hormones (thyroliberin, corticoliberin, somatoliberin, etc.)
Islets of Langerhans (pancreas)		
β-cells	Insulin, C-peptide, Zn^{2+}	High plasma glucose
α-cells	Glucagon	Low plasma glucose
Adrenal medulla	Adrenaline and noradrenaline, opiate peptides, nucleoside triphosphates, chromogranins A & B, ascorbic acid, Ca^{2+}	Acetylcholine (through nicotinic and muscarinic receptors)
Blood plasma constituents		
Liver (hepatocytes)	Albumin, other plasma proteins, very low density lipoprotein (VLDL)	Continuous
Plasma cells	Immunoglobulins (antibodies)	Continuous
Mediation of local inflammatory reactions		
Mast cells	Histamine, with heparin, proteins and Zn^{2+}	Antigen to which cell is sensitive
Plant cell wall synthesis		
Dividing cells	Pectic materials and hemicelluloses	

The Golgi apparatus and condensing vacuoles constitute a complex cellular region that is responsible for many covalent modifications of secretory material, for additions of non-protein materials, for sorting proteins allotted to different destinations (e.g., secretion, lysosomes or the plasma membrane), and for concentrating and packaging the completed secretory cocktail into vesicles. Although the details of many of these processes are not yet understood, it is clear that during transit through this cellular region secretory materials pass sequentially through at least three functionally distinct compartments, namely *cis*-Golgi, *trans*-Golgi and condensing vacuoles.

When *N*-glycosylated polypeptides from the endoplasmic reticulum arrive at the Golgi, an α-1,2-mannosidase of the *cis*-Golgi removes several mannose residues, thus preparing the heterosaccharides for receipt of the characteristic terminal sugar residues (often *N*-acetylglucosamine, galactose, sialic acid and fucose, see p. 37) in the *trans*-Golgi. *O*-linked heterosaccharides (p. 38) are also assembled, probably in the *trans*-Golgi, by direct transfer of sugars from sugar nucleotides. The proportions of the mass of a completed glycoprotein or peptidoglycan that is in the sugar residues is very variable, ranging from a few per cent (e.g., the 10 *N*-linked heterosaccharide chains, total molecular weight approximately 30 000, in a 200 000 molecular weight immunoglobulin, either secreted or membrane-bound) to an overwhelming dominance by carbohydrate (e.g., the predominantly carbohydrate polymers of plant and fungal cell wall precursors, or a heavily glycosylated structure such as a mucin). Further changes in the carbohydrate portion of the molecules sometimes includes the attachment of large numbers of negatively charged sulphate groups (e.g., in mucins).

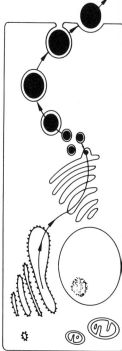

Release by
exocytosis

Storage
vesicles

Condensing
vacuoles
(packaging)

Golgi
complex
(glycosylation
and other
modifications)

Rough
endoplasmic
reticulum
(synthesis)

The caseins, the major soluble proteins of milk, are phosphorylated on a large proportion of their serine residues, a process that occurs in the Golgi. Another phosphorylation reaction, this time characteristic of newly synthesized lysosomal enzymes, is the modification of a heterosaccharide mannose residue which occurs in the *cis* elements of the Golgi. (The function of this modification is discussed in Section 6.9.)

Proteolytic events comprise another major family of post-translational modifications to secretory polypeptides. Although diverse, such reactions have particular importance in the generation of small peptide hormones and neurotransmitters from large polypeptide precursors. Many of these proteolytic events occur in the Golgi region. At their simplest, such processes involve only the proteolytic cleavage of the polypeptide that arrives from the endoplasmic reticulum (having already lost its signal sequence there), releasing the active form of the secretory protein and a small peptide; examples include the removal of *N*-terminal hexapeptide sequences from proparathyroid hormone and from proalbumin. Somewhat more complex is the removal, by two internal proteolytic cleavages, of the 'connecting peptide' from the middle of the proinsulin sequence (p. 136). The nonapeptide neurohormones vasopressin and oxytocin are synthesized as sequences within polypeptide precursors of molecular weight approximately 25000. These are then processed by enzyme(s) with trypsin-like specificity to yield three products, namely a hormone, a second secretory protein (neurophysin, mol.wt 10000) and a glycopeptide (mol. wt 10000). Proteolytic processing, in this case, starts in the neuronal cell body, probably in the Golgi region, and continues during the transit of the secretory vesicles along the axons that lead to the neurohypophysis.

Even more complex is the synthesis of the hormones of the anterior and intermediate lobes of the pituitary and of opiate peptides in the brain and adrenal medulla. One type of anterior pituitary cell (the corticotroph) coordinately secretes at least three hormones (ACTH, β-lipotrophin and some β-endorphin), all of them derived from a single glycopeptide precursor (proopiomelanocortin, mol.wt approximately 30000). The same glycopeptide is used as a hormone precursor in the intermediate lobe of the pituitary, but in this tissue additional proteolytic processing leads to a different set of products that include α-melanocyte-stimulating hormone and β-endorphin (a very potent 30-residue opiate peptide). Met- and leu-enkephalins, two opiate pentapeptides that are both neurotransmitters and secretions of the adrenal medulla, are derived from a precursor that includes within its sequence multiple copies of the enkephalin sequences. Several of these enkephalin sequences are flanked by the pairs of basic amino acid residues which guide the proteolytic excision of the correct sequences.

The *trans* elements of the Golgi and adjacent condensing vacuoles are the cellular sites at which the constituents of blood lipoproteins (triacylglycerol, cholesterol, phospholipids and apoproteins) are assembled into their characteristic organization of a triacylglycerol core stabilized by a cholesterol phospholipid-protein surface coat. The major species are the chylomicrons, synthesized from absorbed fat by intestinal epithelial cells, and the very low density lipoprotein particles (VLDL), in which liver liberates the fat that it synthesizes from carbohydrate.

The final elements of the Golgi cisternae and the adjacent 'condensing vacuoles' convert the relatively dilute secretory macromolecules into the concentrated form that is characteristic of mature secretory vesicles in most cells. Storage of proteins at high concentrations is occasionally in crystalline form (e.g., insulin hexamers containing two Zn^{2+} atoms, glucagon trimers) and, even when the stored materials are amorphous, the presence of complexes with metal ions (e.g.,

ACTH, β-lipotrophin

α-MSH, β-endorphin

enkephalin precursors

blood lipoproteins

complexes with metal ions

Proteolytic processing of proopiomelanocortin in the pituitary

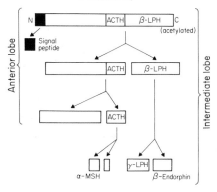

The enkephalin precursor in adrenal medulla and brain (267 amino acid residues)

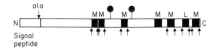

N−glycosylated asparagine residues (●)
Basic residues (↑)
M; met−enkephalin sequences (−tyr−gly−gly−phe−met−)
L; leu−enkephalin sequences (−tyr−gly−gly−phe−leu−)

parotid amylase with Ca^{2+}) or sulphated polyanions probably facilitates storage at high concentration.

In some secretory cells, such as neurones, mast cells and the chromaffin cells of the adrenal medulla, the most important component of the secretion is a small molecule such as a neurotransmitter, histamine or adrenaline. In these cells the secreted material is a mixture of the functional small molecules, characteristic protein(s), highly charged constituents such as sulphated mucopolysaccharide and/or nucleoside triphosphates (most often ATP), and divalent cations (often Ca^{2+}). In such cells, the function of the 'extra' constituents may be to participate in the formation of complexes with the low molecular weight secretion. The presence of such complexes allows small molecules such as neurotransmitters to be stored at total concentrations that would otherwise be osmotically embarrassing for the cell (e.g., approximately 0.8 M acetylcholine in cholinergic synaptic vesicles).

The macromolecular constituents of such secretions (proteins, mucopolysaccharides) arrive by the standard route described above but the small molecules (amines, nucleotides, Ca^{2+}) are added later. Neurotransmitter vesicles become charged during transit down the axon to synapses, and they can also be recycled and recharged with neurotransmitter at the nerve terminal. Many nerve terminals possess active transport systems for effectively recovering released neurotransmitters, for example noradrenaline, or their breakdown products, for example choline released from acetylcholine by synaptic acetylcholinesterase; this is both economical and an important mechanism for the termination of neurotransmitter action (pp. 113 and 191).

The mechanisms by which such small molecules are accumulated are particularly well understood for the adrenal chromaffin granule, but the limited available evidence for other systems (cholinergic synaptic vesicles, platelet 5-hydroxytryptamine granules, etc.) suggests that they probably make use of similar mechanisms. The active transport systems that accumulate catecholamines and adenine nucleotides in chromaffin granules (the catecholamine storage vesicles of adrenal medullary cells) are, like those in classical energy-coupling membranes (see Chapter 4), driven by $\Delta\bar{\mu}_{H^+}$. This is generated by an inward-directed H^+-translocating ATPase present as approximately 15 copies per vesicle. The similarities between this ATPase and the ATP synthase of energy-coupling membranes (p. 91) include:

packaging of
small molecules

retrieval of
secreted
neurotransmitter

adrenal
chromaffin
granule

H^+-ATPase

Contents of isolated chromaffin 'granules'

600 mM catecholamine
180 mM nucleotide (70% ATP)
 18 mM Ca
  5 mM Mg
 24 mM ascorbate
Opiate peptides (esp. enkephalins)
200 mg protein/ml

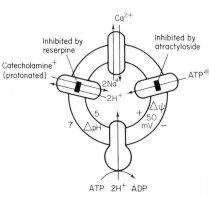

Transport in chromaffin granules

142

sensitivity to some of the same inhibitors (DCCD, but not oligomycin); a similar subunit structure; and a large degree of immunological cross-reactivity with the mitochondrial enzyme. When chromaffin granules at a neutral pH are incubated with $MgATP^{2-}$, the initial resting potential (-70 mV, inside negative) is preserved by inward H^+-pumping to a value of approximately $+50$ mV and there is also a drop in internal pH of approximately 0.8 pH units. The stoichiometry of pumping in this system is at least $2H^+$ per ATP hydrolysed. Coupling of amine transport to dissipation of $\Delta\bar{\mu}_{H^+}$ is achieved by a reserpine-sensitive transporter that will accept a variety of amine hormones or neurotransmitters—dopamine, noradrenaline, adrenaline, 5-hydroxytryptamine, tyramine. This transporter derives its energy from both $\Delta\Psi$ and Δ pH and achieves exchange of one amine molecule for two H^+. The gradient generated is of the order of 30 000-fold (from 10–20 μM in the cytosol to approximately 550 mM inside the chromaffin granule). ATP entry is achieved by electrophoretic movement through an ATP transporter that is, like the mitochondrial ATP/ADP exchange system, sensitive to inhibition by atractyloside. Ca^{2+} enters by exchange with Na^+.

The biosynthesis of noradrenaline and adrenaline from dopamine is achieved within chromaffin granules (and the dense-cored vesicles of noradrenergic nerves) as a result of the activity of dopamine β-hydroxylase in the granule membrane. This copper-containing glycoprotein catalyses the hydroxylation of dopamine using molecular O_2 and a reductant. *In situ*, this reductant may be ascorbate, which is present in the chromaffin granule at a concentration of approximately 20 mM. The chromaffin granule membrane also contains other redox components, including an NADH oxidase and a *b*-type cytochrome, and they may be involved in maintaining the ascorbate pool in reduced form.

Once secretory vesicles have been formed, they usually collect close to the part of the cell surface through which they will release their contents. In relatively unpolarized cells, such as mast cells or the β-cells of islets of Langerhans, this simply means accumulation all around the periphery of the cytoplasm. However, in markedly polarized cells, such as those that surround the lumen of a salivary or pancreatic acinus, the vesicles may be crowded into the luminal pole of the cell. In neurones, this polarization is even more striking, with the maturing secretory vesicles having to traverse the length of the axon before release at a nerve terminal.

electrogenic amine transport

electrophoretic ATP transport

catecholamine biosynthesis

axonal transport

Directed vesicle movements of this type seem often to be driven along the arrays of aligned microtubules that are particularly characteristic of nerve axons; in the presence of colchicine, a compound which causes microtubule dissociation, axonal transport of neurotransmitter vesicles ceases.

In most cases, the material stored in vesicles at the end of this entire sequence of events is potentially capable of fulfilling its full biological function when released. Sometimes, however, the stored form is still a precursor of the final functional form. Examples are the precursor to the hormone angiotensin, precursors to proteins essential for blood-clotting (amongst them prothrombin and fibrinogen), and procollagen which, after several extracellular covalent modifications, is laid down as collagen fibres. An interesting situation arises in the exocrine pancreas, from which some enzymes are released in active form while others emerge as inactive precursors: those which are potentially damaging to the secretory vesicle membrane (proteases and phospholipase A_2 with neutral pH optima) are stored as zymogens whereas others (RNAase, DNAase, lipase, etc.) are stored and released in active form.

6.4 Release and membrane retrieval

In some systems, amongst them secretion of casein from mammary acinar cells, of immunoglobulins from plasma cells, and of albumin and VLDL from liver parenchymal cells, release from the cells appears to be continuous, with the rate of secretion dictated by the rate of synthesis. In most cells, however, secretory vesicles tend to accumulate and then to be discharged in response to some clearly identifiable stimulus such as an action potential, neurotransmitter or antigen (see Table, p. 139). In general, these are stimuli which act at the plasma membrane, but there are a few situations in which control may be exerted through some intracellular 'receptor' mechanism: the best characterized example is glucose-stimulated insulin secretion from pancreatic β-cells, which seems likely to be a response to an, as yet, unidentified intracellular consequence of glucose metabolism.

The final result of the secretory event is the release of most or all of the contents of the secretory vesicle into the extracellular medium, unaccompanied by other cellular constituents such as secretory vesicle membrane or cytoplasmic enzymes. This is achieved by fusion of the secretory vesicle membrane with the plasma membrane so as to bring the ex-

secretion of precursors

release by exocytosis

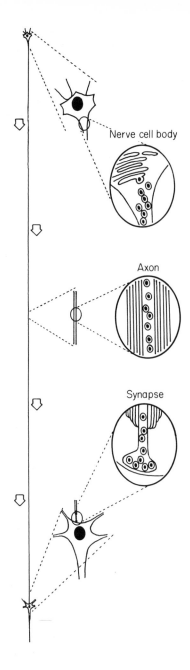

Nerve cell body

Axon

Synapse

144

tracellular medium and intravesicular space into direct continuity: this process is termed exocytosis. Evidence for this conclusion comes mainly from two sources. First, images of such membrane fusion events are observed in electron micrographs of secreting cells: freeze–fracture microscopy has been particularly effective in this field. Second, analysis of the released material demonstrates selective secretion only of the secretory vesicle contents. For example, receptor-stimulated exocytosis in the adrenal medulla selectively releases the contents of the adrenal chromaffin granule (see table).

role of Ca^{2+}

A feature common to most situations involving exocytic secretory processes is control of the final secretory event by a rise in cytosol $[Ca^{2+}]$ in that part of the cell from which secretion occurs. Often this is brought about by ligands that activate Ca^{2+}-mobilizing receptors at the plasma membrane, for example acetylcholine or pancreozymin on exocrine pancreas or antigen on sensitized mast cells. Sometimes, however, the initial stimulus serves to depolarize an electrically excitable secretory cell, with the resulting action potentials in their turn causing the opening of potential-sensitive Ca^{2+} 'gates'. This mechanism is particularly important in controlling the release of neurotransmitters from nerve cells:

neurotransmitter release

action potentials are generated in the dendrites and cell body of a stimulated neurone, rapidly transmitted down the axon, usually as an Na^+/K^+ action potential, and on arrival at nerve terminals this signal is translated into a Ca^{2+} influx that triggers neurotransmitter release.

The classical evidence that exocytic release of secretion is triggered by Ca^{2+} came from experiments in which Ca^{2+}-deprived cells became unresponsive to stimuli and in which admission of Ca^{2+} to cells using an ionophore or micropipette initiated secretion. More detailed information on the control of exocytic events has come from studies of cells rendered leaky to small molecules (mol.wt less than 1000): this is usually done by momentary exposure of cell suspensions to electric fields sufficient to push the plasma membrane well beyond its breakdown voltage (brief transmembrane potentials of approximately 1 V are typical). Treated cells leak

cofactor requirements for exocytosis

their normal complement of small ions and metabolites, whilst retaining all of their intracellular proteins and organelles. Using such leaky adrenal chromaffin cells, mast cells and platelets, it has been demonstrated that exocytosis requires $MgATP^{2-}$ and that it can be switched on by Ca^{2+} concentrations in the micromolar range; no other essential

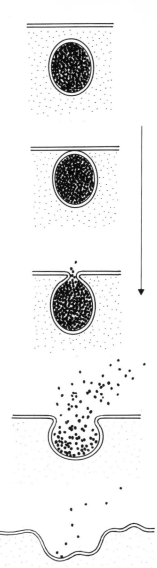

Composition of isolated granules and secreted material in the adrenal medulla

	Isolated granules	Secreted material
Phospholipids	+++	±
Cholesterol	+++	±
Membrane proteins	+++	±
Chromogramins	+++	+++
Catecholamines	+++	+++
Nucleotides	+++	+++
Ascorbate	+++	+++
Opiate peptides	+++	+++
Calcium	+++	+++

Exocytosis induced by Ca^{2+} in permeabilized cells

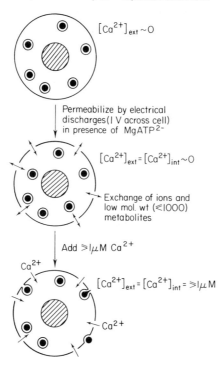

$[Ca^{2+}]_{ext} \sim O$

Permeabilize by electrical
discharges(1 V across cell)
in presence of $MgATP^{2-}$

$[Ca^{2+}]_{ext} = [Ca^{2+}]_{int} \sim O$

Exchange of ions and
low mol. wt (≤1000)
metabolites

Add ≥1μM Ca^{2+}

Ca^{2+}

$[Ca^{2+}]_{ext} = [Ca^{2+}]_{int} = ≥1μM$

Ca^{2+}

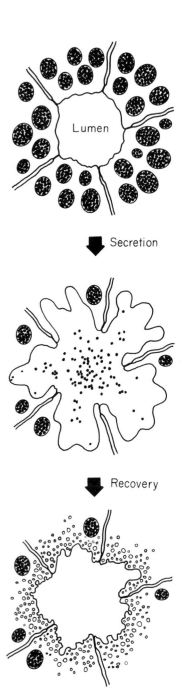

Lumen

Secretion

Recovery

requirements have been found. As with receptor-stimulated exocytosis, the secretion evoked by Ca^{2+} and $MgATP^{2-}$ in permeabilized adrenal chromaffin cells involves release only of the contents of chromaffin granules.

Not all secretory stimuli act directly to mobilize Ca^{2+}: for example, parotid amylase secretion is evoked most effectively as a result of β-adrenergic stimulation of adenylate cyclase. By contrast, accumulation of cAMP in some cells leads to inhibition of secretion: examples include platelets and mast cells. It may well turn out that in all of these situations the dominant control of exocytosis is through local changes in cytosol $[Ca^{2+}]$, with this modulated both directly by ligands acting at the cell surface and indirectly through intermediate signals such as cyclic nucleotides.

The membrane that is added to the plasma membrane during exocytosis would, if left there, lead to a continuous expansion of the surface area of the secreting cells. This is avoided by a continuous retrieval of membrane from the surface back to the Golgi region of the cells. This process, which again requires metabolic energy and is probably controlled by cytosol Ca^{2+}, is readily demonstrated if cells are stimulated to secrete while suspended in a medium containing an

cAMP and
exocytosis

recycling of
membrane

146

electron-dense tracer such as dextran, cationized ferritin or horseradish peroxidase. Under these conditions, the return of membrane vesicles from the plasma membrane is signalled by the appearance of the electron-dense label within Golgi elements, first in cisternae and peripheral vesicles, then in condensing vacuoles and finally in newly formed secretory vesicles. This entire sequence of events can occur within about 15 min of the initiation of exocytosis.

6.5 Membrane interactions during exocytosis and recovery

Secretory proteins take from about 10 min to a few hours to progress from synthesis to availability for secretion from cells (neurotransmitter vesicles, which have to pass down the nerve axon, obviously take very much longer). Once biosynthesis of the protein is completed, the entire secretory sequence can continue even if further protein synthesis is abolished. Metabolic energy is required for at least three of these subsequent steps, namely movement from endoplasmic reticulum to Golgi, release, and membrane retrieval. These observations are all compatible with the idea that the membrane components of the cell can participate in several complete cycles of the secretion/recovery process rather than being synthesized anew in parallel with the secreted material. This has been confirmed by experiments which demonstrate that the rates of biosynthesis of membrane proteins in rapidly secreting cells are very much lower than the rates of synthesis of the secretory proteins.

energy for secretion

The secretory product released in small vesicles from the endoplasmic reticulum is very dilute, but becomes more concentrated as it traverses the Golgi complex and is finally packaged by the condensing vacuoles into relatively large vesicles that contain concentrated secretions. Thus, it seems likely that there are a minimum of three cycles of membrane flux and retrieval within the secretion/recovery sequence; movement from endoplasmic reticulum to *cis*-Golgi and back; retrieval to the Golgi of excess membrane initially present during the generation of secretory vesicles by the *trans*-Golgi and condensing vacuoles; and the recycling of used secretory vesicle membrane from the plasma membrane to the Golgi.

Membrane 'flow' in secretory cells

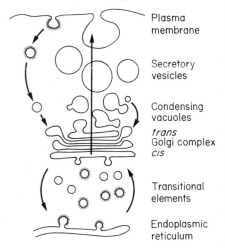

Plasma membrane

Secretory vesicles

Condensing vacuoles

trans
Golgi complex
cis

Transitional elements

Endoplasmic reticulum

During this process each membrane class retains its characteristic composition in terms of lipid, enzyme and (glyco)protein complement. Some enzymes tend to be

constancy of membrane composition

shared by adjacent compartments in the sequence (e.g., *cis*-Golgi elements contain substantial quantities of 'characteristic' endoplasmic reticulum enzymes) but there is no tendency for all of the membranes to move towards an average composition. Thus, the membrane vesiculation and fusion events occurring at each stage in the sequence must be specific mechanisms capable of recycling only that membrane material recently received from the preceding compartment (e.g., retrieval of secretory vesicle membrane, but not of plasma membrane, from the cell surface). These mechanisms are not yet understood.

6.6 Secretion by other mechanisms

Exocytosis is not the only way in which materials are selectively released from cells. In some cases a single type of cell secretes both exocytically and by other mechanisms.

secretion of milk

Mammalian milks, although secreted by a single type of mammary acinar cell, are complex mixtures containing proteins, fat droplets and lactose (a disaccharide, mol.wt 342). Triacylglycerol, the main constituent of the fat droplets, is synthesized by endoplasmic reticulum membranes and then appears as droplets in the cytoplasm. After moving to the apex of the cell these are released by an 'apocrine' mechanism: during this process a fat droplet becomes closely surrounded by a part of the plasma membrane of the secreting cell and the bridge between the particle and the cell pinches off. This mechanism is confirmed by biochemical evidence that the enzymic composition of the membrane enclosing the milk fat globule is typical of a plasma membrane. This apocrine process differs from the exocytic release of other triacylglycerol-rich lipoproteins (e.g., VLDL from liver and chylomicrons from intestine). Casein, the major milk protein, is phosphorylated in the Golgi, and released exocytically, as are other major milk proteins (e.g., α-lactalbumin). Lactose synthesis occurs in the Golgi, in cisternae that are lactose-impermeable, and it may also leave the mammary acinar cell by exocytosis.

secretion of bile

Hepatocytes (the main cell of liver tissue) are the source of a variety of secretory materials, of which the VLDL and albumin of plasma have already been mentioned. Secretion of bile, the emulsifying solution essential to lipid digestion, is less well understood. Most components of this secretion leave the cell through specialized areas of surface membrane that form the boundaries of channels termed bile canaliculi.

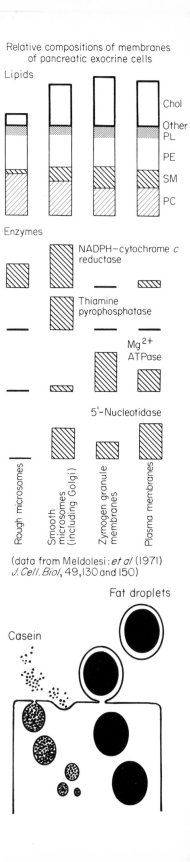

Relative compositions of membranes of pancreatic exocrine cells

Lipids

Chol
Other PL
PE
SM
PC

Enzymes

NADPH—cytochrome *c* reductase

Thiamine pyrophosphatase

Mg²⁺ ATPase

5'-Nucleotidase

Rough microsomes
Smooth microsomes (including Golgi)
Zymogen granule membranes
Plasma membranes

(data from Meldolesi: *et al* (1971) *J. Cell. Biol*, 49, 130 and 150)

Fat droplets

Casein

148

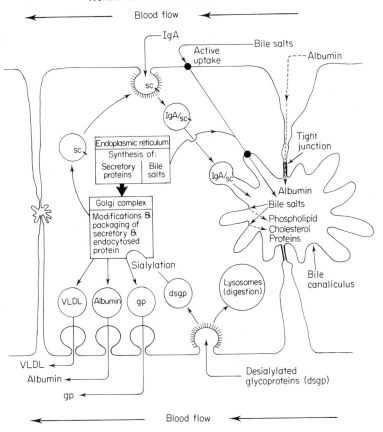

These membrane domains are separated from the remainder of the cell surface by tight junctions, so that the canalicular membranes from two or more apposed cells form a closed channel through which the bile drains away from the cells. The main solutes in bile are bile salts which, being detergents, are potentially damaging to the canalicular membrane. Bile contains substantial quantities of cholesterol and phosphatidylcholine, perhaps derived from this membrane. However, survival of this membrane during bile secretion may be aided by its having a relatively ordered structure rich in sphingomyelin. Plasma proteins are also found in bile. Albumin is present at much lower concentrations than in blood and probably leaks slowly through the tight junctions at the borders of bile canaliculi. However, immunoglobulin A (IgA) is present at a higher concentration than in the circulation, and it is secreted bound to another protein ('secretory component'). Hepatocytes synthesize 'secretory component', and it is thought that this is then transferred in membrane vesicles to the domain of the plasma membrane that is adjacent to blood capillaries (the sinusoidal domain). There it picks up IgA, and the IgA/secretory component complex is then transferred across the liver cell by adsorptive endocytosis at the sinusoidal domain of the plasma membrane followed by exocytosis into bile canaliculi.

fluid secretion

Many secretions come from glands whose acini feed into ducts which carry the secretion to a relatively distant site of action (e.g., secretion of saliva and pancreatic juice). In these circumstances, a flow of fluid is needed to carry the secreted macromolecules through the duct system. In general, these fluids are approximately iso-osmotic with extracellular fluid, although often of markedly different composition: for example, pancreatic juice is alkaline and rich in HCO_3^-, and some types of saliva are K^+-rich. In some tissues, the exocytic acinar cells themselves generate a considerable fluid flow, with subsequent modifications to the ionic composition achieved by cells lining the ducts. For example, the acinar cells of some salivary glands secrete an Na^+-rich fluid, and the duct cells then exchange K^+ for Na^+. In other tissues, for example exocrine pancreas, fluid secretion is almost entirely a function of the ductular cells.

In both situations, bulk fluid flow requires the active pumping of at least one ion through the acinar or ductular cells, so that other ions and water may be drawn osmotically through 'leaky' tight junctions around the ducts. In pancreas, for example, the primary driving force may be an Na^+-linked extrusion of H^+ from the basal surface of the ductular cells.

Thus, membrane transport processes essential to fluid secretion are quite different from those involved in release of macromolecules. They often occur in different cells, and they are frequently under independent control, so that successful generation of a balanced secretion is the result of the physiological integration of two or more quite disparate processes. This is again well illustrated by exocrine pancreas, where Ca^{2+}-mobilizing stimuli (acetylcholine and pancreozymin) are the major controllers of acinar secretion of proteins, whilst control of ductular fluid secretion is mainly achieved through a secretin-activated adenylate cyclase.

6.7 Phagocytosis

Phagocytosis is the process by which cells take in particulate material from the exterior, either as food or to kill it. Morphologically, it is a mirror image of exocytosis and it has therefore been termed endocytosis (as has pinocytosis, Section 6.8). After internalization of a particle within a phagocytic vacuole (endosome), digestive or lethal materials can be added to this new intracellular compartment by fusion with other vesicular organelles such as lysosomes: this is obviously a much more efficient mechanism than wholesale release of these materials to the exterior. In independent organisms such as *Amoeba*, phagocytosis is a form of feeding and the coalescence of a phagocytic vacuole with lysosomes provides an intracellular digestive apparatus in which the macromolecular components of ingested organisms are rapidly dismantled.

In contrast, the more limited activities of mammalian polymorphonuclear leucocytes (polymorphs) and macrophages are designed primarily to locate, capture and kill invading pathogenic microorganisms. Most invading bacteria will have been encountered before by the immune system, and these are immediately attacked, and in the process labelled, by plasma immunoglobulins and the complement system (pp. 109–110). Polymorphs are drawn chemotactically to the site of invasion by bacterial products and also by components released by the complement system and by polymorphs that arrived earlier (pp. 105–106). Bacteria (and other foreign antigenic materials) are recognized and ingested mainly after their interactions with antibodies and with the complement system, both of which facilitate the binding of bacteria to the surface of polymorphs and macrophages. When polymorphs ingest bacteria they kill them within a few minutes, but there is little further degradation of their macromolecules over many hours. Killing is achieved by a variety of bacteriocidal mechanisms, mainly by enzymes that are contributed to the phagocytic vacuole by its fusion with two (or more) different types of vesicular organelles. These are lysosomes (the azurophil granules), which contain a collection of hydrolases with acid pH optima and also a large quantity of peroxidase, and a second, non-lysosomal population (the specific granules) which contain alkaline phosphatase, lysozyme and several antibacterial basic proteins (e.g., lactoferrin). Polymorphs mature from promyelocytes in the bone marrow, and during this process the Golgi elaborates first the azurophil granules and then the specific granules.

After particle ingestion, phagocytic vacuoles fuse first with specific granules and later with azurophil granules. This takes a few minutes, during which time the pH of the vacuole decreases and most bacteria are killed, and it is accompanied by

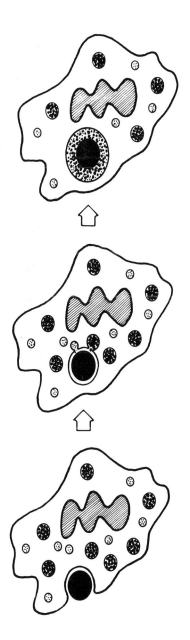

a dramatic increase in O_2 uptake by the polymorphs. Much of this O_2 is converted to bacteriocidal oxygen metabolites (including H_2O_2, O_2^- and hydroxyl radical) within the vacuole by a membrane-bound NAD(P)H oxidase system donated by the plasma membrane and the membrane of the specific granule. An essential component of this oxidase system is a b cytochrome of negative redox potential (-295 mV). A genetic deficiency or malfunction of this cytochrome gives rise to chronic granulomatous disease, a condition in which polymorphs phagocytize bacteria normally but fail to kill them. A second killing mechanism, this time dependent upon a halide (e.g., Cl^-) and H_2O_2 (produced by the oxidase or by the bacteria), is catalysed by the peroxidase from azurophil granules.

membrane
synthesis after
phagocytosis

During phagocytosis, a macrophage can rapidly interiorize up to about one-half of its plasma membrane as phagocytic vacuole membrane, and this has offered an opportunity to observe the degradation and renewal of membrane in these cells. Macrophages normally have a very mobile surface and a large surface/volume ratio, but after such extensive phagocytosis they become rounded and are unable to continue to phagocytize. During the subsequent few hours, the 5′-nucleotidase of the ingested plasma membrane disappears (half-time for its disappearance, $T_{1/2}$, 2 h) but the cholesterol and phospholipid contents of the cells do not change. Subsequently, however, new plasma membranes are elaborated, as measured by parallel rises in 5′-nucleotidase, cholesterol and phospholipid, and the cells regain their ability to phagocytize, pinocytize and spread on surfaces. The requirement for membrane synthesis in this recovery of endocytic function is made apparent by the absence of all of these regenerative changes in cells deprived of cholesterol (macrophages cannot biosynthesize cholesterol from acetate).

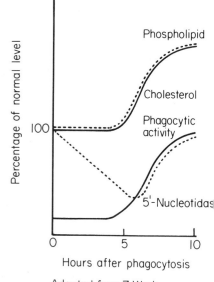

Adapted from Z. Werb
and Z.A. Cohn (1973).
J. Biol. Chem,
247, 2439-2446.

6.8 Pinocytosis

fluid-phase
pinocytosis

Pinocytosis, the other form of endocytosis, is the vesicular uptake of soluble molecules by cells. In fluid-phase pinocytosis a cell invaginates parts of its plasma membrane to form small membrane vesicles containing extracellular medium: good markers of this process are impermeant molecules like sucrose, polyvinylpyrrolidone and horseradish peroxidase which do not readily absorb to cell surfaces.

adsorptive
pinocytosis

Adsorptive pinocytosis is a much more selective process in which certain extracellular molecules are concentrated by adsorption to cell-surface receptors and are then endocytized.

Adsorption is fairly independent of temperature, but endocytosis is temperature-dependent and requires a supply of metabolic energy; this distinction has been of great practical value in experimental dissection of the sequence of events during adsorptive pinocytosis. The discrimination achieved by adsorptive pinocytosis is well illustrated by the fact that macrophages, which possess receptors for the F_c region of immunoglobulins, pinocytize an immunoglobulin–horseradish peroxidase complex about 4000-fold faster than they take up the free enzyme by fluid-phase pinocytosis.

Typical rates of fluid-phase pinocytosis by active cells such as amoeba and macrophages are around $0.1–1.0$ μl fluid per 10^{-6} cells h^{-1}. Addition of proteins and a variety of salts to amoebae leads rapidly to massive fluid intake by the formation of vesicles large enough to be followed by light microscopy. These then fuse with digestive vacuoles: nutrition of these organisms therefore includes the endocytic uptake of both particulate and soluble food.

transcellular transport (diacytosis)

In some cells, material is pinocytized at one pole and released at the other. Such transcellular endocytosis/exocytosis sequences have been termed diacytosis or transcytosis, and they can be of fluid phase or adsorptive type. Fluid-phase diacytosis is particularly important in capillaries, where there is a need for rapid two-way exchange of macromolecules between blood plasma and the extracellular fluid which bathes cells. Endothelial cells form a very thin lining to capillaries, with their edges sealed by tight junctions so that they constitute a continuous tube of cells. However, each endothelial cell contains about 10000 smooth-surfaced membrane vesicles (500–1000 nm diameter) which occupy about 10 per cent of the cell volume and rapidly shuttle fluid back and forth across the cell. A substantial number of these vesicles may be simultaneously fused with the blood and tissue faces of the endothelial cell, forming continuous channels, and some capillary endothelia permanently display large numbers of continuous transcellular channels (fenestrae). Bulk fluid-phase diacytosis, again by smooth-surface vesicles, also serves in the movement of intact colostrum proteins, including immunoglobulins, from gut to blood across the small intestinal epithelium of ungulates (e.g., pig and cow) during the first few hours after birth.

diacytosis in endothelium

diacytosis in gut

Adsorptive pinocytosis is involved in a wide variety of cell functions. Amongst those already mentioned are diacytosis of immunoglobulin A across the hepatocyte (p. 149), the metabolism of receptor-bound hormones and regulation of

adsorptive endocytosis

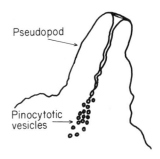

Pseudopod

Pinocytotic vesicles

Pinocytosis in *Amoeba*

Fluid phase pinocytosis through capillary endothelium

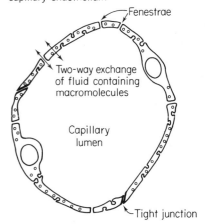

Fenestrae

Two-way exchange of fluid containing macromolecules

Capillary lumen

Tight junction

Extracellular tissue fluid

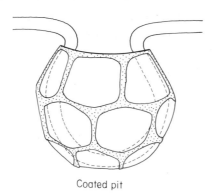

Coated pit

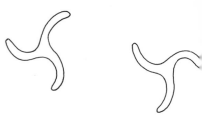

Appearance of clathrin triskelions

'coated' vesicles and pits

receptor numbers (p. 129), and internalization of 'capped' antigens on lymphocytes (pp. 43–44). A common feature of these functions, and of others discussed below, is that during at least a part of the process the participating vesicles (diameters, 50–250 nm) are 'coated'. That is, they display at their cytoplasmic surface a heavily stained fuzzy layer. Detailed examination of isolated coated vesicles (by electron microscopy of negatively stained vesicles) and of the cytoplasmic surface of the coated pits from which they invaginate at the cell surface (by an elegant etching and metal-shadowing technique) reveals that these structures consist of a lipid-rich membrane, to the cytoplasmic surface of which is attached a polygonal protein lattice of 12 pentagons plus a variable number of hexagons. This lattice consists largely of clathrin (mol.wt 180000), with three clathrin molecules contributing to each polygonal vertex and two to each edge, together with smaller quantities of polypeptides of molecular weights 100000 and 35000. Coated vesicles are also involved in non-endocytic events such as the delivery of newly synthesized glycoproteins to the cell surface (p. 170) and the membrane shuttles essential to preparation of secretory materials before exocytosis (p. 146).

clathrin

endocytosis and lysosomes

Probably the most common pattern of adsorptive pinocytosis is that followed by plasma components destined for digestion in lysosomes: examples include insulin, desialylated plasma proteins and low-density lipoprotein (LDL). Each binds to its own specific receptors on appropriate cells: sometimes the receptors are already congregated at coated pits (LDL receptors in fibroblasts), and in other cases they congregate only after binding their ligand (insulin receptors). After endocytosis of a coated vesicle the clathrin coat is lost and the residual smooth-surfaced vesicle fuses with a lysosome. In most cases the adsorbed material then dissociates at the acid pH of the lysosomal interior and is digested, leaving

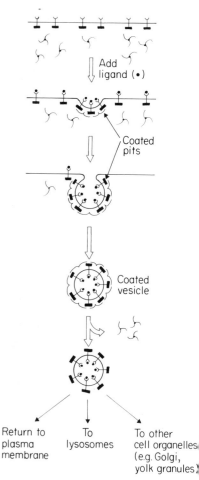

Add ligand (•)

Coated pits

Coated vesicle

Return to plasma membrane

To lysosomes

To other cell organelles (e.g. Golgi, yolk granules)

Receptor-mediated endocytosis in coated vesicles

the receptor-bearing membrane to recycle to the cell surface where it collects another load of ligand. Less commonly, as with the epidermal growth factor (EGF) receptor, the receptor is also degraded, thus reducing the cell's sensitivity to a subsequent hormonal stimulus. The rapidity of receptor (and membrane?) recycling during adsorptive pinocytosis is emphasized by the fact that a macrophage with about 75 000 receptors for mannosylated proteins can endocytose about two million mannosylated protein molecules in an hour, suggesting an endocytosis/exocytosis cycle time of only a few minutes.

Not all ligands that reach lysosomes after adsorptive pinocytic uptake are degraded. The iron-loaded form of the transport protein, transferrin, reaches lysosomes, discharges its iron at the low pH in the lysosome, and is then recycled to the cell surface. The vitamin B_{12}-binding protein of plasma probably behaves similarly. Desialylated plasma proteins have a mixed fate: some are digested; others are transferred to the Golgi complex, have their sialic acid residues replaced, and then return to the circulation. Semliki Forest virus binds to receptors at the cell surface but, unlike many other enveloped viruses, does not then fuse with and inject its infective nucleocapsid through the plasma membrane. Instead, it is endocytized in coated vesicles and then transferred into lysosomes where the low pH triggers the fusion of viral envelope and lysosomal membrane. Confirmation of this mechanism comes from the ability of weak bases (e.g., methylamine, NH_4^+) that equilibrate into and raise the pH of lysosomes to block viral infection. Lysosomal enzymes in the extracellular phase also enter cells and return to lysosomes by adsorptive pinocytosis (see pp. 153–154).

A huge and specialized cell that sends adsorptively endocytized proteins to a different intracellular site is the oocyte. The yolk proteins and lipoproteins of eggs are mainly synthesized in the liver, and a chicken oocyte may transfer 1 g of yolk components per day from blood plasma to developing yolk vacuoles.

Adsorptive pinocytosis can also be the first step in diacytosis, in which the endocytized protein by-passes lysosomes and leaves the cell through a surface different from that at which it entered. Amongst such processes are several which achieve the selective movement of antibodies of the IgG class from mother to offspring. During the latter part of gestation, this is achieved in some species (e.g., rat, rabbit) by the yolk sac and in primates (e.g., man) by the placental

receptor recycling

asialoglycoproteins

virus entry

oocytes

diacytosis of maternal immunoglobulins

Penetration to cytosol of
Semliki Forest virus nucleocapsid

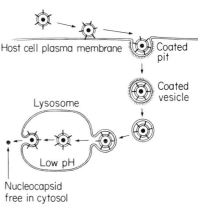

Membrane
Nucleocapsid
'Spike' glycoproteins

Host cell plasma membrane

Coated pit

Coated vesicle

Lysosome

Low pH

Nucleocapsid free in cytosol

155

syncytiotrophoblast. Both are thin epithelial sheets thrown into microvilli on the 'maternal' surface; they take antibodies from the uterine fluid and the maternal bloodstream, respectively. After birth, antibody transfer continues via the milk, especially in the antibody-rich colostrum that is secreted by the mammary gland of some animals immediately after birth. Mammary epithelial cells of the cow, whose calf absorbs antibodies by fluid-phase pinocytosis (see above), can generate a colostrum containing up to 70 mg/ml of IgG_1 and in the process substantially decrease the IgG_1 concentration in the maternal circulation. In the rat, by contrast, the concentrations of IgG in blood and milk are similar, but for the first three weeks after birth the duodenum and proximal jejunum possess a selective mechanism for adsorptive pinocytosis of IgG. In all of these tissues the IgG receptors which initiate adsorptive diacytosis are specific for the F_c region (the heavy chain constant region) of the IgG_1 (and sometimes also IgG_3) subclass.

IgA secretion

The body also has mucous and secretory surfaces that require immune protection: for example in the digestive, respiratory and urinogenital tracts and in secretory epithelia such as salivary, lacrimal and mammary glands. This is achieved by diacytosis on to those surfaces of an IgA-secretory component complex of the type already described above as a component of secreted bile (see pp. 147–148).

6.9 Lysosomes

Degradation of material that enters cells by endocytosis occurs after fusion of an endocytic vesicle with a lysosome, thus mixing the contents of the two vesicles but keeping them separate from other cell components. A lysosome that has not undergone such fusion is termed a primary lysosome, whereas the product of that fusion is a secondary lysosome. Primary lysosomes are small membrane-bounded organelles that contain a wide variety of hydrolytic enzymes, most of which have acid pH optima. In healthy cells lysosomes maintain an acidic internal pH, probably by the activity of an ATP-driven inward proton pump. The combined action of the 50 or more lysosomal hydrolytic enzymes makes these organelles potentially capable of the complete degradation of almost any cellular component or endocytized macromolecule. Once degradation to water-soluble molecules of molecular weights less than about 300 has occurred, these products diffuse out, sometimes helped by facilitated diffu-

primary lysosomes

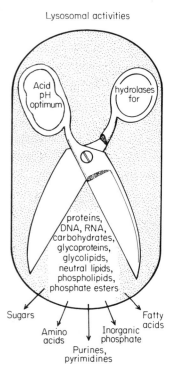

Lysosomal activities

Acid pH optimum

hydrolases for

proteins, DNA, RNA, carbohydrates, glycoproteins, glycolipids, neutral lipids, phospholipids, phosphate esters

Sugars

Amino acids

Purines, pyrimidines

Inorganic phosphate

Fatty acids

156

sion systems in the lysosomal membrane, and are utilized by the cell.

biosynthesis of lysosomes

Lysosomal enzymes, like secreted enzymes, are glycoproteins synthesized by the endoplasmic reticulum/Golgi complex route. Similarly, lysosomal membranes resemble secretory vesicle membranes and plasma membranes by being relatively rich in cholesterol, sphingomyelin and glycosphingolipids. Assembly of the organelles occurs at least partly in a cell compartment (known as GERL: Golgi/endoplasmic reticulum/lysosomes) that includes smooth endoplasmic reticulum and peripheral Golgi elements. The destination of newly synthesized lysosomal enzymes appears to be dictated by their possession, on otherwise typical asparagine-linked heterosaccharide chains, of a phosphorylated mannose residue. This is put on in the *cis*-Golgi to the 6-position of a mannose residue by the addition of *N*-acetylglucosamine-l-phosphate followed by hydrolytic removal of the *N*-acetylglucosamine. Newly synthesized lysosomal enzymes are also proteolytically processed, probably before their arrival at lysosomes. Sometimes the precursor is only slightly larger than the mature protein (e.g., 67 000 versus 61 000 for carboxypeptidase Y) but in other cases a much larger proportion of the precursor is discarded (e.g., 51 000 versus 30 000 for cathepsin D).

mannose-6-phosphate as a signal

Although newly synthesized lysosomal enzymes normally find their way into lysosomes quickly, this process is disrupted if the acid pH of the lysosome is neutralized with 'lysosomotrophic' weak bases such as NH_4^+ or chloroquine. Under these conditions, the newly synthesized enzymes are released into the extracellular medium. A similar loss of newly synthesized lysosomal enzymes to the exterior occurs in cells from patients with I-cell disease, in which there is failure to synthesize the mannose-6-phosphate 'address'. In addition to the direct pathway, many cells possess high affinity mannose-6-phosphate receptors that serve, by adsorptive pinocytosis, to pick up lysosomal enzymes from the exterior and direct them to lysosomes. The selectivity of this system is demonstrated by the inability of cells to endocytize dephosphorylated lysosomal enzymes and by the rapid uptake and transfer of non-lysosomal proteins to which mannose-6-phosphate residues have been artificially attached.

proteolytic processing

Although the digestion of endocytized material is the most easily studied lysosomal function, it is clear that lysosomes are also involved in the normal metabolic turnover of cell components such as soluble proteins and membrane compo-

157

nents. For example, the relative rates of inactivation of different cytosol enzymes by lysosomal enzymes are similar to their relative degradation rates *in vivo*, and the administration to animals of pepstatin, a selective inhibitor of lysosomal cathepsin D, slows the turnover of liver proteins *in vivo*. Such proteins gain entry to lysosomes by an ATP-dependent process. Sometimes, substantial regions of cytoplasm become surrounded by lysosomal membrane, forming large autophagic vacuoles: fusion with primary lysosomes then yields secondary lysosomes in which the organelles are digested. Autophagy tends to be most prominent during times of change in metabolic emphasis, for example during regression of tissue (as in the reabsorption of tadpole tail), starvation (when cell components need to be broken down to provide essential metabolites), or disposal of damaged organelles (as after hypoxia or free radical damage).

autophagy
normal metabolic
turnover

In certain genetic diseases, cells become packed with secondary lysosomes that are filled with undigested cell components (e.g., glycosphingolipids, sphingomyelin or glycogen); these engorged secondary lysosomes are known as residual bodies. Such 'storage diseases' are caused by the absence of individual hydrolases responsible for the breakdown of the accumulated materials (see Chapter 8.2). Once again, this provides firm evidence that lysosomes are essential not only for the digestion of endocytized material but also for the metabolism of normal cell constituents.

Although lysosomes are normally capable of completely degrading the materials they encounter, cells occasionally endocytize indigestible and non-permeant material with which their lysosomes become engorged, for example mineral fragments, colloidal metals, sucrose. Accumulation of non-noxious endocytized macromolecules in lysosomes sometimes greatly changes their buoyant density, providing a valuable experimental tool that aids their isolation in pure form. Sometimes the indigestible materials in these residual bodies damage the lysosomal membrane and lead to leakage of lysosomal enzymes into the cytosol: examples are asbestos and silica in the leucocytes and macrophages of the lungs of asbestosis and silicosis sufferers, and uric acid in the lysosomes of the polymorphonuclear leucocytes that infiltrate into rheumatic and gouty joints. The consequences for the affected cell and, in severe cases, for the surrounding tissue can be serious: inflammation, cell death and necrosis. Lysosomal membranes can also be damaged, with similar consequences, by peroxidative agents (e.g., photosensitive

residual
bodies

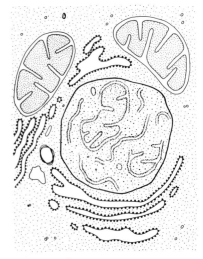

Autophagic vacuole

basic dyes such as phenol red, or CCl_4) or by lipid-disorganizing agents (e.g., retinol, lysophosphatidylcholine).

Further Reading

Hopkins C.R. & Duncan C.J. (eds.) (1979) Secretory mechanisms, *Symposium 33, Soc. Expt. Biol.*, Cambridge University Press.

Royal Society Discussion (1981) The control of secretion. *Phil. Trans. Roy. Soc.* **B 296,** 3–193.

Silverstein S. (ed.) (1978) *Transport of Macromolecules in Cellular Systems.* Dahlem Conferenzen, Berlin.

Palade G. (1975) Intracellular aspects of the process of protein synthesis. *Science* **189,** 347–358.

Davies B.D. & Tai P-C. (1980) The mechanism of protein secretion across membranes. *Nature* **283,** 433–438.

Rothman J.E. (1981) The Golgi complex: two organelles in tandem. *Science* **213,** 1212–1219.

Meyer D.I. (1982) The signal hypothesis—a working model. *Trends Biochem. Sci.* **7,** 320–321.

Schmidt M.F.G. (1982) Acylation of proteins—a new type of modification of membrane glycoproteins. *Trends Biochem. Sci.* **7,** 322–324.

Staneloni R.J. & Leloir L.F. (1982) The biosynthetic pathway of the asparagine-linked oligosaccharides of glycoproteins. *Crit. Rev. Biochem.* **12,** 289–326.

Elbein A.D. (1981) The tunicamycins—useful tools for studies of glycoproteins. *Trends Biochem. Sci.* **6,** 219–221.

Herbert E. (1981) Discovery of pro-opiomelanocortin, a cellular polyprotein. *Trends Biochem. Sci.* **6,** 184–188.

Marx J.L. (1983) Synthesizing the opioid peptides. *Science* **220,** 395–397.

Hammerschlag R. & Stone G.C. (1982) Membrane delivery by fast axonal transport. *Trends Neurosci.* **5,** 12–15.

Holtzmann E. (1977) The origin and fate of secretory packages, especially synaptic vesicles. *Neuroscience* **2,** 327–355.

Winkler H. (1977) The biogenesis of adrenal chromaffin granules. *Neuroscience* **2,** 657–683.

Apps D.K. (1982) The uptake of amines by secretory granules. *Trends Biochem. Sci.* **7,** 153–156.

Schekman R. (1982) The secretory pathway in yeast. *Trends Biochem. Sci.* **7,** 243–246.

Åkerman K.E.O. & Nicholls D.G. (1983) Ca^{2+} transport and regulation of transmitter release in isolated nerve endings. *Trends Biochem. Sci.* **8,** 63–64.

Smolen J.E., Korchak H.M. & Weissman G. (1982) Stimulus–secretion coupling in neutrophils. *Trends Pharmacol. Sci.* **3,** 483–485.

Silverstein S.C., Steinman R.M. & Cohn Z.A. (1977) Endocytosis. *Ann. Rev. Biochem.* **46,** 669–722.

Besterman J.M. & Low R.B. (1983) Endocytosis: a review of mechanisms and plasma membrane dynamics. *Biochem. J.* **210,** 1–13.

Herzog V. (1981) Pathways of endocytosis in secretory cells. *Trends Biochem. Sci.* **6,** 319–322.

Pearse B.M.F. & Bretscher M.S. (1981) Membrane recycling by coated vesicles. *Ann. Rev. Biochem.* **50,** 85–101.

Ungelwickell E. & Branton D. (1982) Triskelions: the building blocks of clathrin coats. *Trends Biochem. Sci.* **7,** 358–361.

Lentz T.L. (1983) Cellular membrane reutilization and synaptic vesicle recycling. *Trends Neurosci.* **6,** 48–53.

Stahl P.D. & Schlesinger P.H. (1980) Receptor-mediated pinocytosis of mannose/*N*-acetylglucosamine terminated glycoproteins and lysosomal enzymes of macrophages. *Trends Biochem. Sci.* **5,** 194–196.

Cuatrecasas P. & Roth T.F. (eds.) (1983) Receptor-mediated endocytosis. *Receptors and Recognition,* Volume 15, Chapman & Hall, London.

Hasilik A. (1980) Biosynthesis of lysosomes. *Trends Biochem. Sci.* **5,** 237–240.

Mullock B.M. & Hinton R.H. (1981) Transport of proteins from blood to bile. *Trends Biochem. Sci.* **6,** 188–191.

Kuhn L.C. & Kraehenbuhl J-P. (1982) The sacrificial receptor: translocation of a polymeric IgA across epithelia. *Trends Biochem. Sci.* **7,** 299–302.

Brown M.S., Kovanen P.T. & Goldstein J.L. (1981) Regulation of plasma cholesterol by lipoprotein receptors. *Science* **212,** 628–635.

See also pp. 212, 213.

7 Biosynthesis and turnover

Biosynthesis of membrane molecular components or of their precursors is continuous in almost all cells irrespective of their state of development or of their activities. A significant proportion of this biosynthetic activity may be devoted, in dividing and/or differentiating cells, to extension or modification of existing membranes. However, a major proportion of the biosynthetic activity of most cells is devoted simply to maintaining existing membranes.

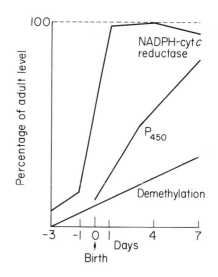

Cells proliferate by growing and dividing, with the mass of membrane approximately doubling between cell divisions. In unicellular organisms, which usually multiply rapidly, membrane growth is a dominant feature of cell activity and membrane biosynthesis may be devoted largely to this end. However, in multicellular organisms relatively few cells show rapid division but even the non-dividing cells may markedly change their membrane complement during maturation and differentiation. Thus, bacteria can, in response to a particular nutrient in their environment, develop an appropriate mediated transport system. This involves the synthesis and insertion of specific molecular components into the existing plasma membrane. In mammalian systems, differentiation to functional maturity may be accomplished by specific modifications to the enzyme complement of existing membranes. For example, the liver of a rat just before birth already has an endoplasmic reticulum which is morphologically normal but which lacks a functional electron transfer system. In the first week of postnatal life this activity develops, probably under hormonal control; the membranes do not, however, change their appearance. During this development the proteins comprising the individual segments of the electron transfer chain appear at different times: they are added to the membrane asynchronously rather than as organized arrays.

An example in which a massive increase in the amount of membrane occurs is provided by the response of the endoplasmic reticulum in liver to the introduction of drugs such as ethylmorphine and phenobarbital. When first administered

cell growth

neonatal changes

asynchronous addition

response to phenobarbital

161

these narcotics are effective in low doses but subsequently it becomes necessary to take higher doses to maintain narcotic levels of the drugs in tissues and blood. This is because within a few days the liver develops enzyme systems capable of inactivating these drugs. The livers of the drug-tolerant animals are larger than normal and electron microscopy reveals that much of the cytoplasm of their hepatocytes is packed with smooth endoplasmic reticulum. Fractionation of homogenates of such livers yields a microsomal fraction which is larger than normal and consists mainly of smooth-surfaced vesicles with very high activities of detoxifying enzymes. The biosynthesis of this membrane involves both the synthesis of enzymes and the synchronous accumulation of phospholipid and some cholesterol. Cessation of drug administration allows a return to lower levels of enzyme activity and a regression of the smooth endoplasmic reticulum.

differentiation of promitochondria and of plastids

Other extensively studied examples of simultaneous changes in metabolic activities and in membrane morphology which can be induced experimentally include the differentiation of the promitochondria of anaerobic yeasts into the mitochondria of aerobic cells and the differentiation of the plastids of etiolated plants into the fully functional chloroplasts of green plants (Section 7.4). The transformation of promitochondria to mitochondria features the acquisition by the inner membrane of the proteins of electron transport and this is accompanied by a dramatic change in lipid composition from a dominance (>80 per cent) of lipids with relatively short (C_8–C_{16}) and fully-saturated chains in promitochondria to a dominance (>90 per cent) of monounsaturated chains in mitochondria.

A good illustration of the speed with which a cell can respond to a functional demand on one part of its membrane complement is the relatively rapid biosynthesis of new plasma membrane which occurs in a macrophage soon after an extreme bout of phagocytosis (Chapter 6.7).

During cell division and differentiation the extension and elaboration of membranes may require a major share of the cell's biosynthetic activity, but mature, differentiated cells often show no net change in their membrane content. Despite this, radioactive membrane components of such cells show, after pulse-labelling *in vivo,* a steady decline in radioactivity which indicates that they are continuously being destroyed and replaced. This metabolic turnover is usually measured by administering a radioactive precursor of a component to an organism and determining the half-life ($T_{1/2}$: the

turnover of components

Normal

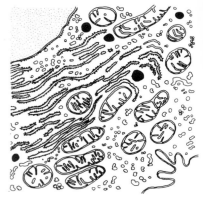

Response to phenobarbital

time during which half is destroyed or lost) of the component *in vivo*. The turnover rates determined for membrane constituents reveal that they may be renewed many times during a cell's lifespan. Old membranes are not, however, simply replaced by new ones since, in a single type of membrane, the rates at which different components are renewed varies widely. In the endoplasmic reticulum of liver different enzymically active proteins may be renewed every few hours (e.g., hydroxymethylglutaryl-CoA reductase shows rapid diurnal variations) or every few weeks (e.g. NAD glycohydrolase).

Turnover rates of membrane lipids show somewhat less variety; marked differences, though, are observed between the turnover rates of different lipid classes and between different parts of each type of phospholipid molecule. Moreover, within a single class of phospholipids there may be more than one kinetically distinguishable population of molecules, each having a distinctive rate of turnover. Such variations may be related in part to the use of some membrane lipids as raw materials for metabolic processes. In brain, for example, the only sufficiently large reservoir of choline to supply the synthesis of acetylcholine would appear to be the choline-containing phospholipids. Prostaglandins and leukotrienes (see Chapter 5.10) are synthesized from arachidonic acid, most of which resides in membrane phospholipids. The many steroid hormones largely concerned with the body's mineral and carbohydrate balance and reproductive functions are derived from cholesterol. The latter is also the precursor of bile acids.

Tissues such as liver and small intestinal mucosa also have to supply the cholesterol and phospholipid (mainly phosphatidylcholine) needed to form the stabilizing surface layer of the lipoprotein particles which they secrete into the bloodstream. If this coat is not formed correctly, as in liver poisoning caused by ethanol or agents which provoke lipid peroxidation (e.g. CCl_4), triacylglycerol accumulates in the tissue (fatty liver). Lipids and membrane proteins are also secreted into bile (Chapter 6.6).

Such losses to metabolism are presumably made good through biosynthesis and will be included in turnover measurements. However, there are also protein and lipid components that are not required for any known metabolic purpose outside the membrane but which are continuously removed from functioning membranes and replaced by new, apparently identical, molecules. Such continuous turnover

membrane lipids as metabolic precursors

lipoprotein synthesis

significance of turnover

Turnover of membrane components (liver)

Proteins	$T_{1/2}$(h)
nuclear	~120
endoplasmic reticulum	~ 50
plasma membrane	~ 50
mitochondria	~110

Proteins (endoplasmic reticulum)	
HMG-CoA reductase	2–3
NADPH-cyt *c* reductase	~ 70
cytochrome b_5	~100
NAD glycohydrolase	~400

Lipids (endoplasmic reticulum)	
phospholipid	15* & 80**
cholesterol	24* & 140**

Phospholipids (endoplasmic reticulum)	
phosphatidylcholine	14*
phosphatidylethanolamine	16*
phosphatidylserine	23*
sphingomyelin	38*

*, ** represent pools with different turnover rates.

163

maintains membranes in a dynamic state that would enable the cell to respond rapidly to any changing demand on its membrane functions. It also ensures that molecules which become modified whilst in the membrane are rapidly replaced, thus contributing to the maintenance of membranes in a fully functional state.

reutilization

A complication in simple interpretation of turnover data is the reutilization of the products of membrane degradation for subsequent membrane synthesis. In metabolism this frequently serves to effect economies in the use of valuable materials such as cofactors, essential amino acids and essential fatty acids. In emergency situations, such as starvation, reutilization decreases and the products of membrane degradation are used for energy provision; the amount of membrane material in the cell may, as a result, markedly decrease.

7.1 Lipid synthesis and transfer

An explanation, in a cellular context, of the biosynthesis and turnover of cell membranes must include mechanisms for the synthesis of the necessary molecules and their transfer to the site(s) at which they function. They must then be incorporated in the correct membrane(s) and appropriately positioned and oriented in relation to its (their) overall organization. Both incorporation and subsequent removal must be achieved without disturbing the overall structure. Sometimes the molecules may be synthesized as precursors which need to be chemically modified to fulfil their function correctly. All these processes must be under the guidance of systems which modulate the rates of biosynthesis and/or degradation of each type of molecule and which thus determine the cellular complement of each membrane.

lipid
biosynthesis

Membrane phospholipids and sterols are synthesized from cytosolic precursors largely by membrane-bound enzymes exposed at the cytoplasmic surface of the endoplasmic reticulum. Newly synthesized lipid molecules are therefore likely to be incorporated first into the cytoplasmic half of the lipid bilayer and some of them subsequently translocated to the lumenal half. This translocation may provide some selectivity which could contribute to an asymmetric distribution of lipids across the membrane. Phospholipids may also undergo subsequent modification, perhaps at another site. For example, the fatty acid patterns of phospholipids may be remodelled by a cycle of fatty acid removal and replacement. Many membranes contain phospholipases A_1 and A_2, which remove, respectively, the 1-

164

and 2-acyl groups from glycerophospholipids, and also possess acyltransferases which attach fatty acyl groups onto these positions. The probable importance of such deacylation/acylation cycles is illustrated by the observation that in liver newly synthesized phosphatidylinositol contains only one double bond per molecule, but that this lipid is later converted to the 1-stearoyl, 2-arachidonyl pattern (four double bonds) characteristic of this lipid in many animal tissues. Other modifications include the phosphorylation of phosphatidylinositol (PI) to polyphosphoinositides (PI-4P and PI-4,5P$_2$), possible interchanges between different head group components and, in bacteria, the aminoacylation of phosphatidylglycerol. The synthesis of glycosphingolipids almost certainly starts at the endoplasmic reticulum but addition of the sugar residues probably involves glycosyltransferases located in the Golgi complex and in the plasma membrane. Only mitochondria and chloroplasts appear to have independent capabilities for the synthesis *de novo* of complete lipids (diphosphatidylglycerol in mitochondria and digalactosyldiacylglycerol in chloroplasts).

Movement of lipid components from endoplasmic reticulum and their insertion into other membranes must be sufficiently selective to preserve the specific compositions of different cellular membranes. One type of transfer mechanism which can achieve the selection of particular lipid molecules is the exchange of phospholipid and cholesterol between membranes that is catalysed by transfer proteins present in the cytosol of many cells: different proteins appear to catalyse the transfer of different phospholipids. The best characterized is a phosphatidylcholine transfer protein with a molecular weight of about 20 000 which binds one molecule of phosphatidylcholine and catalyses its transfer between different subcellular organelles or lipid structures (liposomes or monolayers). The non-covalent binding of lipid to protein is such as to protect the lipid from attack by phospholipases but leave it accessible to displacement by detergents. Such transfer proteins probably contribute to the rapid equilibration of newly synthesized phospholipids amongst the different cell membranes: this takes only a few minutes (phosphatidylinositol) or hours (phosphatidylcholine and phosphatidylethanolamine). They do not, however, appear to provide any explanation of the specific lipid compositions of membranes.

lipid transfer

7.2 Protein synthesis

Some membrane polypeptides are synthesized on polyribosomes (polysomes) attached to cytoplasmic surfaces of

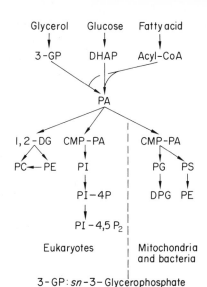

3-GP: *sn*-3-Glycerophosphate
DHAP: Dihydroxyacetone phosphate
PA: Phosphatidate
1,2-DG: 1,2-Diacylglycerol
CMP-PA: CMP-Phosphatidate
(CDP-Diacylglycerol)
PC: Phosphatidylcholine
PE: Phosphatidylethanolamine
PI: Phosphatidylinositol
PG: Phosphatidylglycerol
PS: Phosphatidylserine
PI-4P: PI 4-Phosphate
PI-4,5 P$_2$: PI 4,5-Bisphosphate
DPG: Diphosphatidylglycerol

membranes (endoplasmic reticulum in eukaryotes and plasma membranes in prokaryotes) and others on polysomes free in the cytosol. Most intrinsic proteins of the plasma membrane are probably synthesized and simultaneously inserted into membranes by membrane-bound polysomes, but most extrinsic and some intrinsic proteins are generated by free polysomes and subsequently attached to or inserted into the appropriate membrane. The majority of mitochondrial and chloroplast polypeptides are encoded in nuclear DNA and their precursors are synthesized in polysomes free in the cell cytosol before translocation to the appropriate membrane or compartment in the organelle. Thus, two sources of polypeptides and a variety of mechanisms of insertion into membranes are involved in membrane biogenesis.

Polypeptide chain synthesis and simultaneous insertion into the membrane by membrane-bound polysomes (cotranslational insertion) is similar in many ways to the mechanism already described for the formation of secretory proteins (Chapter 6), the major difference being that the product of synthesis remains embedded in the membrane. The most detailed and direct studies of this mechanism have been made with the spike glycoproteins of enveloped viruses and with histocompatibility antigens.

The viral RNA that is present in the cytosol of an infected cell dictates the production by the host cell's biosynthetic machinery both of complete replicas of the viral nucleic acid and of RNA copies of specific segments that function as messenger RNAs for polypeptides which are eventually incorporated into new virus particles (see Chapter 8). These include the spike glycoprotein(s) of the viral envelope.

The mRNAs for these (glyco)proteins have been translated both in cell-free systems which lack microsomal membranes and in systems to which membranes have been added at various times after the initiation of polypeptide chain biosynthesis. These *in vitro* biosynthesizing systems permit the use of terminators of chain growth (e.g., puromycin) and inhibitors of glycosylation (e.g. tunicamycin) and, in addition, the liberation of exposed polypeptide sequences by proteolytic enzymes. Systematic application of these experimental manipulations, together with amino acid sequence analysis of the entire polypeptide transcript and of the proteolytically cleaved fragments, have established the sequence of events which lead to the generation of the polypeptide chain of the spike glycoprotein (G protein) of vesicular stomatitis virus (VSV) and to its correct insertion into the endoplasmic reticulum of the host cell (see margin).

Polypeptide chain biosynthesis is initiated whilst the polysome is still free in the cytosol; attachment to the endoplasmic reticulum is not possible until at least 40 residues have been generated, presumably because the growing chain is initially contained within the ribosome and its emergence is required for the attachment to the membrane. There is also an upper limit to the length of chain that can initiate the interaction with the membrane (70 residues for VSV). This may be because the exposed, growing polypeptide chain has to fold into a secondary configuration that is compatible with the aqueous environment, and in this process obscures the site through which it interacts with the membrane.

The timing of the glycosylation of the G-protein polypeptide chain as it emerges on the non-cytoplasmic side of the membrane is also established by these experiments. For VSV spike glycoprotein, two identical asparagine-linked core heterosaccharides are introduced by transfer from a dolichol pyrophosphoryl carrier (see Chapter 6) before the polypeptide chain is completed. There is modification of these core heterosaccharides by the removal of glucose and some mannose residues while still in the endoplasmic reticulum, followed in the Golgi region by the removal of further mannose residues and addition of *N*-acetylglucosamine, galactose, sialic acid and fucose residues to yield the completed heterosaccharide.

There is also evidence that fatty acids are esterified to at least some completed polypeptide chains, probably in the Golgi complex just before the removal of the last mannose residues. These fatty acid residues, which may contribute to the anchoring of the polypeptide chain in the membrane, are probably attached to hydroxyls of serine, threonine or tyrosine residues at or near the carboxy-terminal end of the polypeptide.

Similar sequences of events have been identified during the biosynthesis of a number of normal mammalian plasma membrane glycoproteins which span the membrane once. These include erythrocyte glycophorin A and the heavy chains of lymphocyte IgM and of mouse H-2D^d histocompatibility antigen. The H-2D^d antigen has been assembled *in vitro* and experiments similar to those described above for VSV G-protein have established the disposition of the polypeptide chain in the membrane (see diagram, p. 168).

For all such single-spanning glycoproteins the molecular mechanisms of polypeptide chain generation, insertion into

time
sequence

glycosylation

fatty acid
attachment

single-span
polypeptides

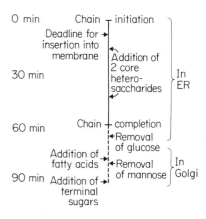

Time sequence for generation
of VSV G-glycoprotein

membranes and modification at the non-cytoplasmic face of the membrane are very similar to those proposed for secretory proteins in that they involve a signal or precursor extension sequence which guides the growing polypeptide chain through the membrane, with cotranslational modification by proteolysis and glycosylation, and perhaps also sulphydryl bridging, occurring at the non-cytoplasmic surface of the endoplasmic reticulum. The signal sequences of these polypeptides may also interact with the same 'target' proteins in the endoplasmic reticulum membrane. The extrinsic protein complex that interacts with signal sequences of secretory proteins (see Chapter 6) also binds signal sequences of precursors of intrinsic membrane polypeptides synthesized *in vitro*. These proteins may thus serve as a target for all polypeptides which traverse the endoplasmic reticulum in any way. It is also evident that a common mechanism is involved in the channelling of both secretory and membrane polypeptides across the membrane. If this mechanism involves membrane-spanning proteins, their arrangement must be such as to allow the membrane-spanning segments of membrane polypeptides to be liberated into the lipid hydrocarbon of the membrane interior.

The *N*-terminal signal sequences of precursor peptide extensions of membrane proteins appear to be from 15 to 29 residues long. They are generally, but not invariably, removed soon after they emerge on the non-cytoplasmic side of the membrane (ER). The 'signal' sequence starts with a short, polar segment and this is followed by a substantial hydrophobic segment (at least nine residues) which terminates at a cleavage site characterized by an amino acid with short side-chain (glycine, alanine or serine). The growing polypeptide chain that subsequently emerges at the non-cytoplasmic surface of the membrane may be very long, has predominantly polar characteristics and commonly has core heterosaccharides immediately attached at one or more asparagine residues. The membrane-spanning segment that is translated next is a sequence of 20 to 28 uncharged or hydrophobic amino acids bounded at the non-cytoplasmic side by either a basic or an acidic (or a proline) residue and on the cytoplasmic side by lysine or arginine residues. The C-terminal sequence that remains exposed on the non-cytoplasmic surface is polar and very variable in length (from four residues in immunoglobulins to 40 in glycophorin A).

Multiple-chain spanning proteins may be generated using similar mechanisms. For example, the three (glyco)polypep-

amino acid
sequence

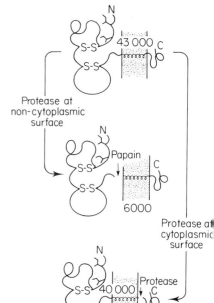

H-2D^d antigen — synthesized by membrane-bound ribosomes

43 000

Protease at non-cytoplasmic surface

Papain

6000

Protease at cytoplasmic surface

40 000

Protease

Tunicamycin present during synthesis

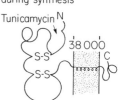

Tunicamycin

38 000

Synthesized in membrane-free system

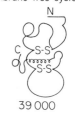

39 000

tide chains that form the Semliki Forest Virus (SFV) spike glycoprotein are initially inserted into the membrane co-translationally and sequentially as two spanning polypeptides. One of these is subsequently hydrolysed at a point in the large and exposed N-terminal region so as to give a short stretch of polypeptide (E_3) which remains associated (as an extrinsic component) with the two intrinsic, membrane-spanning polypeptides (E_2 and E_1). The three glycosylated polypeptides together form the complete SFV spike glycoprotein.

An association between extrinsic and intrinsic polypeptides may also be formed by two independently synthesized polypeptides, one a membrane-spanning polypeptide and the other a polypeptide that is released (secreted) into the endoplasmic reticulum and subsequently associated at the non-cytoplasmic surface with the membrane-spanning unit. An example is the association of β_2-microglobulin with the heavy chains of the Type I histocompatibility antigens (Chapter 5.2).

The polypeptide chains of some proteins span (or are inserted into) the membrane several times, and their biosynthesis and insertion probably involves a more complex sequence of events; there is, as yet, very little direct information on these mechanisms of synthesis and insertion. For example, the single polypeptide chain of bacteriorhodopsin forms seven membrane-spanning segments, several of which include polar residues. It is probable that these polar residues are accommodated deep in the membrane as a result of the polypeptide chain being folded so as to expose only lipophilic residues to its hydrocarbon environment. The capacity of many large membrane polypeptides to organize themselves in stable configurations that include internal polar regions that are protected from the lipid environment by a lipophilic surface is probably just as essential to the correct functioning of membrane proteins as the well-known tendency of the proteins dissolved in the aqueous compartments of a cell to adopt a configuration that exposes polar residues and buries apolar ones. Such arrangements of membrane polypeptides can be generated by multiple membrane-spanning polypeptide sequences, by complex folding patterns or by oligomeric interactions between polypeptides.

In gram-negative bacteria, mechanisms are also required for transferring newly synthesized polypeptides to the periplasmic space and to the outer membrane. There seems little doubt that such polypeptides are synthesized at the cytoplas-

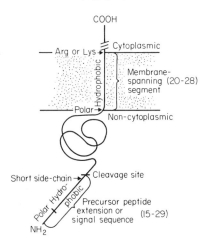

Generalized structure of a membrane-spanning polypeptide

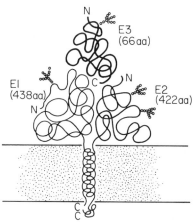

SFV spike glycoprotein

mic membrane, predominantly by a cotranslational mechanism, and that translocation into the periplasmic space is equivalent to translocation of eukaryote secretory polypeptides into the cisternae of the endoplasmic reticulum. Insertion into the outer membrane, however, is generally more rapid than into the periplasmic space; this seems to preclude the intermediate accommodation of outer membrane polypeptides in this space. The speed of transfer and the subsequent orientation of the polypeptides in the outer membrane appear to favour a direct transfer through areas of contact between the cytoplasmic membrane and the outer membrane (Bayer's junctions, zones of adhesion).

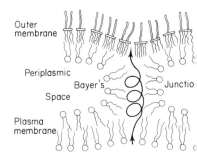

Addition of proteins, synthesized on free polysomes, to the cytoplasmic face of the plasma membrane is also established as a mechanism for further elaborating membrane structure. Studies of reticulocytes have revealed that polypeptides 4.5 and 6 of erythrocyte membranes (Chapter 2 are synthesized on free polysomes in the reticulocytes and then added to the cytoplasmic surface of the plasma membrane. Such post-translational additions of proteins to membranes probably contribute substantially to the overall structure of the plasma membrane and also of other organelles. For example, cytochrome b_5 (Chapter 2) and NADH-cytochrome b_5 reductase are synthesized on free polysomes and post-translationally anchored into membranes of several intracellular organelles by a hydrophobic C-terminal segment. Post-translational incorporation of polypeptides into mitochondria and chloroplasts will be discussed in Section 7.4.

gram-negative bacteria

addition of extrinsic protein

7.3 Transfer and redistribution

Polypeptides synthesized in the endoplasmic reticulum may be destined to function in membranes of other organelles such as plasma membrane, lysosomes and peroxisomes. Specific transfer processes are required to ensure that such molecules reach their correct destinations and, in some cases, become active only when they have arrived there. Experiments using either radioactive labelling and cell fractionation or immunocytochemical labelling and electron microscopy have permitted many individual molecules to be traced through the membrane system, but the identification of functionally significant packages of membrane molecules at intermediate stages of processing is more difficult.

Many lipid and protein molecules can move laterally in membranes (Chapter 2.5) and this may provide a mechanism for the transfer of membrane components from one site to another either in a continuous membrane system or between separated organelles through the process of vesiculation and transfer across the intervening cytosol. Vesiculation from the Golgi complex is involved in the formation of lysosomes and secretory vesicles, and the formation of peroxisomes appears to involve vesiculation from the endoplasmic reticulum. Vesiculation followed by fusion transfers membrane material from the Golgi complex to the plasma membrane in exocytosis (Chapter 6.4) and probably also in the normal provision of new components for plasma membranes: examples include the movement of membrane vesicles from dictyosomes into the developing cell plate during cell division in plants and probably also the migration of 5'-nucleotidase-rich vesicles from the Golgi in hepatocytes. Unfortunately, it is not yet clear how general and quantitatively important this mechanism of membrane biosynthesis is, nor how such mechanisms achieve selectivity amongst particular membrane components. The molecular components of membranes themselves may have specific interaction requirements which contribute substantially to this selectivity. There are many examples of preferential protein–protein and lipid–protein interactions among membrane components, but factors which determine the patterns of molecules in individual membranes have not yet been identified.

transfer
as vesicles

Some specific factors which might be involved in selective control of the incorporation of new materials into existing membranes have been studied both in model systems and within cells. Observations on the fates of new radioactive molecules have often indicated that such molecules are evenly distributed throughout a particular membrane even at the earliest times examined. However, experiments involving the immobilization of outer membrane antigens of *E. coli* by dual antibody cross-linking and the use of immunofluorescent labels have demonstrated the existence of growth zones which otherwise would be rapidly dispersed by lateral diffusion. Most evidence favours the idea that all membrane synthesis occurs by enlargement of existing membranes.

Attempts to reconstitute functional multienzyme systems from isolated membrane constituents have revealed that for two proteins of a sequence to interact normally they must be incorporated into a pre-existing lipid structure containing the correct lipid class(es): they may be introduced into this struc-

171

ture either simultaneously or at different times. In addition, experiments with bacterial mutants incapable of synthesizing phospholipids if starved of glycerol have shown that an existing membrane system need not be enlarged by synthesis of new phospholipids before the membrane proteins of a transport system can be inserted; in such circumstances the functional efficiency of the system may be somewhat impaired. When fatty acid-requiring mutants are grown in media containing different fatty acids the physical properties of the membrane lipids are varied. For each batch of cells there is a temperature below which the proteins of a transport system cannot be efficiently incorporated into the membranes; this temperature seems to reflect the need, if correct insertion is to occur, for fluidity in the membrane lipids. If an inducer of a transport system is added below this temperature, the proteins of the system are synthesized but transport is not initiated: such a system cannot be 'rescued' by raising the temperature.

A piecemeal mode of assembly is consistent both with the independence of the turnover rates of different constituents within individual membranes and with the largely random distribution of the newly inserted constituents throughout the area of the membranes. It does not, however, explain how areas of membranes which are in physical continuity can include segregated areas containing only certain proteins. For example, when an enveloped virus multiplies the nucleo-capsids are synthesized within the cell. Simultaneously, the proteins and glycoproteins of the future viral envelopes (which are also synthesized within the cell) appear in the plasma membrane of the host cell, where they form patches from which the typical proteins of the host cell plasma membranes are excluded (see Chapter 8).

patches of
specific proteins

Similarly, during the differentiation of embryonic myotubes into mature muscle fibres the distribution of cell-surface acetylcholine receptors changes. They are initially evenly dispersed but during development they become congregated into patches with which the growing nerve axons then interact to form neuromuscular junctions. Functionally significant clusters of protein molecules are also found at tight junctions (Chapter 1.1), at gap junctions (Chapter 5.2) and in the 'purple patches' of bacteriorhodopsin molecules in the plasma membrane of *Halobacterium halobium* (Chapter 2.1).

7.4 Assembly of mitochondria and chloroplasts

The assembly and organization of the inner membranes of mitochondria and chloroplasts present special complications as both have probably evolved from prokaryotic organisms which colonized other cells and became endosymbionts early in evolution. In addition to their characteristic content of diphosphatidylglycerol (Chapter 2.2), mitochondria have a complement of DNA which, like that of bacteria, consists of double-stranded closed circles. In yeast, each mitochondrion contains up to five identical DNA molecules of molecular weight about 5.10^7 and, depending on the species, this contributes about 10–25 per cent of the total cell DNA. Mitochondria also contain a unique RNA complement transcribed from this DNA, and ribosomes which are attached to the inner surface of the inner membrane during periods of active protein synthesis. Like bacterial ribosomes, these ribosomes are smaller than eukaryotic cytoplasmic ribosomes, and mitochondrial protein biosynthesis is inhibited by many of the inhibitors which block bacterial protein biosynthesis; these inhibitors have been essential tools in the identification of proteins coded by the mitochondrial genome.

Information on mitochondrial differentiation has come mainly from studies with yeasts, *Neurospora crassa* and rat liver. Yeasts, which can be grown aerobically or anaerobically, have been especially useful because of the existence of *petite* mutants, in which protein biosynthesis in mitochondria is defective, and because mitochondrial differentiation can be suppressed by growing under anaerobic conditions (or in the presence of high concentrations of glucose). Anaerobically grown yeasts are devoid of mitochondria, but possess organelles termed promitochondria. These lack cristae and are filled with densely staining material, and they can only be detected in the cytoplasm by electron microscopy after either special types of fixation or freeze–fracture. Promitochondria, which are extremely fragile and difficult to isolate, have a low content of tricarboxylic acid cycle enzymes and cytochromes and a low level of ATPase activity (which is insensitive to oligomycin) and they do not exhibit mitochondrially directed protein synthesis. The promitochondria of anaerobic cells contain phospholipids with mainly medium-chain saturated fatty acids (see p. 162), are more permeable than mitochondria and lack diphosphatidylglycerol. If unsaturated fatty acids are supplied then the membranes assume a more

mitochondrial DNA

promitochondria

Specific inhibitors of protein synthesis

Mitochondrial ribosomes
Chloramphenicol
Mikamycin
Ethidium bromide

Cytoplasmic ribosomes
Cycloheximide
Emetine

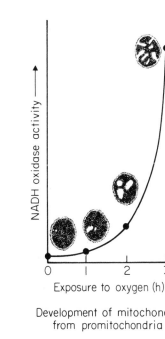

Development of mitochondria from promitochondria

173

'mitochondrial' configuration, but the organelles still do not show respiration-linked phosphorylation. Transformation of promitochondria to fully functional mitochondria requires aeration of the medium.

Differentiation of promitochondria to mitochondria is prevented if protein synthesis is inhibited either in the cytoplasm or in mitochondria. Cytoplasmic protein biosynthesis appears to contribute the proteins of the outer membrane and the matrix and also some of the respiratory apparatus of the inner membrane, while the mitochondrial genome directs synthesis of about 10 per cent of the proteins of yeast mitochondria, including the mitochondrial ribosomal proteins and some components of the inner membrane which are rich in hydrophobic amino acids and which are embedded in the lipid layer: in the cytochromes they do not include the subunits which bear the haem prosthetic groups.

mitochondrial and cytoplasmic protein synthesis

Some, at least, of the cytoplasmically synthesized polypeptides destined for the inner mitochondrial membrane are synthesized and released in soluble form before entering the mitochondrion. In most cases, the precursor polypeptide that is initially synthesized is larger in molecular weight than the mitochondrial polypeptide by 1500 to 6000 (examples include subunits α, β and γ of F_1 and subunits IV to VI of cytochrome oxidase), but in several cases (e.g., the adenine nucleotide transporter and cytochrome c) the mature protein appears to be the same size as the initial translation product. In each case, studies both of intact cells and using the incorporation of preformed precursors into isolated mitochondria have demonstrated that the uptake, proteolytic processing (where necessary) and integration of the polypeptide only occur in energized mitochondria: import appears to be the energy-dependent step.

precursor polypeptides

The processing and incorporation of cytoplasmically synthesized mitochondrial components involve transfer of individual polypeptide species to any of the compartments of the mitochondrial interior. Cytochrome c peroxidase, an enzyme found in the intermembrane space of yeast mitochondria, is synthesized as a precursor that is proteolytically processed during its entry into the mitochondrion, possibly without an energy requirement. The adenine nucleotide transporter and components of the electron transfer chain have to become integrated into the inner membrane, and subunits of F_1 are destined for incorporation into an extrinsic protein at the matrix face of the inner membrane. The enzymes of the matrix also enter from the cytoplasm. There

174

must be mutual recognition elements built into the cytoplasmic precursor molecules and the two mitochondrial membranes that allow each polypeptide correctly to traverse either one or two membranes and then find its correct location.

chloroplast differentiation

A general situation similar to that in mitochondria exists in the chloroplast, where proteins, lipids and pigments are incorporated into pre-existing membranes and the chloroplasts then divide to produce daughter chloroplasts. Plants grown in the dark contain etioplasts; these have a rudimentary inner membrane system consisting of a 'crystalline' prolamellar body which is connected to a few more extended areas of membrane. These are converted to chloroplasts containing highly complex systems of lamellae and grana under the influence of light. Like mitochondria, chloroplasts have a population of circular DNA and their own ribosomes. The proteins contributed by the chloroplast during its differentiation are less well characterized than for yeast mitochondria, but they include chloroplast ribosomal proteins and the large subunit of ribulose 1,5-bisphosphate carboxylase. The gene that codes for the small subunits (mol. wt 15000) of this enzyme is derived from the nucleus. It codes for a polypeptide, synthesized on cytoplasmic polysomes, which has a molecular weight about 4000 larger than the mature subunit protein. This N-terminal extension or 'transit peptide' is significantly longer than the 'signal peptide' of secretory polypeptides; it lacks the 9–18 amino acid sequence of hydrophobic residues and it has charged residues scattered throughout its sequence.

Plastocyanin (mol.wt 10000) is synthesized as a precursor on cytoplasmic ribosomes and post-translationally passes through three membranes to function at the inner surface of the thylakoid. The molecular weight of the precursor is 25000, suggesting that its 'transit peptide' is larger than the mature protein.

Further Reading

Bell R.M., Ballas L.M. & Coleman R.A. (1981) Lipid topogenesis. *J. Lipid Res.* **22,** 391–403.

Kader J.C., Douady D. & Mazliak P. (1982) Phospholipid transfer proteins. In *Phospholipids* (eds. Hawthorne J.N. & Ansell G.B.) *New Comprehensive Biochemistry* **4,** 279–311.

Lodish H.F. & Rothman J.E. (1979) The assembly of cell membranes. *Scientific American* Jan., 38–53.

Simons K., Garoff H. & Helenius A. (1982) How an animal virus gets into and out of its host cell. *Scientific American* Feb., 46–54.

Kreil G. (1981) Transfer of proteins across membranes. *Ann. Rev. Biochem.* **50,** 317–348.

Warren G. (1981) Membrane proteins: structure and assembly. In *Membrane Structure* (eds. Finean J.B. & Michell R.H.). *New Comprehensive Biochemistry* **1**, 215–257.

Strauss A.W. & Boime I. (1982) Compartmentation of newly synthesized proteins. *CRC Critical Rev. Biochem.* **12**, 205–235.

Sabatini D.D., Kreibich G., Morimoto T. & Adesnik M. (1982) Mechanisms for incorporation of proteins into membranes and organelles *J. Cell Biol.* **92**, 1–22.

Osborne M.J. & Wiu M.C.P. (1980) Proteins of the outer membrane of gram-negative bacteria. *Ann. Rev. Microbiol.* **34**, 369–422.

Inouye M. & Helegoua S. (1979–1980) Secretion and membrane localization of proteins in *Escherichia coli. CRC Critical Rev. Biochem.* **7**, 339–371.

Schatz G. & Butow R.A. (1983) How are proteins imported into mitochondria? *Cell* **32**, 316–318.

Ellis R.J. (1977) Protein synthesis by isolated chloroplasts. *Biochim. Biophys. Acta* **463**, 185–215.

See also pp. 212, 213.

8 Membrane variations and membrane pathology

The preceding chapters have all been concerned with elements of membrane structure and function that are common to many membranes and cells. As with other cell components, however, the various membranes display considerable natural variation from tissue to tissue and also variations arising from environmental changes or due to genetic mutations. Membrane function may be modified to the benefit or to the detriment of the organism. Furthermore, damage to membranes or interference with membrane functions often lead to biochemical changes that are invaluable in diagnosing and following the progression of human disease. It is to topics such as these that this final chapter is devoted.

8.1 Variability between membranes

Although all membranes appear to be fundamentally similar in overall plan, their details show considerable variation. Each cellular membrane has its own specific complement of enzymes and a particular lipid composition, although the association of these two patterns usually has no obvious functional significance. For example, plasma membranes are rich in cholesterol and relatively saturated glycosphingolipids, which will restrict passive permeability to water and ions, and they also include the Na^+/K^+-pump responsible for maintaining the Na^+ and K^+ gradients between extracellular medium and cytoplasm; specific lipid requirements for the Na^+/K^+-ATPase are probably restricted to PI and/or PS, two anionic phospholipids that are widely distributed amongst cell membranes and make up only a small fraction of plasma membrane lipids. By contrast, diphosphatidylglycerol is a lipid found in eukaryotes only in the inner mitochondrial membrane (Chapter 2), where it may be essential for the function of the cytochrome oxidase segment of the respiratory chain.

Even within a single membrane there are substantial local variations in protein and lipid composition. The plasma

lipid
patterns

177

functionally
differentiated
domains

membrane of the mammalian enterocyte (intestinal epithelial cell) is differentiated into two readily recognizable domains, a digesting and absorbing apical domain (the brush border) and a basolateral domain which exchanges materials and information with the rest of the body. The hepatocyte plasma membrane is differentiated into at least three domains: the sinusoidal domain, which exchanges material and information with the blood; the contiguous domain responsible for cell–cell contact; and the bile canaliculus domain through which bile is elaborated and which also resists the damaging effects of high concentrations of extracellular bile salts. Such lateral differentiation is probably produced by specific direction of newly synthesized material early in the life of the cell by mechanisms as yet unknown. A tendency of such differentiated domains to undergo randomization by lateral diffusion may be restrained by the tight junctions which separate these domains and perhaps also by interactions of components of these domains with elements of the submembrane cytoskeleton, which is particularly well developed in the microvilli of the intestinal brush border and of the bile canaliculus (see p. 5).

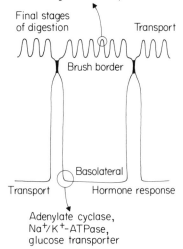

Plasma membrane domains of mammalian
enterocyte

species and
tissue
variations

Differences in the functions of the same type of membrane in different tissues are achieved by variations in composition. Thus, the cristae of mitochondria from insect flight muscle largely contain the proteins of energy metabolism supported by transport systems for ATP/ADP and for glycerophosphate, their primary energy-yielding substrate. On the other hand, the much more varied functions of the mitochondria in mammalian liver require the presence of many other transport systems (for citrate, aspartate, etc. Chapter 4).

Variations in abundance of a single protein from cell to cell may have a substantial effect on membrane function. For example, the different sensitivities of various cells to a given chemical stimulus are usually due to differences in the number of the appropriate receptors at the cell surface. Possession of an active transport system for bile salts allows hepatocytes to concentrate bile salts from blood for secretion into bile. Perversely, this transport system may also be responsible for the specific hepatotoxicity of the fungal toxin, phalloidin; although phalloidin can irreversibly polymerize actin in any cell, it is specifically accumulated by hepatocytes and hence is more toxic to these cells.

Specialization of function, and therefore of composition, is carried to extremes in some membranes. Thus, one or a few

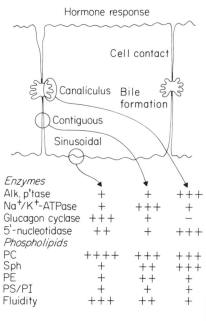

Plasma membrane domains of mammalian
hepatocyte

protein species dominate the membranes of the sarcoplasmic reticulum, the electroplax, and the retinal discs.

8.2 Genetic variability and genetic diseases

Most genes encode the amino acid sequences of proteins, many of which are either incorporated into membranes or are enzymes responsible for the synthesis or degradation of membrane components. Variations in the base sequences of genes often lead to functionally neutral changes in the amino acid sequences of gene products; this accounts for much normal genetic polymorphism. Some mutations, however, lead either to synthesis of a functionally defective protein or to abortion of polypeptide synthesis. Mutations in regulatory genes lead to changes in the rates of expression of structural genes and hence to changes in the cellular complements of the proteins they encode.

Deliberate induction of mutations and careful selection of mutants are extremely powerful tools in the biochemical analysis of membrane function. For example, bacterial mutants deficient in periplasmic solute-binding proteins (p. 66), β-galactoside transport (p. 67) and various components of the PEP-linked phosphotransferase system (p. 72) have played a key role in the understanding of membrane transport processes. Genetic polymorphism is a relatively common phenomenon in man (and other animals). For example, the expression of A, B and O antigens on the surface of erythrocytes is a function of the presence or absence of glycosyltransferases which, respectively, add terminal N-acetylgalactosamine (A) or galactose (B) residues to H-antigen oligosaccharide sequences (Chapter 2.3).

A second group of blood group antigens is expressed through glycophorin, the major erythrocyte sialoglycoprotein. M-antigen is expressed by individuals in which glycophorin has an N-terminal serine and N-antigen by those with N-terminal leucine; MN individuals carry both the M and N genes. In addition, there are individuals (E_{na}^-) whose erythrocytes lack glycophorin. Those who are homozygous for the E_{na}^- gene express no glycophorin whereas heterozygotes have erythrocytes with about one-half the normal quantity. The erythrocytes of homozygous E_{na}^--individuals contain an increased complement of heavily glycosylated band 3, another glycoprotein, maybe to partially compensate for the absence of glycophorin. These cells show no obvious defect of function.

genetic
polymorphism

mutants

blood group
antigens

glycophorin
deficiency

179

Other inherited abnormalities of the human erythrocyte membrane include some in which the defect is confined to the erythrocyte and others in which it is shared with the plasma membranes of other cells, but is most easily studied in the erythrocyte. Hereditary spherocytosis (HS) is an autosomal dominant condition characterized by haemolytic anaemia, spleen enlargement and jaundice. Normal erythrocytes are flexible biconcave discs but those of HS patients are fragile, inflexible spheres that are rapidly removed from the circulation by the spleen. Normal erythrocytes have a lifetime of 120 days but HS erythrocytes survive for only 20 days even if they are transfused into a normal individual, thus indicating that the defect is intrinsic to the erythrocyte. Removal of the spleen increases the cells' lifespan and ameliorates the jaundice but does nothing to correct the underlying membrane defect. HS erythrocytes lose membrane by outward vesiculation, and this is probably responsible for their spherical and inflexible form. They are also abnormally permeable to Na^+ and K^+ and contain more Ca^{2+} than normal cells.

Hereditary stomatocytosis is a somewhat similar inherited haemolytic anaemia. Again, the cells are almost spherical, are abnormally permeable to Na^+ and K^+ and have a shortened lifespan. However, there is no substantial loss of plasma membrane and they are therefore rendered spherical by osmotic swelling. This may be due to a primary defect in ionic homeostasis.

The spectrin of the submembrane filaments in erythrocytes is widely believed to play an important role in the maintenance of erythrocyte shape and integrity. One of the few direct indications in favour of this view comes from an inherited haemolytic anaemia of mice in which the erythrocytes lack spectrin. An abnormal spectrin has been described in hereditary pyropoikilocytosis in which erythrocytes severely distort on mild heating.

Membrane problems are also characteristic of some erythrocyte diseases in which the genetic lesion dictates the synthesis of an abnormal haemoglobin. In β-thalassaemia the erythrocytes accumulate aggregates of denatured haemoglobin (Heinz bodies) and in sickle cell disease there is reversible aggregation of deoxyhaemoglobin S. Heinz bodies render limited areas of membrane less flexible and aggregated haemoglobin S imposes a 'sickled' shape upon the cells. These distorted cells lose small amounts of membrane, probably during passage through the spleen, and they accumulate abnormally large quantities of Ca^{2+}. If these erythrocytes are extracted with a non-ionic detergent such as Triton X-100, then the residual cell profile consists of the submembrane filamentous network and this retains the distorted shape of the intact cell.

Several congenital erythrocyte defects are mirrors of membrane defects elsewhere. Duchenne muscular dystrophy is an X-linked recessive disease characterized by progressive skeletal muscle degeneration due to leakage of enzymes through an abnormal muscle cell plasma membrane. There are also signs of abnormality in the plasma membranes of the erythrocyte of these patients in terms of increased ion permeability, higher intracellular Ca^{2+} concentration and increased phosphorylation and cross-linking of spectrin. The erythrocytes are less deformable than normal, but not sufficiently to cause a haemolytic anaemia.

The erythrocytes, leucocytes and platelets of patients with paroxysmal nocturnal haemoglobinuria are abnormally sensitive to attack by the complement system of the plasma. The major problem is the irregular occurrence of spontaneous episodes of haemolysis, mainly at night, caused by small amounts of activated complement in the plasma. The activated complement, in addition, causes serotonin secretion by platelets.

Glanzmann's thrombasthenia, an autosomal recessive condition, is a platelet disease in which the cells are unable to cross-link to one another and consolidate a clot. Plasma membranes from these platelets are deficient in a membrane glycoprotein of molecular weight 100 000, which may therefore be involved in cross-bridging. In Bernard–Soulier syndrome, another autosomal recessive disease, platelets fail to attach normally to exposed subendothelial tissue in damaged arteries. The plasma membranes of these platelets are deficient in a glycoprotein of molecular weight 150 000.

Sometimes a single disease may take more than one form. Polymorphonuclear leucocytes from patients with chronic granulomatous disease phagocytize bacteria normally but fail to kill some of them. An essential component in one of the killing mechanisms is a cytochrome b of very negative redox potential that is present in the plasma membrane and secretory vesicles (p. 152). An X-linked form of the disease is characterized by the absence of this cytochrome, whereas leucocytes from patients with the autosomal recessive variant have a normal amount of the cytochrome but this fails to become reduced during phagocytosis.

Duchenne muscular dystrophy

platelet defects

chronic granulomatous disease

Other defects of plasma membrane function include defects in receptors and in transport systems. A striking example of the former is familial hypercholesterolaemia. Low density lipoprotein (LDL) is normally cleared from plasma by adsorptive endocytosis in coated vesicles (p. 154), but patients homozygous for this condition fail to do this. Again, the defect can take at least two different forms: either the LDL receptors are absent from peripheral cells such as fibroblasts or else they are present and bind LDL normally but the receptor–LDL complexes are not endocytized.

Hereditary defects in transport systems are often displayed most strikingly in the brush-border membranes of intestinal epithelial cells and of the absorbtive epithelium of the renal tubule. These two membranes have very similar complements of hydrolytic enzymes and transport systems, and factors secondary to the central genetic lesion often determine whether a defect is most obviously expressed in intestine or kidney. For example, an autosomal recessive condition in which the glucose/galactose transporter is absent from both tissues shows itself primarily as a problem in which babies fail to thrive because they develop an osmotically generated diarrhoea, caused by unabsorbed glucose and galactose. By contrast, genetic deletion of one or other of the brush-border amino acid transporters leads to an aminoaciduria, with attendant problems such as precipitation of 'stones' of pure cystine in the kidneys of cystinuric individuals. The presence of transporter(s) for small peptides and some overlap between the substrate specificities of the various amino acid transporters of the intestine allow some absorption of most amino acids. Several of the amino acids excreted in aminoacidurias are non-essential amino acids that can be synthesized in adequate amounts within the body.

Defective absorption of a dietary constituent can be due to absence of the hydrolytic enzyme whose action precedes the transport process. Such is intestinal sucrase deficiency. In various forms of this disease the brush-border membranes show a deletion of the sucrase, a decrease in its concentration, or the presence of a non-functional protein.

The lysosomal storage diseases constitute another important group of hydrolase deficiencies. Amongst these diseases are several in which individual enzymes required for degradation of membrane sphingolipids are absent. Although these enzyme deficiencies (the lipidoses) usually affect most or all tissues, their damaging effects tend to be concentrated in tissues such as brain and kidney, which are rich in plasma

Examples of inherited transport disorders in man

Renal glycosuria	(sugars)
Glucose/galactose malabsorption	(sugars)
Cystinuria	(amino acids)
Hartnup disease	(amino acids)
Iminoglycinuria	(amino acids)
Familial rickets	(phosphate)

membranes (and hence in sphingolipids). The spleen, which has to digest much of the membrane lipid of cells cleared from the bloodstream, may also be severely affected. Commonly, these diseases lead to mental retardation, neural degeneration and early death. Lipidoses in which glycerophospholipid degradation is impaired are not observed, maybe because these lipids perform such a key role in the structure of intracellular membranes that any such defect would immediately be lethal to cells.

8.3 Cell proliferation and differentiation

Normal development of a multicellular organism involves multiplication and differentiation of the early progeny of the fertilized egg into a series of stem cell lines. These stem cells then proliferate before further differentiating into the multitude of different types of mature tissue cells. Some types of stem cell die out early in the lifespan of the organism and thus limit the total population of a long-lived cell type (e.g., neurones, muscle cells) and some persist as a source from which short-lived cells can constantly be replenished (e.g., the blood cell precursors of the bone marrow and the germinal cell progenitors of sperm). Sometimes the differentiated cells retain a capacity for division (e.g., hepatocytes, fibroblasts, vascular endothelium). These immensely complicated processes of proliferation and differentiation are orchestrated by an incompletely understood system of neural and hormonal controls, both during development and during adulthood. Control mechanisms in the adult must be adequate both for the normal maintenance of cell populations and for those special situations in which an increased supply of new cells is required: examples include proliferation of particular lymphocyte clones in response to antigens, the monthly growth and loss of the myometrium during the menstrual cycle and the growth of mammary epithelial tissue during pregnancy. Sometimes cells proliferate profusely, leading to a cancer. Although it seems likely that this is usually the result of a mutation, malignant tumours can also arise from the uncontrolled growth of cells that find themselves in the wrong environment. Omnipotent embryonic stem cells give rise to normal tissues if they multiply within the inner cell mass of an embryo but develop into teratocarcinomas—cancers that contain grotesque mixtures of 'differentiated' structures such as fingers and hair—when they multiply at sites outside the embryo.

Lysosomal enzyme deficiencies in some lipidoses

The myriad changes in cell character that occur during the progression from zygote to fully differentiated cell obviously include numerous changes in membrane function. For example, the transition from promyelocyte to mature polymorphonuclear leucocyte involves the elaboration of the granule apparatus and oxygen-dependent killing mechanisms essential to the mature cell (see p. 152). Thus, the cytochrome b_{-245} of the plasma membrane appears during this transition, but the transferrin receptor that was needed to keep the multiplying cells supplied with iron disappears during the same period. Another striking example of the emergence of an essential membrane characteristic is the acquisition of 'fusion competence' by myoblasts. These cells first divide rapidly and then both stop dividing and acquire the ability to spontaneously fuse into the multinucleate myotubes that are the precursors of mature muscle fibres.

The emphasis in studies of erythrocyte differentiation in response to the polypeptide hormone erythropoietin is usually put upon the control of haemoglobin biosynthesis. However, elimination of intracellular organelles and maturation of the erythrocyte membrane are of equal importance. Once the stem cells have multiplied most organelles are degraded and the nuclei are expelled. The major period of plasma membrane protein synthesis thus occurs before the onset of haemoglobin synthesis, with spectrin and actin synthesized first, followed by glycophorin A and band 3.

Occasionally, differentiation may involve a cell's extreme commitment to the synthesis and function of a particular membrane, as in the synthesis and maintenance of the nerve myelin sheath by Schwann cells and oligodendroglial cells. At other times, it may take the form of a detailed change in the function of an existing membrane. For example, the sarcoplasmic reticulum of 'slow' muscle fibres contains far less Ca^{2+}-pump ATPase than that of 'fast' fibres, but if 'slow' fibres are functionally connected to nerve that normally innervates a 'fast' muscle then the fibres take on a 'fast' phenotype that includes a sarcoplasmic reticulum rich in Ca^{2+}-pump ATPase.

Studies of cancer cells from natural tumours (e.g., leukaemias) and of tissue culture cells transformed to a malignant phenotype by oncogenic viruses have revealed diverse detailed changes in these rapidly proliferating cells. Examples include increased membrane 'fluidity', decreased cell-surface fibronectin, simplified cell-surface carbohydrate structure, a decrease in Ca^{2+} requirement for growth and in-

cell
differentiation

leucocyte

myoblasts

erythrocyte

myelin

muscle

membrane
changes in
cancer

184

creased glucose transport (which supports an enhanced rate of glycolysis). However, it is remarkably difficult to assign a key role in malignancy to any of these changes; many of them are, in fact, correlates of rapid cell division, of cells at particular stages in the cell cycle or of the fact that natural tumours often arise from immature cells (e.g., myeloid stem cells).

An important clue to a possible role for one group of membrane enzymes in the uncontrolled growth associated with malignant transformation has, however, come with the identification of the transforming gene products of some oncogenic viruses as tyrosine-directed protein kinases, whose substrates include plasma membrane proteins of unidentified function. Support for this idea comes from the observation that peptide growth control signals such as epidermal growth factor (EGF) and platelet-derived growth factor (PDGF) also control the activities of tyrosine kinase activities: the EGF receptor (mol.wt 170000) seems to express this protein kinase activity and to phosphorylate itself. Another protein kinase—phospholipid-dependent protein kinase C—appears to be the cellular receptor for tumour promoters such as TPA (tetradecanoyl phorbol acetate). These molecules facilitate the tumour-promoting activity of carcinogens and also have other diverse effects on cell state, ranging from potentiation of fibroblast proliferation to induction of macrophage differentiation.

8.4 Effects of temperature on membranes

Cell membranes, especially those of homeotherms such as mammals and birds, generally perform their normal functions within a narrow temperature range, and excursions outside this range often cause a marked decline in activity. Moreover, membrane enzyme activities frequently show patterns of temperature-dependence different in form from those typical of soluble enzymes. This is most readily demonstrated when an Arrhenius plot (log activity *vs* absolute temperature^{-1}) can be resolved into two or more straight lines with different gradients, indicating different 'apparent activation energies' over different temperature ranges. This most often happens in the temperature range 10–40°C, and a frequent interpretation is that these discontinuities arise as responses to changes in the physical state of the lipid environment of the enzyme molecules. Sometimes several enzymes in a single membrane will show the same 'transition

185

temperature', but it is not unusual for different enzymes in the same membrane to show activity transitions at different temperatures, perhaps indicating heterogeneities in the lipid environment even within a single membrane.

membrane changes in hibernation

A particularly striking example of this type of pattern, and of its natural regulation, is seen in the plasma membranes of the livers of active and hibernating hamsters. Activities of the Na^+/K^+-ATPase, Mg^{2+}-ATPase, and 5'-nucleotidase of membranes from active animals show two discontinuities, at 25°C and 13°C, whereas in those from hibernators the latter discontinuity occurs at a lower temperature (4°C). Glucagon-stimulated adenylate cyclase activity, which entails the co-operation of proteins at both surfaces of the plasma membrane (pp. 122–124), shows the same pattern. By contrast, alkaline phosphodiesterase I, an enzyme located at the outer surface of the plasma membrane, shows only the low-temperature discontinuities, and F^--stimulated adenylate cyclase and cAMP phosphodiesterase, both located at the cytoplasmic surface, show only the discontinuity at 25°C. These results suggest that each of these enzymes is sensitive to its general lipid environment and that a phase transition occurs in the inner leaflet of the membrane at 25°C, irrespective of the state of the animal. In the outer leaflet, however, the temperature of this transition falls by approximately 9°C in hibernating animals, possibly as a result of a change in membrane fatty acid composition.

cold acclimatization

Relative increases in the concentration of unsaturated fatty acids in the phospholipids of organisms acclimatized to cold have frequently been reported. For example, the brain and intestinal mucosa of cold-acclimatized fish have phospholipids with enhanced proportions of $C_{20:4}$ and $C_{22:6}$, and both fatty acid and phospholipid patterns of the protist *Tetrahymena* adapt to changed temperature within about 4 h, maintaining at all temperatures a constant value of membrane 'fluidity' (measured by polarization of the fluorescence of a lipophilic probe). The mechanisms responsible for such changes are difficult to ascertain in complex animals and plants, but are much more amenable to study in microorganisms. *E. coli* can make only one unsaturated fatty acid (*cis*-vaccenic acid), and cold acclimatization enhances the rate of its biosynthesis *de novo*. *Bacillus megaterium*, by contrast, has the ability to Δ_5-desaturate existing saturated fatty acids. On reduction of its growth temperature from 35°C to 20°C there is a rapid induction of Δ_5-desaturase that is complete within 1–2 h.

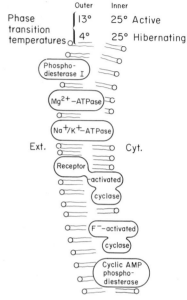

Enzyme activities in liver plasma membranes active and hibernating hamsters

Major fatty acids of Tetrahymena *phospholipids (% of total fatty acids)*

	Growth temp.	
	15°	39.5°
14:0	7	7
16:0	9	13
16:1	9	9
18:0	0.6	2.1
18:1	10	11
18:2	20	15
18:3	31	25
Saturated/ unsaturated ratio	0.26	0.5

temperature
and
permeabilities

The permeability characteristics of membranes are sensitive to temperature. Mediated permeation processes that involve specific proteins frequently display discontinuities in their Arrhenius plots similar to those noted above for intrinsic membrane enzymes, indicating that the function of the transport proteins is affected by the physical state of the lipid in which they find themselves. Passive diffusion of lipophilic molecules through membranes shows a high sensitivity to temperature, suggesting that permeation is greatly affected by the structure of the lipid layer as dictated by its lipid composition, degree of unsaturation and temperature. By contrast, water movement through natural membranes shows little effect of temperature, suggesting passage through water-filled structures rather than the lipid bilayer.

cryofixation
and
cryopreservation

In all of these cases, the demonstrated sensitivity to temperature seems to relate to the physical state of the membrane lipid; the general structural organization of membranes appears to survive until temperatures are reached at which ice crystals begin to form. However, membrane survival is essential if tissues are to survive freezing. Cryobiology distinguishes between two types of objective, namely cryofixation and cryopreservation. The aim of cryofixation is to freeze tissue in a way that preserves morphological relationships precisely, primarily by preventing movement of water and formation of ice crystals during freezing. This is most effectively done by very rapid freezing to $-196°C$ (the boiling point of liquid N_2) in the presence of a 'cryoprotectant' such as glycerol or dimethylsulphoxide. Although membranes are damaged by such techniques they preserve their normal morphology for as long as they remain frozen, and these frozen structures can be examined in detail by freeze-fracture techniques (see p. 4). It is also possible to examine unstained, ultrathin frozen sections using an electron microscope, usually of the STEM (Scanning-Transmission) type, that has a cooled specimen holder. Cryopreservation, on the other hand, has as its aim the survival of cells or tissues after freezing and thawing. In this case, migration of water through membranes during freezing may be acceptable, but formation of intracellular ice crystals of appreciable size is obviously unacceptable. Successful techniques have now been developed for the long-term preservation of several types of cell, including sperm, fertized ova and tissue-culture cell lines. Cooling of the cells is usually in two stages, with the first, slower stage allowing the formation of small extracellular ice crystals and causing

187

partial dehydration of the cells. Samples are then quickly frozen to liquid nitrogen temperature and stored at −80°C. When required, they are thawed relatively quickly, so as to minimize the growth of ice crystals. Cryoprotectants are usually included during these procedures so as to minimize damage to the partially dehydrated and frozen cells and to inhibit growth of ice crystals.

8.5 Membrane fusion

Fusion between membranes is an essential feature of many normal cell functions. Fusion of two or more cells occurs during tissue differentiation (e.g., the fusion of myoblasts to form the precursors of muscle fibres) and during fertilization (egg and sperm). Such events are initiated during contacts between the outer surfaces of the plasma membranes of participating cells. Phagocytosis and pinocytosis (Chapter 6) are initiated by invagination of plasma membrane so that again outer membrane surface is involved in the fusion that allows a vesicle to bud off into the cytoplasm. Conversely, cell division and the release of structures that are surrounded by plasma membrane (e.g., milk fat droplets, many enveloped viruses; see pp. 148, 204) involve membrane fusion that is initiated through contacts at the cytoplasmic surface of a plasma membrane. Exocytotic secretory events (Chapter 6) involve contact and fusion of Golgi-derived secretory vesicles with the cytoplasmic surface of the plasma membrane. Many intracellular membrane interactions involve membrane fusion events, particularly with the elements of the Golgi–lysosome system; each involves a fusion of two cytoplasmic or two extracytoplasmic (e.g., Golgi luminal) membrane surfaces. Each of the many membrane fusion events appears to be relatively specific and under effective cellular control.

Information on the molecular events involved and on their control has been sought by using cellular models in which fusion events can be controlled (e.g., by physiological stimuli or ions) and artificial membrane systems. Different studies have tended to emphasize either the importance of lipid physical characteristics or of particular proteins to fusion events: their relative contributions may well vary from situation to situation.

Cell fusion can be promoted *in vitro* by a variety of mildly polar amphiphilic molecules that include a fluid hydrocarbon substituent (e.g., unsaturated or medium-chain fatty acids or

Ext. − ext. fusions

Cyt. − cyt. fusions

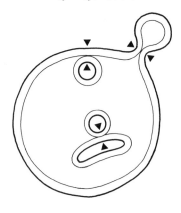

lipids and fusion

monoacylglycerols). Phospholipase C treatment, which converts a polar membrane phospholipid molecule to a less polar and still membrane-associated diacylglycerol or ceramide, sometimes induces membrane vesiculation from the untreated surface of the membrane. In some cases, sites of membrane fusion are depleted of intrinsic proteins and therefore lipid-enriched. For example, freeze-fracture electron microscopy suggests the generation of such areas during the fusion of plasma membrane and secretory vesicle membranes in stimulated mast cells. Protein depletion is also characteristic of the membrane vesicles that bud off erythrocytes that are either old or loaded with unphysiological concentrations of Ca^{2+}. In particular, these vesicles are devoid of extrinsic membrane proteins such as spectrin that normally associate with the cytoplasmic surface of the plasma membrane.

protein
depletion

Evidence for the involvement of specific proteins in cell–cell fusion has come particularly from studies of viruses (e.g., Sendai virus) that induce such fusion. In the case of influenza virus, the viral protein responsible for initiating the membrane fusion necessary for viral entry into host cells is a glycoprotein (haemagglutinin HA) consisting of two disulphide-linked polypeptides, HA_1 and HA_2 (mol.wts 46000 and 30000). The gene for this protein has been cloned and used to confer a cell-fusing capability upon a normally nonfusogenic virus. Specific proteins are almost certainly essential to many membrane fusion events within cells. For example, a protein (synexin) has been isolated from adrenal medulla that mediates a specific Ca^{2+}-dependent interaction between isolated chromaffin granules (see p. 142) and plasma membranes.

fusogenic
proteins

Ca^{2+} ions appear to play an essential role in many membrane fusion events. Intracellular fusions essential to exocytosis, membrane recovery after exocytosis, and transport of macromolecules between endoplasmic reticulum and Golgi are all at least partially controlled by cytoplasmic $[Ca^{2+}]$. Some fusion events require the millimolar concentrations of Ca^{2+} normally found outside cells (e.g., myoblast fusion) whereas others do not (e.g., phagocytosis). Such concentrations of Ca^{2+} are capable of causing both vesicle fusion and lysis in liposomal membrane models that incorporate anionic lipids such as phosphatidate and phosphatidylserine.

role of
Ca^{2+}

Artificial methods designed to provoke the occurrence of unnatural fusion events have recently become important as experimental and industrial tools. Widely used techniques include the use of fusogenic viruses or their isolated membranes (e.g., Sendai), high concentrations of polyethylene glycol (mol.wt 1000–6000) or momentary exposure of cells to high electric potentials. Such methods can sometimes yield novel information on the mechanisms of action of membrane-located processes, for example the mode of coupling of hormone receptors to adenylate cyclase (pp. 122–124). More often, however, they are used to make genetic hybrids of two cells that would normally never fuse. Examples include fusion of an activated B-lymphocyte with a myeloma cell to create a 'hybridoma' that secretes monoclonal antibody, and attempts to introduce genes for resistance to pests into commercially important plants.

8.6 Drugs that act at membranes

Since many aspects of cellular function are mediated by the activities of membranes it is hardly surprising that many of the most widely used drugs exert their therapeutic or harmful effects upon membrane functions.

anaesthetics

Local anaesthetics are usually partially charged amine derivatives that block axonal conduction in nerve fibres, whereas the most widely used general anaesthetics include relatively inert gases such as nitrous oxide, diethyl ether, cyclopropane and fluorinated hydrocarbons (e.g., halothane). Despite their great chemical variety, the relative anaesthetic potencies of these molecules correlate very well with their ability to partition from water into the slightly polar solvent octanol, suggesting that some amphiphilic site is involved in their action. Many anaesthetics both expand the packing of membrane lipid and increase the fluidity of the lipid, leading to increases in the passive permeability of membranes to ions. However, they probably also interact with some membrane proteins and these may include the molecular targets for the anaesthetic actions of these drugs.

drugs acting
on receptors

Although receptor-directed drugs have been used therapeutically for many years, recent interest in the actions of drugs on neurotransmitter systems has been particularly spurred by the realization that many of the most widely used psychoactive drugs act in the brain either at neurotransmitter receptors or on systems that modify the amounts of neurotransmitter seen by the receptors. For example, the anti-schizophrenic actions of phenothiazine tranquillizers (e.g., chlorpromazine) appear to be mediated mainly by blockade of the D_2-subclass of dopamine receptors.

Chlorpromazine

190

The analgesic, euphoria-inducing and addictive activities of plant alkaloids such as morphine and its derivative, diamorphine (heroin), appear to arise entirely from their interactions with receptors whose true endogenous ligands are peptides of the endorphin and enkephalin families. Indeed, the recognition of the existence of these neuropeptides came from experiments designed to identify endogenous ligands that competitively inhibit morphine binding to membrane receptors. A second group of drugs whose effects were discovered empirically but whose investigation seems likely to reveal new neurotransmitter systems are the benzodiazepine antianxiety agents (e.g., diazepam). The mode of action of the receptors for these drugs appears to be to facilitate the opening of hyperpolarizing Cl^- channels by the inhibitory transmitter GABA. There is also a possibility that a second class of agonist active at benzodiazepine receptors may inhibit GABA-controlled opening of Cl^- channels and hence induce anxiety, hyperactivity and even convulsions. In Huntington's chorea, uncontrolled body movements develop as a result of the progressive loss of inhibitory GABA neurones. The extreme excitatory action of the poison strychnine, which is included in small quantities in some 'tonics', can also be ascribed to its antagonism of the inhibitory effects of GABA.

In general, high levels of neurotransmitter release in the noradrenergic and 5-hydroxytryptamine pathways of the CNS tend to lead to alertness and excitation, whereas suppression of activity in these pathways can cause depression. Reserpine, which reduces output of these neurotransmitters by virtue of its ability to prevent their accumulation in presynaptic storage vesicles (see p. 142), has been used in treatment of hypertension. However, its use is now discouraged because it also causes depression. By contrast, widely used tricyclic antidepressant drugs (e.g., imipramine) enhance the activity of released noradrenaline and 5-hydroxytryptamine by inhibiting the active transport systems responsible for their uptake from the synaptic cleft (see p. 142). Another approach to antidepressive therapy is to inhibit breakdown of these monoamine neurotransmitters by administration of inhibitors of mitochondrial monoamine oxidase (e.g., isocarboxazid).

Drug therapy directed at particular activities of peripheral tissues is often much more securely based upon experimental observation. For example, a clearly defined action of β-adrenergic agonists (e.g., isoprenaline) is to relax the con-

opiate analgesics

benzodiazepines

Huntington's chorea

antidepressants

β-adrenergic drugs

Diazepam

Imipramine

tracted circular muscle in the bronchioles of a lung subject to an asthmatic attack. However, a potential disadvantage of this type of treatment is that β-adrenergic agonists have an excitatory action on the heart. This has been ameliorated in two ways: the first is to take the drug by inhalation; the second has been the development, based on the fact that the β-receptors of the heart (β_1) and of the lung (β_2) have slightly different ligand selectivities, of agonists (e.g., salbutamol) which act more effectively at β_2-receptors than at β_1-receptors.

antihistamine

Antihistamines have long been used for suppressing the inflammatory effects of histamine released from antigen-triggered mast cells. These H_1-receptor antagonists (e.g., promethazine) effectively suppress symptoms such as urticaria, but they do not inhibit gastric secretion of HCl, even though this is also controlled by histamine. This observation led to the design of a second class of histamine antagonists, the H_2-blockers (cimetidine and ranitidine), and these anti-ulcer agents are now amongst the most widely prescribed drugs in the world.

cardiovascular drugs

A variety of drug interventions is useful in treating various disorders of the cardiovascular system such as coronary artery disease, disturbances of normal heart rhythm or high blood pressure. In general, such treatments are directed at improving coronary circulation, improving the heart's rhythm and reducing its workload. The earliest drugs used for these purposes were the cardiac glycosides (e.g., digoxin, a congener of ouabain), the only known effect of which is to inhibit Na^+/K^+-ATPase; it is thought that reduced Na^+ transport suppresses the electrical activity of the sinoatrial node which controls the rhythm of the heartbeat. Impulse conduction in the heart is also suppressed by 'calcium antagonists' such as verapamil, since much of the inward current of action potentials traversing the conducting system in cardiac tissue is carried by ions moving through Ca^{2+} 'gates' rather than through classical tetrodotoxin-sensitive Na^+ 'gates'. Ca^{2+} 'gates' are also important in controlling the contraction of coronary arteries, so calcium antagonists—particularly, in this case, nifedipine—are useful for relief of angina pectoris. Catecholamines increase both the force and the amplitude of the heartbeat, so another route to suppression of cardiac activity is through blockade of β-adrenergic receptors. Some of the antagonists used are equipotent at all β-receptors (e.g., propranolol) whereas others bind more avidly to β_1-receptors and are therefore somewhat car-

Salbutamol

Cimetidine

Verapamil

192

dioselective (e.g., atenolol). Sometimes the drug chosen is a weak partial agonist rather than a pure antagonist (e.g., pindolol), thus providing some protection against excessive slowing of the heart. A normal physiological control of heart rate occurs when there is stimulation of the vagus nerve, an effect that can be mimicked by administration of a muscarinic cholinergic stimulus. However, this is not usually employed as a pharmacological intervention since it can, in extreme cases, bring the heart to a halt.

High blood pressure both overworks the heart and tends to precede other circulatory problems. It can be counteracted in several ways, including: reducing the output of the heart using β-adrenergic blockade; relaxation of peripheral vasculature by blockade of α_1-adrenergic receptors with prazosin; and stimulation of urine output by diuretics.

A fundamentally different way to interfere with cell communication processes is to prevent production of the signal. This is the mechanism of action of aspirin and other non-steroidal **anti-inflammatory drugs** (e.g., indomethacin, naproxen). They block the activity of the endoplasmic reticulum cyclo-oxygenase that is the first step on the pathways that convert arachidonate ($C_{20:4}$) and other polyunsaturated fatty acids to a variety of prostaglandins. Although this discovery led to recognition of the key position of prostaglandins in pain and inflammation, the details of these processes are still obscure. Recognition that polyunsaturated fatty acids are also metabolized to leukotrienes, a group of lipid derivatives involved in mediating anaphylactic responses to antigens, suggests that inhibition of the 5-lipoxygenase which initiates this biosynthetic sequence might inhibit processes as diverse as spasm in asthmatic bronchioles and migration of leucocytes to sites of inflammation.

A major problem with any therapy aimed at modification of a normal cellular activity is the body's ability to adapt to changed circumstances. One reaction is to develop tolerance to a previously effective dose of a drug, often by increasing the rate of its metabolism (see pp. 161–162 and 196).

Severe problems of **drug dependence**, leading to overt symptoms or to return of the original problem being treated, sometimes in exacerbated form, can arise from prolonged use of drugs that interfere with the function of neurotransmitter systems. Such reactions are probably largely the result of the ability of receptor systems to adapt to chronically increased or reduced levels of stimulation by, respectively, decreasing and increasing their sensitivity to sub-

anti-inflammatory drugs

drug dependence

Nifedipine

Atenolol

193

sequent stimuli. The classic example is opiate addiction, in which receptors that normally encounter modest quantities of endogenous opiate peptides are bombarded with very large quantities of opiate alkaloids. The precise nature of the adaptive process in this case is unknown, but the withdrawal symptoms provoked by abrupt withdrawal of opiate drugs are so severe as to make the drugs extremely addictive. A similar, but milder, response is seen on sudden withdrawal of benzodiazepine anti-anxiety drugs from chronically treated patients; the withdrawal pattern sometimes includes expression of an anxiety state worse than that for which the treatment was originally given. In these two examples, the pattern is one in which withdrawal of an unnatural level of external stimulation leads to deficient responses to the small quantities of endogenous neurotransmitters. In other cases, such as the rapid rise in blood pressure that can occur on abrupt withdrawal of chronic α_1-adrenergic blockade, problems arise from the excessive response to normal levels of endogenous neurotransmitters that is shown by tissue that has been supersensitized by prolonged exposure to a receptor antagonist.

8.7 Detoxification of lipid-soluble materials

Many lipid-soluble or partially lipid-soluble materials, if allowed to accumulate in membranes, would cause membrane damage either due to their effects on specific membrane components or upon the properties of the lipid bilayer. Some of these potentially damaging materials are produced as a result of normal metabolism (e.g., hormonal steroids, bilirubin, certain bile salts) and must be eliminated from the body before toxic levels are attained. Other molecules are taken into the body as natural or added components of foodstuffs (preservatives, colourings, added flavours), food contaminants (e.g., components eluted from packaging), drugs, or environmental pollutants (solvents, pesticides, herbicides, etc.).

For such lipid-soluble materials to be eliminated from the body they must first be converted to water-soluble metabolites that can be excreted via the liver (into bile and thence to the faeces) and kidneys. These conversions often occur in two 'phases'. Phase I reactions introduce a polar and reactive chemical grouping, thus increasing water solubility and, more important, yielding suitable substrates for Phase II reactions. The Phase II reactions then couple the unwanted compound to some endogenous polar acceptor molecule, giving a water-soluble conjugate that can readily be excreted. However, some compounds (e.g., bilirubin) usually proceed directly to a Phase II reaction.

mixed function
oxidases
(monooxygenases)

Most Phase I reactions are carried out in the liver by mixed function oxidase systems. Such enzyme systems also occur elsewhere, for example in kidney, lung and tissues involved in steroid hormone synthesis. The mixed function oxidase systems of the liver are involved in the metabolism of endogenous molecules (e.g., conversion of cholesterol to bile salts, desaturation of fatty acyl-CoA) and in the detoxification of xenobiotic (foreign) molecules. The key reactions in these processes are catalysed by the P_{450}/P_{448} family of cytochromes which split O_2, with one oxygen atom forming water and the other either being introduced into the substrate or reduced concurrently with the oxidation of the substrate (e.g., in desaturation reactions). Reactions catalysed by these cytochromes include hydroxylation of aliphatic and aromatic compounds, epoxidation, dealkylation, desaturation, desulphuration and the oxidation of N, P or S substituents.

Example of mixed function oxidase action

$$RH + O_2 + NADPH + H^+$$

Mixed function (MFO) oxidase

$$ROH + H_2O + NADP$$

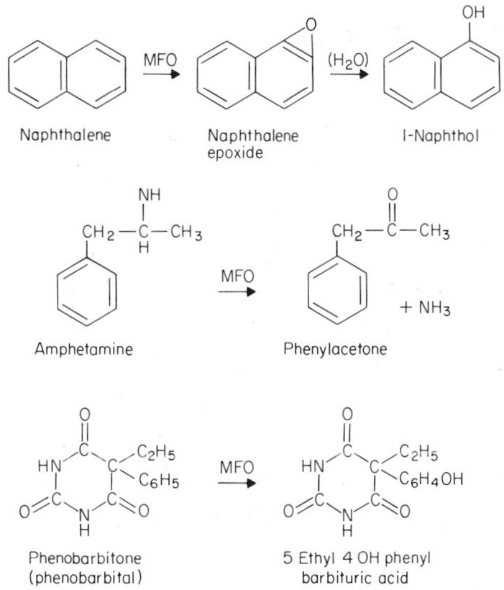

Examples of reactions involving
mixed function oxidase

cytochromes
P_{450}/P_{448}

Cytochromes of the P_{450}/P_{448} family are named after the absorption maxima of the CO derivatives of their reduced forms. The family includes many cytochromes, each of which is a different gene product. These are distinguished by their distinct immunological characteristics, differential isolation,

195

detailed differences in their absorption spectra and differential inducibility by various xenobiotics. They also display different, but overlapping, substrate specificities. For example, mammalian liver can express several phenobarbitone-inducible cytochrome P_{450} variants and several cytochrome P_{448} species that are inducible by 3-methylcholanthrene.

These cytochromes are intrinsic membrane proteins with a requirement for an appropriate phospholipid environment. In addition, the lipid and protein together provide a hydrophobic site that will accommodate hydrophobic substrates. Since each cytochrome P_{450} variant has a relatively broad specificity, its reaction pattern is largely dictated by which substrates gain access. P_{450} cytochromes usually receive two electrons from an associated electron transport chain which includes an NADPH-linked flavoprotein and iron–sulphur protein. In some tissues (e.g., liver) one electron may be supplied by an electron transfer system consisting of an NADH-linked flavoprotein and cytochrome b_5. These enzyme systems are generally localized in the endoplasmic reticulum, and analytical subfractionation of liver microsomal fractions has indicated that different P_{450} variants may be differently distributed in the endoplasmic reticulum system.

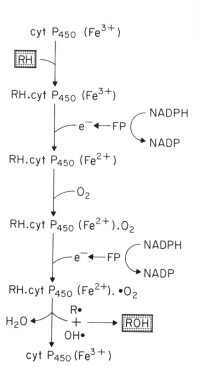

variations
in MFO
activities

Mixed function oxidase (monooxygenase) activity is low at birth, but develops rapidly thereafter. This explains why fetal and newborn mammals are more sensitive to many drugs than are adults. A loss of smooth endoplasmic reticulum, together with its mixed function oxidase activity, is a consequence of starvation or of protein undernutrition; affected individuals are therefore more than usually susceptible to the effects of drugs and other foreign molecules. This is also true with ageing animals and people, where there is a decline in normal liver (and renal) functions.

proliferation
of endoplasmic
reticulum

Prolonged, or occasionally single, exposure to some xenobiotic compounds causes an induction of mixed function oxidase activity that is sometimes accompanied by proliferation of the endoplasmic reticulum and enlargement of the liver. This probably occurs as a result of the derepression of regulator genes. The sensitivity of animals to many drugs, and also their duration of action, is thereby decreased. For example, a rat that would normally sleep for an hour after a particular dose of barbiturate drug might awake after only 15 min if its mixed function oxidase has been induced by repeated doses of this or a related drug. In such animals, the newly proliferated endoplasmic reticulum, with its associated

196

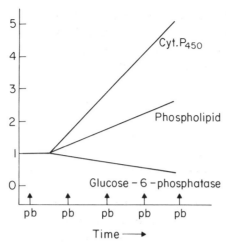

Change in liver composition (relative to control=1)
of rats treated with daily doses of phenobarbital (pb)

P_{450} mixed function oxidase system, is atypical since it lacks those endoplasmic reticulum proteins that are not constituents of the mixed function oxidase system. Most xenobiotics induce proliferation of a P_{450}-rich endoplasmic reticulum, but exposure to polycyclic hydrocarbons (e.g., 3-methylcholanthrene, benzpyrene) induces cytochrome P_{448} without an accompanying proliferation of membrane.

conjugation
reactions

There are many Phase II reactions appropriate to different types of substrate. These include conjugation with glucuronic acid, sulphate, phosphate, glutathione or various amino acids. Glutathione conjugates are often further metabolized to cysteine or mercapturic acid conjugates. The Phase II reactions occur at various sites in the liver cell, with the polar metabolites then being excreted in the bile and urine. Glucuronidations, using UDP-glucuronate as donor, are catalysed by a family of enzymes present in the endoplasmic reticulum. Conjugations with glycine (e.g., of p-aminobenzoic acid) occur within mitochondria. Conjugations with glutathione are achieved by a family of glutathione-S-transferases. These are proteins (mol.wt 40 000) which account for about 6 per cent of the total protein of liver cytosol and which have a variety of substrate specificities. In addition, they possess binding sites for hydrophobic molecules that are of high affinity but low specificity: they therefore seem likely to act as important intracellular carriers of hydrophobic molecules such as bilirubin. Due to the non-specificity of this binding function, this group of proteins has gathered a variety of names, for example ligandin, corticosteroid binding protein and protein Y.

glutathione-
-S-transferase

197

Enzymes of Phase II metabolism occur in different relative amounts in different animals. For example, lithocholate is a monohydroxy bile salt that is produced by bacterial action in the gut and then reabsorbed. In humans it is successfully detoxified by sulphation, but in rats it accumulates and causes severe liver damage. This toxicity is due to attack upon the membrane of the bile canaliculus, inhibiting bile formation and causing the accumulation of toxic biliary materials both in the liver and in the circulation. Many Phase II enzymes are, like those responsible for Phase I reactions, induced by the presence of their substrates.

Phase II enzyme activities are usually low at birth, and many babies show a transient postnatal jaundice until induction of adequate amounts of bilirubin glucuronyltransferase. This can be particularly severe in the babies of rhesus factor-incompatible mothers; sometimes blood bilirubin levels can become neurotoxic, leading to a need for exchange transfusion of bilirubin-free blood, while the UDP-glucuronyltransferase activity develops. Such babies are sometimes treated with inducers of Phase II reactions (phenobarbitone).

Most of the metabolites produced by Phase II reactions are anions, and their entry into bile is facilitated by an anion transport system of wide specificity in the bile canalicular membrane (see p. 149). The driving force of this process may be the membrane potential across the canalicular membrane. However, only anionic metabolites above a certain molecular weight appear in the bile of a particular animal: smaller metabolites go to the kidney for excretion. This 'threshold' molecular weight for biliary excretion varies between species (approximately 325 in rat, 400 in guinea-pig and 475 in human and rabbit). One effect of Phase II conjugation reactions is of course to increase the molecular weight of the molecules being processed (by about 180 during glucuronidation and by about 300 when glutathione conjugates are formed). Factors that may determine the molecular weight threshold for biliary secretion include the specificity of the anion transporter and the permeability characteristics of the tight junctions that form a seal between the cells lining the biliary tract. One mechanism by which cholestatic drugs decrease bile flow is through increasing the 'leakiness' of these junctions so that materials initially secreted into bile find their way back into the bloodstream.

The reactions discussed above usually produce molecules that are either of lower pharmacological activity or less potentially toxic than the original molecule. Sometimes, however, the action of the mixed function oxidase renders a molecule more, rather than less, active than its parent. Thus, some drugs are administered in inactive form, only to be activated by metabolism, and the toxicity of some compounds is enhanced by the action of the mixed function oxidase. For example, the epoxidation and hydroxylation of polycyclic hydrocarbons (such as those in coal tar and tobacco smoke) converts them to potent carcinogens.

Detoxification

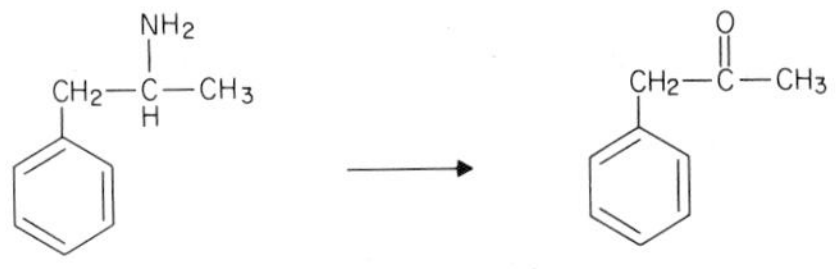

Amphetamine → Phenylacetone

Activation and enhanced toxicity

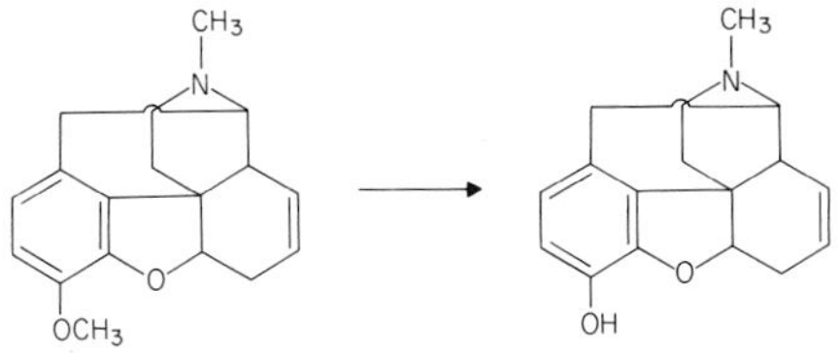

Codeine → Morphine

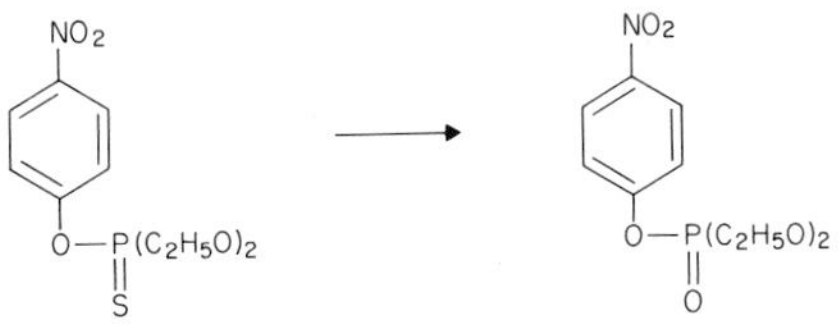

Parathion (insecticide) → Paraoxon (acetylcholinesterase inhibitor)

Side-products from normal activity of the mixed function oxidase system include the free radicals $\cdot O_2^-$ (superoxide) and $\cdot OH$ (hydroxyl) and, derived from them, H_2O_2 (hydrogen peroxide). Provided that these potentially toxic water-soluble materials are produced only in small quantities, they can readily be destroyed by catalase (H_2O_2), superoxide dismutase ($\cdot O_2^-$) and glutathione (all three). If, however, the cellular levels of glutathione and other antioxidants (e.g., ascorbate, tocopherol) fall abnormally low or cells are exposed to excessive quantities of xenobiotics, these oxygen metabolites may accumulate to cytotoxic levels. In addition, the reaction mechanism of the mixed function oxidase includes a

free radicals

Catalase

$$2H_2O_2 \longrightarrow H_2O + O_2$$

Superoxide dismutase

$$\cdot O_2^- + \cdot O_2^- + 2H^+ \longrightarrow O_2 + H_2O_2$$

Glutathione oxidation

$$2R\cdot + 2GSH \longrightarrow 2RH + GSSG$$

199

free radical intermediate produced from the lipophilic substrate. This usually reacts immediately with $^{\bullet}O_2^-$ or $^{\bullet}OH$, but when produced in excess it may escape from the local environment of the oxidase and be removed by free radical 'scavengers' such as glutathione. If a xenobiotic is especially lipophilic, its free radical may partition into the lipophilic core of the endoplasmic reticulum and attack the membrane components. Thus, xenobiotics such as chlorinated hydrocarbons (e.g., CCl_4) are powerful hepatotoxins. Oxidation of CCl_4 yields $^{\bullet}CCl_3$ which, in the polyunsaturated hydrocarbon environment of the membrane interior, initiates a chain of reactions producing lipid free radicals, lipid hydroperoxides and aldehydes, and malonyldialdehyde. These reactions are self-sustaining and, since they occur in a lipophilic environment, they are partially protected from termination by soluble free-radical scavengers such as glutathione. They can, however, be terminated either by a lipophilic free-radical scavenger such as tocopherol or butylated hydroxytoluene (BHT) or by reacting with one another.

When membranes are extensively damaged through modifications to the lipid phase their passive permeability to ions rises and membrane enzyme activities are modified. Amongst the most cytotoxic of these changes are increased inward leakage of Ca^{2+} and Na^+. Cells tend to become ATP-depleted as a result of a futile expenditure of energy on trying to pump the ions out. Na^+ influx causes cell swelling, and raised intracellular Ca^{2+} activates proteases and phospholipases that are normally inactive. A variety of toxins and other agents that kill cells probably share an ability to raise cytoplasmic Ca^{2+} levels either by enhancing its entry or inhibiting its extrusion.

In many diseases, the evidence provided to the clinical biochemist by the effects of a membrane damage may be of positive diagnostic value. For example, cytosol enzymes are normally retained effectively by the plasma membrane, but if this membrane becomes damaged, for example during ischaemia at a site of myocardial infarction, enzymes leak out into the extracellular fluid and hence to the blood. Minor lesions can be repaired, but serious ones lead to cell death and the release both of massive amounts of cytosol enzymes and of enzymes characteristic of intracellular organelles. A rather different situation occurs in obstructive jaundice, when bile ducts become blocked and newly formed bile cannot leave the liver. In this case, it is 5'-nucleotidase, a plasma membrane enzyme located particularly around the bile

lipid
peroxidation

Ca^{2+} leakage
and
cell death

enzymes in
blood plasma

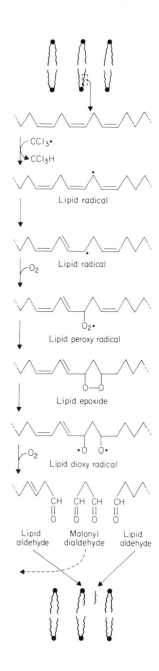

Lipid radical

Lipid radical

Lipid peroxy radical

Lipid epoxide

Lipid dioxy radical

Lipid   Malonyl   Lipid
aldehyde   dialdehyde   aldehyde

canaliculi, which appears selectively in the blood. Clinical studies of the levels, types and order of appearance of enzymes in blood plasma can give invaluable information concerning the severity, location and history of a disease process.

8.8 Toxins and venoms

A wide variety of organisms elaborate cytotoxic materials as normal tissue constituents (e.g., plant alkaloids), in concentrated form as venoms (e.g., snakes, bees) or directly into their environment (e.g., exotoxins of pathogenic micro-organisms). To exert their toxic effects, these compounds must either perturb or traverse the plasma membrane of their target cells.

channel-forming molecules

The simplest of these perturbations is destruction of the normal permeability barrier to ions, and sometimes also to larger molecules, by insertion of water-filled channels through the plasma membrane. Many pathogenic staphylococci produce water-soluble protein α-toxins (mol. wt 34 000) which, when they come into contact with lipid structures, aggregate into lipophilic annular hexamers that serve to introduce 2–3 nm wide water-filled pores. These lesions can readily be seen by electron microscopy of negatively stained membranes. Rather similar, but larger, lesions

complement action

are formed when the plasma complement system attacks membranes that display bound cytolytic immunoglobulins. In this case, component C5b, formed as a result of the activation of the complement cascade, associates with components C6, C7 and C8 and several molecules of C9 to form transmembrane structures of one to two million molecular weight that are penetrated by channels up to 10 nm wide. The formation of much narrower water-filled channels has already been mentioned as the mechanism of action of gramicidin (Chapter 3), and it also explains the cytotoxic action of melittin, a peptide from bee venom. Diffusing ionophores (Chapter 3) can be cytotoxic by virtue of their ability to dissipate normal transmembrane gradients of particular ions (e.g., K^+, H^+, Ca^{2+}).

toxin–sterol interactions

Membrane sterols sometimes provide a specific target for toxins. These include thiol-activated cytolysins from streptococci (e.g., streptolysin O), plant alkaloids (saponins) and certain antifungal polyenoic agents (filipin, amphotericin, etc.). In each case, it appears that toxin–sterol complexes form aggregates, leading to the formation of water–filled pores in the affected membranes.

The integrity of membranes can also be compromised as a result of the action of toxins possessing phospholipase activity, although many membranes survive at least partial destruction of their lipids by such enzymes. Phospholipase toxins include the α-toxins (phospholipases C) of clostridia, phospholipases C specific for various individual phospholipids (e.g., phosphatidylinositol, sphingomyelin) that are secreted by other bacteria, phospholipase A_1 of bee venom and phospholipases A_2 from snake venoms. The phospholipases A_2 from snake venoms include a group of enzymes, exemplified by β-bungarotoxin, which act specifically on nerve terminals.

Some toxins interfere with normal mechanisms of ion movement through membranes. For example, tetrodotoxin and some scorpion and sea anemone toxins prevent the propagation of nerve action potentials by preventing the opening of potential-sensitive Na^+ 'gates' (Chapter 4), whereas veratridine and related neurotoxic alkaloids bring about persistent nerve depolarization by inhibiting the closing of open Na^+ gates.

Some bacterial toxins consist of pathogenic and non-pathogenic segments: these may be on separate polypeptides (e.g., cholera toxin) or on a single polypeptide chain that is very susceptible to proteolytic cleavage (e.g., diphtheria toxin). The role of the non-pathogenic (B) components appears to be to procure the access of the pathogenic (A) components to their cellular targets. In the case of cholera toxin, this target is the stimulatory guanyl nucleotide-binding protein (G_s) of the adenylate cyclase system at the cytoplasmic surface of the plasma membrane, whereas the A subunit of diphtheria toxin acts on an analogous protein that is involved in protein synthesis at ribosomes (Chapter 5).

Cholera toxin consists of an A subunit (or, more usually, A_1 and A_2 segments of the A subunit linked together by a disulphide bridge) of molecular weight 28 000 surrounded by a ring of five B subunits of molecular weight 11 600. In infected individuals it is secreted by toxigenic *Vibrio cholerae* present in the intestinal lumen. Attack is through the binding of the B subunits to the monosialoganglioside G_{M1} at the brush border of the enterocyte, this somehow allowing the A_1 fragment to gain access to the adenylate cyclase of the enterocyte's basolateral plasma membrane. In the case of diphtheria toxin, it is very likely that the analogous process involves endocytosis of the bound toxin, followed by transfer of the A subunit into the cytoplasm only after the toxin has

phospholipases

bacterial toxins

cholera toxin

Cholera toxin

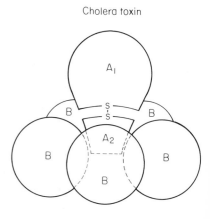

been transferred into lysosomes. Once the A subunit of cholera toxin is within the enterocyte it catalyses an NAD-dependent ADP-ribosylation of the guanyl nucleotide-binding protein responsible for activating adenylate cyclase. This turns off the GTPase activity of the G_s protein and a sustained full activation of adenylate cyclase ensues (see Chapter 5). The result of this massive rise in cAMP level in the enterocyte is to stimulate a gross fluid secretion (i.e., diarrhoea) that is sufficient to kill an untreated patient. Toxigenic strains of *E. coli* produce a toxin with a structure and mechanism of action very similar to that of cholera toxin.

Cholera is a toxin-induced disease of the intestinal mucosa because *Vibrio cholerae* multiplies only in the intestine. Isolated cholera toxin will activate adenylate cyclase in any cells bearing surface G_{M1} ganglioside. In addition, isolated A or A_1 fragments of the toxin are fully active against the adenylate cyclase of isolated membrane preparations: the toxin has therefore been invaluable in elucidating the function of the G_s regulatory component of the cyclase system. *Corynebacterium diphtheriae* infects the throat, and the diphtheria toxin is blood-borne; it switches off protein biosynthesis in a wide variety of cells.

neurotoxins

Other A/B subunit toxins include neurotoxins. Botulinus toxin, produced by *Clostridium botulinus* growing anaerobically in ill-cooked food, binds to the presynaptic elements of neuromuscular junctions where it prevents acetylcholine release and hence causes paralysis. Tetanus toxin is formed in infected wounds, but its targets are inhibitory spinal synapses involved in reflex control of voluntary muscles. To reach these sites it is taken up by nerve endings close to the infection site and then somehow travels through the nervous system, crossing synapses *en route,* finally to act mainly by inhibiting glycine release from the nerve terminals of neurones that constitute the inhibitory arm of a spinal reflex arc.

8.9 Viral infection

Viruses are intracellular parasites, so viral infection and virus release both involve the viral genome penetrating the barrier presented by the host cell plasma membrane.

virus
'receptors'

The first step is the binding of viruses to 'receptors' on the surface of susceptible cells. These binding sites are present in variable numbers, often of the order of hundreds per square micrometre, and they presumably reflect the presence of membrane components with some normal function other than virus attachment. Treatment with degradative enzymes such as neuraminidase has established that these 'receptors' include oligosaccharide groupings on glycoproteins such as major histocompatibility antigens and maybe also on glycolipids. Cells differ greatly in their susceptibility to virus infections, and different strains of a single virus may vary greatly in their infectivity towards a single type of cell. Some cells can be infected by many viruses and some viruses infect a wide variety of cells, at least in tissue culture: in such cases the chemical groupings that act as 'receptors' must be widely disseminated on cell surfaces. In general, the key interactions appear to be between (glyco)proteins of the viral coat (e.g., the protein fibres at the pentons of an adenovirus capsid) or envelope (e.g., the HA glycoprotein of the surface 'spikes' of influenza virus) and these 'receptors' on the host cell surface.

membrane penetration Once bound, some viruses inject their nucleocapsids into the cytoplasm simply by fusing with the plasma membrane (e.g., Sendai virus); the viral glycoproteins then remain associated with the host cell plasma membrane. Other viruses undergo endocytosis before infection occurs; these include influenza and Semliki Forest viruses (Chapter 6.8). These viruses enter cells in pinocytic vesicles that fuse with lysosomes, and the virus membranes then fuse with the lysosomal membrane, thus introducing the viral nucleocapsid into the cytosol. Fusion of viral and lysosomal membranes requires the low pH found within lysosomes, and treatment with agents that raise intralysosomal pH (e.g., methylamine) inhibits infection. Fusion between these viruses and membrane models such as liposomes can be triggered by acid pH.

virus assembly and release Once infection (penetration of the nucleocapsid into the cytosol) has occurred, the viral genome is replicated and translated, leading to the accumulation within infected cells of the molecular components needed for assembly of new viruses. Synthesis and intracellular transit of viral envelope glycoproteins is discussed in Chapter 7. Once patches of viral glycoproteins have been established, usually in the plasma membrane, other viral components (e.g., the matrix protein and nucleocapsid in the case of vesicular stomatitis virus) associate with the cytoplasmic membrane surface and virus particles bud off into the extracellular medium. These particles consist of a virally encoded nucleocapsid and other proteins, surrounded by a membrane consisting of virally coded (glyco)proteins in a lipid bilayer derived from the host cell plasma membrane. Some viruses are released into membrane-

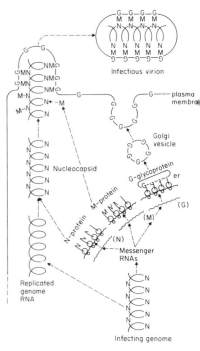

Assembly and release of vesicular stomatitis virus (VSV)

204

bounded compartments within the cell, for example with Golgi elements or into the intermembrane space of the nuclear envelope, and leave the cell either exocytically or during virus-induced cell lysis.

induced
cell fusion

The presence of viral gene products in the plasma membranes of infected cells often leads to a tendency for these cells to fuse with one another or with uninfected cells. Sometimes the fusogenic (glyco)proteins are those that become incorporated into virus particles and enable them to fuse with host cell membranes, but in other types of infection (e.g., herpes, pox) cell fusion is induced by (glyco)protein viral gene products that are not incorporated into released viruses. Such cell fusion processes may accelerate the spread of infection through a tissue.

host
response

Infection by a virus not previously encountered leads quickly to abundant replication of virus in infected cells, after which the virus and virus-infected cells are usually eliminated effectively by activated macrophages and by antigen-specific immunological mechanisms. In animals that have encountered the virus before, these latter mechanisms come into play immediately. Binding of specific antibodies to virus-infected cells facilitates their recognition by macrophages and K (killer) cells and lysis of the cells by the complement system. Infected cells are also targets for cytotoxic T-lymphocytes, with the lymphocytes of the appropriate clone(s) binding to and lysing cells that display the pattern of 'altered self' that is characteristic of virus infection (see p. 108). This lysis involves close membrane–membrane contact between the attacking and the attacked cells and requires extracellular Ca^{2+}. Its mechanism is unknown and the attacking lymphocyte survives to attack other infected cells. Most virus infections are transient, with the infected cells rapidly replaced. However, sometimes attack may be upon cells that no longer multiply (e.g., the permanent depletion of spinal motor neurones that characterizes paralytic poliomyelitis) or virus may integrate into the genome of cells only to re-emerge at intervals and initiate new bouts of disease (e.g., herpes).

immunity

Viral infection may confer long-lasting immunity against subsequent bouts of disease: vaccination with cowpox (variola) virus protects against smallpox for many years. However, infection may still occur on contact with a closely related virus that is antigenically different from that causing the first infection. For example, influenza viruses fall into three broad antigenic groupings (A, B and C), in each of which are many individual virus strains whose antigenic dis-

205

plays differ in detail. Major epidemics of influenza have been attributed to various strains of influenza A virus. These have two main antigenic surface glycoproteins (the HA haemagglutinin and a neuraminidase), both of which sometimes show dramatic 'shifts' in antigenicity. Such shifts sometimes produce antigenically novel virus strains that rapidly spread through the non-immune populations of large areas of the world. Crystallographic analysis of the haemagglutinin of 'Hong Kong/1968' virus revealed four major antigenic sites on the region of the glycoprotein that is displayed on the virus surface; amino acid sequencing reveals that various epidemic strains of influenza virus have mutations in one or more of these sites.

antigenic variability

8.10 Intracellular parasitism and immunological disguise

Bacteria generally grow outside cells and are readily located by the body's immune defences. Strategies evolved by pathogens that escape this surveillance include 'hiding' within cells and presenting a false and 'friendly' immunological face to the host.

concealment within cells

Mycobacterium leprae, which are responsible for leprosy, are phagocytized by macrophages. However, they survive the killing mechanisms within the phagocytic vacuole and multiply within the secondary lysosomes of the macrophages. *Trypanosoma cruzi,* the protozoan pathogen of Chagas' disease, is also phagocytized by macrophages. In this case many of the trypanosomes are killed but some escape from the phagocytic vacuoles and multiply in the cytoplasm of the macrophages. Their progeny then go on to infiltrate within the cells of many tissues, with the most dangerous attack being upon the muscle cells of the heart.

malaria

Plasmodium merozoites, like infective trypanosomes, are introduced into the bloodstream by an insect bite, and the plasmodia then parasitize erythrocytes. Contact between merozoite and erythrocytes leads to a close membrane apposition and thickening of the erythrocyte membrane image. This contact then spreads around the circumference of the merozoite, so that within 1 min the merozoite is taken into the erythrocyte surrounded by a vacuole of erythrocyte plasma membrane. Within the K^+-rich cell interior the merozoite differentiates into a trophozoite and this in turn yields 12–24 merozoites that are released by cell lysis and infect additional red cells. The malaria resistance of people heterozygous for sickle cell anaemia probably arises because malaria-infected heterozygous erythrocytes are abnormally susceptible to sickling and lysis when the parasites are at the trophozoite stage and cannot survive exposure to the K^+-deficient extracellular environment.

A different method of concealment is adopted by the schistosomes (platyhelminth worms) responsible for schistosomiasis (bilharzia). The infective agents in this disease are tiny water-borne cercaria, released from water snails (the alternate host), which gain entry by burrowing through the skin. At this stage they bear a full surface array of schistosome antigens and are therefore vulnerable to immunological assault, but within a few hours they take on a disguise, making them appear immunologically indistinguishable from their hosts. This is done by the secretion from subsurface cells of multilamellar lipid bodies that spread an extra bilayer of lipid over the entire surface of the worm. Into this are passively absorbed antigenic components, such as major histocompatibility antigens from adjacent host cells. This immunological disguise facilitates the establishment of a chronic infection.

Another form of immunological disguise is not to hide, but to change identity frequently. This is the strategy evolved by the extracellular trypanosome responsible for African sleeping sickness. Its antigenicity is dictated by a family of cell-surface glycoproteins. These are encoded in a complex of genes of which only a few are expressed at any one time, and the pattern expressed is changed often. As a result, a single infection with this agent tends to be long-lasting and gives only limited immunity against subsequent infections; the challenge of devising an effective vaccine has so far proved insuperable.

8.11 Autoimmune interference with membrane function

Although the immune system's function is to eliminate invading pathogens it sometimes makes the error of attacking normal tissues. Sometimes the attack upon the cell surface is sufficient to kill cells. For example, the most probable explanation for development of juvenile insulin-dependent diabetes is autoimmune attack upon pancreatic β-cells; this may occur as a secondary autoimmune phenomenon following some form of viral infection (e.g., mumps) and is most common in individuals of histocompatibility genotypes

DW3-DR4 and DW4-DR4. Other endocrine deficiencies can arise from autoimmune attack on other glands (e.g., the thyroid in chronic thyroiditis).

multiple sclerosis

Multiple sclerosis, in which the main neural lesion is demyelination of nerve axons, is another disease which is suspected to have an autoimmune aetiology, possibly following infection by an as yet unidentified virus. Some of its manifestations are mimicked in experimental allergic encephalomyelitis (EAE), a demyelinating condition induced by injection into animals of purified preparations of the A_1 basic protein of the myelin membrane (mol.wt 18400). The demyelinating areas of brain tissues are infiltrated with lymphocytes both in multiple sclerosis and EAE, and EAE can be passively transferred from animal to animal by transfusion of lymphocytes but not of immunoglobulins.

myasthenia gravis

Autoimmune attack on individual membrane components, with the attacked cells surviving but showing changed function, has probably been studied most fully in autoimmune antireceptor conditions. Myasthenia gravis is a disease characterized by progressive development of muscle weakness as a result of immune attack upon the nicotinic acetylcholine receptors arrayed on the postsynaptic folds of the neuromuscular junction. In this case, the patients' blood contains antireceptor antibodies and these, together with the complement system and the cellular components of the immune system, attack and greatly reduce the normally extensive and convoluted postsynaptic surface of the junction. An important effect of antinicotinic receptor antibody may be to stimulate receptor endocytosis and destruction; in cultured myoblasts antibody application reduces the half-life of the receptor from 18 to six hours. A model of myasthenia gravis is readily induced in experimental animals by immunization with purified preparations of nicotinic receptors isolated from the electric organs of electric fish (e.g., *Torpedo* sp.), despite the fact that the mammalian and fish receptors only show limited immunological cross-reactivity.

insulin-resistant diabetes

Although most patients with severe diabetes are insulin-deficient, a few have very high levels of circulating insulin to which normally responsive tissues (e.g., adipose) fail to respond. Such patients frequently possess circulating antibodies to their own insulin receptors; these antibodies bind to receptors, restricting the access of insulin. Some of these antibodies, in addition to inhibiting insulin binding, are capable of either partially or fully mimicking the actions of insulin at

antibodies that activate receptors

208

the receptors. This continuous 'false' activation of receptors initiates endocytosis of the activated receptors, thus down-regulating the cells' already compromised ability to respond to circulating insulin.

Graves' disease is an autoimmune receptor disease in which the major action of circulating antireceptor antibodies is activation of the TSH receptors of the thyroid. The result is excessive secretion of thyroid hormones in patients in which circulating TSH levels may be normal or even subnormal.

Antibodies can move intact from mother to offspring, either across the placenta or during intestinal absorption (Chapter 6). One consequence of this diacytosis of immuno-globulin can be a transient expression in newborn infants of the symptoms of autoimmune diseases such as myasthenia gravis or Graves' disease.

Graves' disease (margin note)

Further Reading

Wallach D.F.H. (1979) *Plasma Membranes and Disease.* Academic Press, New York.

Trump B.F. & Arstila A.V. (1980) *Pathobiology of Cell Membranes.* Volume 2. Academic Press, New York.

Biochem. Soc. Colloquium (1980) Cell-surface membranes and disease. *Biochem. Soc. Trans.* **8**, 686–702.

Evans W.H. (1980) A biochemical dissection of the functional polarity of the plasma membrane of the hepatocyte. *Biochim. Biophys. Acta* **604**, 27–64.

Adelberg E.A. & Slayman C.W. (1980) Genes and membranes. In *Membrane Physiology* (eds. Andreoli T.E., Hoffman J.F. & Fanestil D.D.). Plenum, New York. pp. 357–368.

Rice-Evans C.A. & Dunn M.J. (1982) Erythrocyte deformability and disease. *Trends Biochem. Sci.* **7**, 282–286.

Zucker M.B. (1980) The functioning of blood platelets. *Scientific American* June, 70–89.

Brady R.O. (1973) Hereditary fat-metabolism diseases. *Scientific American* August, 88–97.

Greaves M.F. (1979) Cell surface characteristics of human leukaemic cells. *Essays Biochem.* **15**, 78–124.

Nicolson G.L. (1979) Cancer metastasis. *Scientific American* March, 50–60.

Bishop J.M. (1982) Oncogenes. *Scientific American* March, 69–78.

Martin G. (1980) Teratocarcinomas and mammalian embryogenesis. *Science* **209**, 768–776.

Weinstein I.B. (1983) Protein kinase, phospholipid and control of growth. *Nature* **302**, 750.

Houslay M.D. & Palmer R.W. (1978) Changes in the form of Arrhenius plots of the activity of glucagon-stimulated adenylate cyclase and other hamster liver plasma-membrane enzymes occurring on hibernation. *Biochem. J.* **174**, 909–919.

de Mendoza D. & Cronan J.E. (1983) Thermal regulation of membrane lipid fluidity in bacteria. *Trends Biochem. Sci.* **8**, 49–52.

Franks F. (1978) Biological freezing and cryofixation. In *Low Temperature Biological Microscopy and Microanalysis.* The Royal Microscopical Society.

Poste G. & Nicolson G.L. (1978) Membrane Fusion. *Cell Surface Review* Volume 5. Elsevier/North Holland Amsterdam.

Schramm M., Oates J., Papahajopoulos D. & Loyter A. (1982) Fusion and implantation in biological membranes. *Trends Pharmacol. Sci.* **3**, 221–229.

Cooper J.R., Bloom F.E. & Roth R.H. (1978) *The Biochemical Basis of Neuropharmacology.* 3rd edn. Oxford University Press, Oxford.

Hodgson E. & Guthrie F.E. (eds.) (1980) *Introduction to Biochemical Toxicology.* Blackwell Scientific Publications, Oxford.

Smith R.L. (1973) *The Excretory Function of Bile.* Chapman & Hall, London.

Kappas A. & Alvares A.P. (1975) How the liver metabolizes foreign substances. *Scientific American* June, 22–31.

Bus J.S. & Gibson J.E. (1979) Lipid peroxidation and its role in toxicology. *Rev. Biochem. Toxicol.* **1,** 125–149.

Farber J.L. (1981) The role of calcium in cell death. *Life Sciences* **29,** 1289–1295.

Stephen J. & Pietrowski R.A. (1981) *Bacterial Toxins.* Nelson, London.

Bhakdi S. & Tranum-Jensen J. (1983) Membrane damage by channel-forming proteins. *Trends Biochem. Sci.* **8,** 134–136.

Holmgren J. (1981) Actions of cholera toxin and the prevention and treatment of cholera. *Nature* **292,** 413–417.

Helenius A., Marsh M. & White J. (1980) The entry of viruses into animal cells. *Trends Biochem. Sci.* **5,** 104–106.

Webster R.G., Laver W.G., Air G.M. & Schild G.C. (1982) Molecular mechanisms of variation in influenza viruses. *Nature* **296,** 115–121.

Mahy B.W.J., Minson A.C. & Darby G.K. (eds.) (1982) Virus Persistence. *Soc. Gen. Microbiol., Symposium 33.*

Bernards A. (1982) Transposable genes for surface glycoproteins in trypanosomes. *Trends Biochem. Sci.* **7,** 253–255.

Rubenstein E. (1980) Diseases caused by impaired communication among cells. *Scientific American* Feb., 78–87.

Rose N.R. (1981) Autoimmune diseases. *Scientific American* Feb., 70–81.

See also pp. 212, 213.

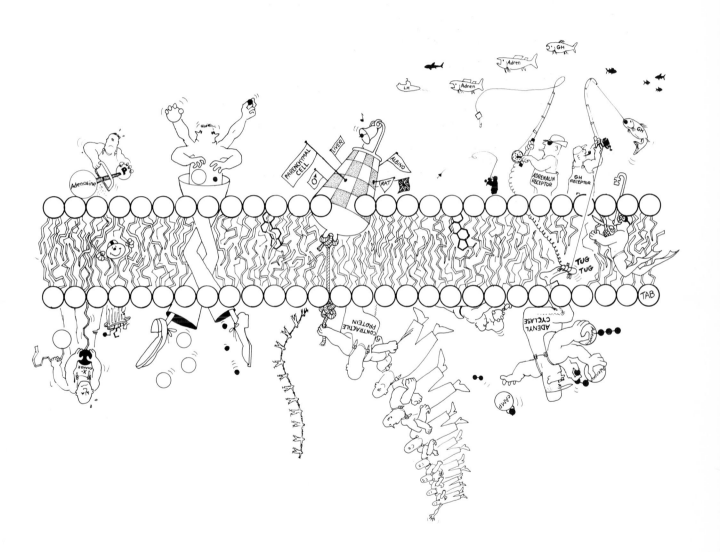

Some suggestions for additional sources of current information on membranes

Reviews on membrane topics appear in a variety of publications: the following may help students in search of additional up-to-date information.

Series of books

Several series are devoted solely to membrane topics, some of them published as complete sets and others continuing to have new volumes added at intervals.

Biological Membranes. Chapman D. & Wallach D.F.H. (eds). Academic Press, London & New York.

Biomembranes. Manson L.A. (ed.). Plenum Press, New York.

Cell Surface Membranes. Poste G. & Nicholson G.L. (eds). North Holland Publishing Co., Amsterdam.

Cell Membranes. Methods and Reviews. Elson E., Frazier W. & Glaser L. (eds). Plenum Press, New York.

Membranes and Transport. Martonosi A.N. (ed.). Plenum Press, New York.

Some review publications and journals devoted to membrane topics

Biochimica et Biophysica Acta
    Biomembranes section
    Reviews on Biomembranes
Current Topics in Bioenergetics
Current Topics in Membranes and Transport
Journal of Membrane Biology

Serial publications which frequently include reviews on membrane topics

Annual Reviews of Biochemistry (also of *Biophysics and Bioengineering, Immunology, Microbiology, Neurobiology, Pharmacology, Physiology and Plant Physiology*). Collected in *Annual Reviews Reprints* 1975–7 and 1978–80.

Biochimica et Biophysica Acta
  Reviews on Bioenergetics
  Reviews on Cancer
Biochemical Journal
FEBS Letters (Annual list of reviews)
Immunology Today
Journal of Cell Biology
Methods in Enzymology
Nature
Pharmacological Reviews
Physiological Reviews
Progress in Biophysics and Molecular Biology
Quarterly Reviews of Biophysics
Recent Progress in Surface Science
Science
Scientific American
Trends in Biochemical Sciences
Trends in Neurosciences
Trends in Pharmacological Sciences

New publications

Titles of new publications on cell membranes (and on a number of other topics in which membranes are implicated) are listed monthly by the Biomedical Information Service, University of Sheffield. Biological Membrane Abstracts are published monthly by Information Retrieval Limited, London.

Index

216

219